Mathematics Level

Mathematics Level 1

ERIC WALKER, MA(Cantab.)

Formerly Head of the Mathematics Department and Deputy Headmaster of Sir Roger Manwood's School, Sandwich; later at the South Kent College of Technology, Folkestone.

HOLT, RINEHART AND WINSTON
LONDON · NEW YORK · SYDNEY · TORONTO

Holt, Rinehart and Winston Ltd: 1 St Anne's Road,
Eastbourne, East Sussex BN21 3UN

British Library Cataloguing in Publication Data

Walker, Eric
  Mathematics Level 1
  1. Shop mathematics
  I. Title
  510'.2'46   TJ1165

ISBN 0–03–910314–5

Typeset by J. W. Arrowsmith Ltd, Bristol.
Printed in Great Britain by Richard Clay (The Chaucer Press) Ltd, Bungay,
Suffolk.

Last digit is print no: 9   8   7   6   5   4   3   2   1

Introduction

The contents of this book cover the syllabus laid down for pre-entry and Level 1 in the Bank of Objectives for TEC Mathematics dated July 1978.

As far as possible and practicable, the approach to the subject is through simple examples leading to the rules, laws and general principles in each section. It is hoped that students will exploit the use of calculators to assist in these preliminary explorations. In many cases guidance towards that end is indicated in the chapters.

Perhaps the most important aim of the book is to help the student, often by simple numerical calculations, to discover the method before being confronted by a rule or law. Where that objective is successful the laws are usually understood better and retained more readily in the memory.

Many students begin the course with a severe handicap: they do not understand much of the very basic arithmetic. Consequently, unless some attempt is made to rectify their lack of numerical skills, such students flounder along for the whole course. At worst they understand little. At best they experience great difficulty and appreciate the subject only after very strenuous efforts. Merely to repeat the methods they have previously encountered frequently produces boredom, provoking the reaction, 'I've done this before'. For these reasons Chapter 1 has been written with the specific aim of presenting basic concepts in what, for most students, will be a new light. At the same time it deals with the early parts of the syllabus and lays down the foundations for an effective understanding of later work. In particular this applies to the study of fractions, ratio and proportion, the solution of simple equations, the manipulation of formulae and facility with algebra.

For most students a slow and thorough beginning to new work is essential. The rules come at the end of the introductory period to summarize the early discoveries. Anything which can be used to show the way to the end product –a simple calculation, a diagram, the use of a mechanical aid, the pocket calculator, collective calculations by the class – should be exploited to the full.

A reference is provided after the contents list to indicate in which chapters the various units of the Bank of Objectives U78/911 are located.

E. WALKER

To the memory of my father and mother,
Albert and Elizabeth Walker.
For their love and encouragement.

Contents

Unit Reference

1

Basic Arithmetic Operations

These operations, which are of the utmost importance in later work, will be introduced by means of the simplest fundamental ideas. Some students will be able to read through much of this section quickly and omit many of the problems in the exercises. It will repay those who are uncertain of arithmetic processes to go carefully through the detailed explanations so that basic laws are fully grasped.

1.1   Representation of numbers

One method of representing numbers is by measuring distances along a line. Consider the line $ABCDE$ ... in Fig. 1.1, which is marked off in equal intervals (or units).

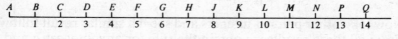

Figure 1.1

AB represents 1 unit, or 1; AC represents 2 units, or 2; AE represents 4; AH represents 7 and so on. AL represents 10 units, or 10, or 1 (unit of ten). AC is not the only length which represents 2. Others are BD, CE, DF, etc.

1

Now, from the diagram, $AC + CF = AF$
So we obtain $\qquad\qquad\qquad\qquad 2 + 3 = 5$

In this + is taken to mean 'add'. It is an operation on the numbers 2 and 3. The rules governing the operation of addition with the whole numbers (integers) 1, 2, 3, etc. are thus obtained:

$$1 + 1 = 2 \quad \text{because } AB + BC = AC$$
$$2 + 1 = 3 \quad \text{because } AC + CD = AD$$
$$3 + 1 = 4 \quad \text{because } AD + DE = AE$$

By drawing an extended line and considering many more cases we can build up a table (Table 1.1) showing how to add together

Table 1.1 *Table for addition*

+	1	2	3	4	5	6	7	8	9	10
1	2	3	4	5	6	7	8	9	10	11
2	3	4	5	6	7	8	9	10	11	12
3	4	5	6	7	8	9	10	11	12	13
4	5	6	7	8	9	10	11	12	13	14
5	6	7	8	9	10	11	12	13	14	15
6	7	8	9	10	11	12	13	14	15	16
7	8	9	10	11	12	13	14	15	16	17
8	9	10	11	12	13	14	15	16	17	18
9	10	11	12	13	14	15	16	17	18	19
10	11	12	13	14	15	16	17	18	19	20

various pairs of integers from 1 to 10. The first number is in the left-hand column and the number to be added to it is in the top row. From the table we see that

$$5 + 2 = 7 \text{ and } 2 + 5 = 7$$
$$\text{So } 5 + 2 = 2 + 5$$
$$\text{Again, } 7 + 6 = 13 \text{ and } 6 + 7 = 13$$
$$\text{So } 7 + 6 = 6 + 7$$

Now take other pairs of integers and see if a similar result follows. From all these results we obtain the rule for any integers a and b.

$$a + b = b + a \qquad\qquad\qquad 1.1$$

Look again at the line AL. It measures 10 units of 1, or 10 units, or 1 unit of 10. Suppose we have a length which is 23 units. It is also 2 units of ten (or 2 tens) + 3 units of 1. So 75 means 7 tens + 5 units, and 249 means 2 units of 100 (hundreds) + 4 tens + 9 units.

Exercise 1.1

1. Express in units and tens the following: 35, 47, 56, 63, 82, 50, 30, 92, 71, 44.
2. Express in units, tens and hundreds: 174, 196, 238, 587, 923, 102, 105, 206, 609, 750, 800.

(Note that 307 means 3 hundreds + 0 tens + 7 units.)

1.2 Place values of digits

In the number 427 the 4, 2 and 7 are called digits. In a number with many digits each digit represents a unit ten times bigger than the unit of the digit to its right. For example, in the number 546 287 the digit 2 represents hundreds and the digit 6 represents thousands.

To make the addition of large numbers easier we place them vertically one below the other, so that all digits with the same unit value are in the same column. Therefore we write 4582 + 617 + 28 + 9164 as:

$$
\begin{array}{r}
4582 \\
617 \\
28 \\
9164 \\
\hline
14391 \\
\hline
\text{edcba}
\end{array}
$$

Adding column (a) we get 4 + 8 + 7 + 2 = 21, that is, 2 tens + 1 unit. We place only 1 unit in column (a) in the answer and we combine the 2 tens with the digits in column (b) because all these units are units of ten (tens).

Column (b) gives 2 (carried over from column (a)) + 6 + 2 + 1 + 8 = 19, i.e. 19 tens which is 9 tens and 10 tens. 9 tens we place in column (b) in the answer. Now 10 tens is 1 hundred, and that is a unit which must go in column (c).

Column (c) gives 1 (carried over from column (b)) + 1 + 6 + 5 = 13, which is 3 hundreds + 10 hundreds. 3 hundreds we place in column (c) in the answer, and 10 hundreds, i.e. 1 thousand, goes in column (d).

Column (d) gives 1 (carried over from column (c)) + 9 + 4 = 14, i.e. 4 thousands + 10 thousands. 4 thousands we place in column (d) in the answer; 10 thousands is like 1 unit of ten thousand, which we must place in column (e).

We abbreviate our working as follows:

```
       4582
        617
         28
       9164
       1112    This line is the carry-over line
      ─────
      14391
      ─────
```

Exercise 1.2

In questions 1 to 5 find the values of each of the following:

1. 37 + 59 + 28
2. 438 + 586 + 923
3. 50 487 + 37 459 + 452 + 20 376
4. 61 682 + 20 409 + 74 931 + 8179
5. 78 462 + 45 879 + 989 + 57 + 999 989.
6. The total voltage drop in a series circuit is the sum of the voltages across each element in it. If there are five elements with voltage drops of 23, 49, 205, 174 and 586 what is the total voltage drop in the circuit?
7. The boundary for a civic centre is the shape of an irregular hexagon (6 sides). The sides are of length respectively 183, 196, 215, 198, 205 and 176 metres. What is the total distance round the boundary?

Check your answers to questions 1 to 5 by performing the calculations on your calculator. In a later chapter we shall be dealing with operations using a calculator in some detail, but students should find continued addition quite straightforward without guidance.

1.3 Multiplication

Consider a rectangle, length 4 and breadth 3 (Fig. 1.2). We can divide the rectangle into squares, each of which is 1 unit by 1 unit

Figure 1.2

square (called 1 unit squares). The total number of unit squares required to fill the rectangle is $4 + 4 + 4 = 12$. If our rectangle had been length 4 and breadth 17 the number of squares would have been:

$$4 + 4 + 4 + 4 + 4 + 4 + 4 + 4 + 4 + 4 + 4 + 4 + 4 + 4 + 4 + 4 + 4$$

But this is too complicated a way of writing it down. We have written down 4 seventeen times, so we abbreviate it to 17×4.

Therefore, in Fig. 1.2 we write $4 + 4 + 4 = 3 \times 4$, which is equal to 12. We call the operation $\times$ multiplication. If we draw other diagrams for rectangles of all lengths and breadths from 1 to 10 we obtain the following table, Table 1.2, for multiplication.

Table 1.2 *Table for multiplication*

$\times$	1	2	3	4	5	6	7	8	9	10
1	1	2	3	4	5	6	7	8	9	10
2	2	4	6	8	10	12	14	16	18	20
3	3	6	9	12	15	18	21	24	27	30
4	4	8	12	16	20	24	28	32	36	40
5	5	10	15	20	25	30	35	40	45	50
6	6	12	18	24	30	36	42	48	54	60
7	7	14	21	28	35	42	49	56	63	70
8	8	16	24	32	40	48	56	64	72	80
9	9	18	27	36	45	54	63	72	81	90
10	10	20	30	40	50	60	70	80	90	100

In this table we take the first number in the multiplication to be in the left-hand column and the second to be in the top row. So, for example, $6 \times 8 = 48$.

But also $8 \times 6 = 48$
Thus $6 \times 8 = 8 \times 6$

Again, $7 \times 9 = 63$ and $9 \times 7 = 63$
Thus $7 \times 9 = 9 \times 7$

Look at Table 1.2 carefully for combinations of other pairs of integers to see if similar results apply. In fact they do. This leads us to believe that, where a and b are any integers:

$$a \times b = b \times a \qquad\qquad 1.2$$

Exercise 1.3

Using your calculator and the operation multiplication, verify that Law 1.2 applies when a and b take the following pairs of values:

1. 13 and 12
2. 14 and 17
3. 18 and 21
4. 34 and 47
5. 85 and 73
6. 193 and 102
7. 4562 and 3451
8. 1089 and 7304
9. 6345 and 7875

1.4   Combination of two operations

Suppose we wish to carry out two operations, one after the other: first addition, then multiplication. For example, find $2 + 3$ then multiply by 7. We write this as follows:

$$(2 + 3) \times 7$$

We insert the bracket to make sure it is understood that the addition is to be done first and the multiplication second.

By Table 1.1, $2 + 3 = 5$, so $(2 + 3) \times 7 = 5 \times 7$
By Table 1.2, $5 \times 7 = 35$
But look at Table 1.2 and notice that $2 \times 7 = 14$
   and $3 \times 7 = 21$
And we know that $14 + 21 = 35$
This means that $(2 \times 7) + (3 \times 7)$ gives the same
   answer as $(2 + 3) \times 7$

Example

By calculator show that $(329 + 576) \times 698 = (329 \times 698) + (576 \times 698)$

Step 1	$329 + 576 = 905$
Step 2	$905 \times 698 = 631\,690$
Step 3	$329 \times 698 = 229\,642$
Step 4	$576 \times 698 = 402\,048$
Step 5	$229\,642 + 402\,048 = 631\,690$

Exercise 1.4

Using Tables 1.1 and 1.2, and applying the method above, show that:

$$(a + b) \times c = (a \times c) + (b \times c)$$

where a, b and c take the following sets of values:

1. 3, 4 and 5
2. 4, 5 and 6
3. 5, 4 and 4
4. 7, 2 and 9
5. 8, 2 and 7
6. 2, 7 and 10

By calculator show that the rule applies when a, b and c take the values:

7. 28, 37 and 29
8. 39, 42 and 58
9. 47, 61 and 88
10. 93, 94 and 95
11. 105, 158 and 177
12. 432, 47 and 561
13. 5961, 2304 and 4758

All the above calculations lead us to believe that the following law is true:

$$(a + b)c = ac + bc \qquad\qquad 1.3$$

where ac is a short way of writing 'a multiplied by c', and so on.

Another way of establishing the same result is by drawing the diagram in Fig. 1.3. In Fig. 1.3 the area of the large

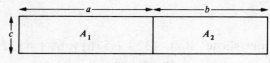

Figure 1.3

rectangle $= A_1 + A_2$. The length of the large rectangle $= (a + b)$. The breadth of all the rectangles $= c$. The area of the large rectangle is $(a + b)c$. The area of $A_1 = ac$. The area of $A_2 = bc$. This means that:

$$(a + b)c = ac + bc$$

Law 1.3 explains the method which we use when we multiply two numbers which are bigger than ten. For example:

$$53 \times 47 = 53(40 + 7) = (40 + 7)53 \quad \text{(by Law 1.2)}$$
$$= (40 \times 53) + (7 \times 53) \quad \text{(by Law 1.3)}$$

This is what we do when we write the sum as:

$$
\begin{array}{r}
53 \\
47 \\
\hline
371 \\
2120 \\
\hline
2491 \\
\hline
\end{array}
$$

   371   this is 7×53
2120   this is 40×53

It is necessary to study and understand these laws, because what we do in our problems is based upon a correct use of the laws. In fact, if we examine some of the things we take for granted we will see that they are based upon the laws we have already discussed, and other methods we use are based upon laws which we have still to discover.

If asked to solve the problem $(17 \times 4) \times 25$ many of us would say $4 \times 25 = 100$ and then $17 \times 100 = 1700$ and give that as the answer. Yet the problem does not tell us to do it that way. We have altered the order of operations. If we do carry out the instructions, first find 17×4 and then multiply the result by 25, we obtain exactly the same answer, namely 1700. This means, then, that:

$$(17 \times 4) \times 25 = 17 \times (4 \times 25)$$

Look at Table 1.2 again:

$2 \times 3 = 6$ and $6 \times 5 = 30$, so $(2 \times 3) \times 5 = 30$
Again, $3 \times 5 = 15$ and $2 \times 15 = 30$, so $2 \times (3 \times 5) = 30$
Therefore $(2 \times 3) \times 5 = 2 \times (3 \times 5)$

Example

By calculator show that $(732 \times 494) \times 63 = 732 \times (494 \times 63)$

Step 1 $732 \times 494 = 361\,608$
Step 2 $361\,608 \times 63 = 22\,781\,304$
Step 3 $494 \times 63 = 31\,122$
Step 4 $732 \times 31\,122 = 22\,781\,304$
It appears that $(a \times b) \times c = a \times (b \times c)$
or, in abbreviated form, $(ab)c = a(bc)$

1.4

Exercise 1.5

Where appropriate use Table 1.2 and where not use your calculator to verify Law 1.4 when a, b and c take the following sets of values:

1.   2, 3 and 4
2.   2, 4 and 6
3.   13, 14 and 17
4.   19, 23 and 34
5.   18, 43 and 56
6.   98, 58 and 62
7.   103, 29 and 35
8.   66, 72 and 54
9.   123, 231 and 321
10.   203, 218 and 227

Another law we obtain by using Table 1.1 is:

$$(a + b) + c = a + (b + c) \qquad 1.5$$
From Table 1.1, $(2 + 3) + 4 = 5 + 4 = 9$
and $2 + (3 + 4) = 2 + 7 = 9$

Example

By calculator verify Law 1.5 where a, b and c take the values 66 784, 593 270, 11 034 907.

Step 1 $66\,784 + 593\,270 = 660\,054$
Step 2 $660\,054 + 11\,034\,907 = 11\,694\,961$
Step 3 $593\,270 + 11\,034\,907 = 11\,628\,177$
Step 4 $66\,784 + 11\,628\,177 = 11\,694\,961$

Exercise 1.6

By calculator verify Law 1.5, where a, b and c take the following values:

1. 23, 34 and 57
2. 48, 68 and 83
3. 79, 54 and 40
4. 124, 348 and 539
5. 670, 4329 and 50 567
6. 110 523, 2 396 574 and 451 938
7. 23, 4589 and 675
8. 718, 85 643 and 939 047

Another way of arriving at this conclusion is by referring to the triangle represented in Fig. 1.4. The sides of the triangle are a, b

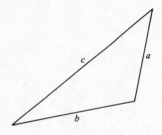

Figure 1.4

and c. The total perimeter (distance round) can be found either by adding a and b together and then adding c to that, i.e. $(a + b) + c$, or by adding the total of b and c to a, i.e. $a + (b + c)$. So:

$$(a + b) + c = a + (b + c)$$

Quite frequently we make use of this law when we are adding columns of figures together. We do not always add up the digits in the order in which they occur in a column, but jump about selecting digits which are easier to add to our existing total.

   Another law which we make much use of later can be found by applying extended Tables 1.1 and 1.2, or by using a calculator, or by means of Fig. 1.5. In Fig. 1.5 the area of the complete rectangle is:

$$\text{length} \times \text{breadth} = (a + b)(c + d)$$
$$\text{But it also equals } A_1 + A_2 + A_3 + A_4$$
$$= ac + bc + ad + bd$$

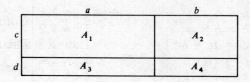

Figure 1.5

Thus we arrive at the law:

$$(a + b)(c + d) = ac + bc + ad + bd \qquad 1.6$$

Example

By calculator verify Law 1.6 where a, b, c and d take the following values: 35, 67, 49, 84.

    Step 1 $35 + 67 = 102$
    Step 2 $49 + 84 = 133$
    Step 3 $102 \times 133 = 13\ 566$
    Step 4 $35 \times 49 = 1715$
    Step 5 $67 \times 49 = 3283$
    Step 6 $35 \times 84 = 2940$
    Step 7 $67 \times 84 = 5628$
    Step 8 $1715 + 3283 + 2940 + 5628 = 13\ 566$

Exercise 1.7

By calculator verify Law 1.6 when a, b, c and d take the following sets of values:

1.   5, 4, 7, 9
2.   7, 9, 8, 9
3.   9, 12, 15, 14
4.   23, 45, 72, 63
5.   56, 92, 43, 51
6.   94, 32, 112, 59

We will put down, for reference later, the laws which we have already obtained.

$$a + b = b + a \qquad \text{Law 1.1}$$
$$a \times b = b \times a \qquad \text{Law 1.2}$$
Commutative law

$$(a + b)c = ac + bc \qquad \text{Law 1.3} \quad \text{Distributive law}$$

$$(ab)c = a(bc) \qquad \text{Law 1.4}$$
$$(a + b) + c = a + (b + c) \qquad \text{Law 1.5}$$
Associative law

$$(a + b)(c + d) = ac + bc + ad + bd \qquad \text{Law 1.6}$$

Up to now, in this chapter, all the arithmetic we have done has been confined to numbers which are counting numbers and the two operations + and ×. But we know there are other kinds of numbers and operations. We will show how these arise naturally from using the numbers and operations referred to so far, and, in that way, arrive at a greater understanding of them.

For the rest of the chapter, then, we shall be embarking on the discovery of new elements and new operations through a clear understanding of the laws above.

1.5 Subtraction

First we will go back to addition. By extending Table 1.1 we ought to be able to answer any question which asks, 'what is the sum of a and b?', i.e.

$$a + b = ? \quad \text{e.g.} \quad 21 + 15 = ?$$

But suppose we ask the question of addition in a different way. By using Table 1.1 answer the following question: $3 + ? = 7$.

We look for 3 in the left-hand column and along the row to find the answer 7. 7 comes under 4 in the top row. So 4 is the answer.

We can answer such questions with many different numbers, and we would ask the question by saying, 'what number must be added to 3 to give an answer of 7?'. After a time, however, we would tire of using so many words to describe how to find the answer, so we invent a new idea to meet the requirement. We say the answer is 7 subtract 3, or $7 - 3$. And thus we have invented a new operation: subtraction, or $-$.

If we go back to Fig. 1.1 we can interpret this:

$$7 - 3 = AH - AD = AH - EH = AE = 4$$

In other words, start at A, go right 7 (taking us to H) and from there go left 3 (bringing us to E). So we started at A and ended up at E, and distance $AE = 4$.

Exercise 1.8

Using Fig. 1.1 explain subtraction with the following pairs of numbers:

1. $5 - 2$
2. $4 - 3$
3. $8 - 6$
4. $11 - 8$
5. $11 - 6$
6. $11 - 3$
7. $12 - 9$
8. $13 - 7$

Extending this operation to larger numbers we have:

$$\begin{array}{r} 5347 \\ 2235 \\ \hline 3112 \\ \hline \text{dcba} \end{array}$$

column (a) $7 - 5 = 2$; column (b) $4 - 3 = 1$;
column (c) $3 - 2 = 1$; column (d) $5 - 2 = 3$

$$\begin{array}{r} 5347 \\ 2358 \\ \text{Carry line } 111 \\ \hline 2989 \\ \hline \text{dcba} \end{array}$$

column (a) $7 - 8 = 9$ carry 1;
column (b) $4 - 5 - $ carry $1 = 8$ carry 1;
column (c) $3 - 3 - $ carry $1 = 9$ carry 1;
column (d) $5 - 2 - $ carry $1 = 2$

Exercise 1.9

Carry out the following subtractions. Check your answers with your calculator.

1. $456 - 345$
2. $579 - 357$
3. $468 - 246$

4. $432 - 345$
5. $642 - 246$
6. $8642 - 6824$
7. $12\,854 - 8625$
8. $623\,821 - 49\,276 - 745$
9. An electric circuit consists of a voltmeter, a capacitor and a resistor in series. The voltage drops across the whole circuit, the voltmeter and the capacitor respectively are 243 V, 149 V and 32 V. Calculate the voltage drop across the resistor.
10. The mass of a truck and its load is 38 546 kg. The mass of the truck is 6538 kg. What is the mass of the load?

1.6 The number zero

We are now in a position to discover a new number. We have already encountered it as a digit in a number, but we have not yet explained it. Suppose we ask the questions:

$$5 + ? = 5 \quad \text{and} \quad 6 - 6 = ?$$

Using Fig. 1.1 we start at A and end at A, which is no distance from A. We call this answer 0, and we would mark A by this value. It means that:

$$5 + 0 = 5 \quad \text{and} \quad 6 - 6 = 0$$

In fact, for all integers a:

$$a + 0 = a \quad \text{and} \quad a - a = 0 \qquad 1.7$$

Zero is the only number which, when added to any number, leaves that number unchanged. So we have discovered a new number. But that is only the beginning: there are many more to be found.

1.7 Negative numbers

Suppose we try to explain $3 - 4$ using Fig. 1.1. We would start at A, go 3 units to the right (taking us to D) and from there go 4 units to the left. This would take us 1 unit to the left of A. But there is no point so marked, and no number attached to it, so it would appear that there is no answer.

However, there is a solution to this problem. When we add a number we move to the right along the line, and when we subtract we go left along the line. So let us call distances to the right along the line from *A* positive (+) and distances to the left along the line from *A* negative (−). This means that we are now going to attach two meanings to each of the signs + and −.

One unit to the left from *A* would therefore be −1, and every extra unit to the left of that would be another −1. So we would get Fig. 1.6.

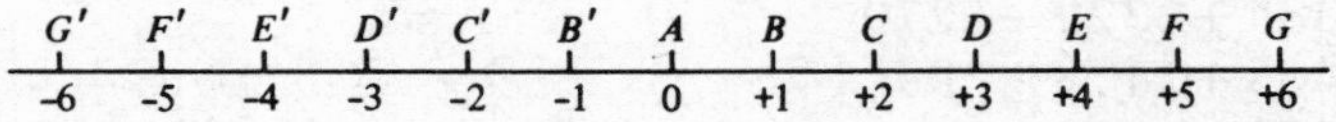

Figure 1.6

Now we have introduced a new kind of number – a negative integer. Because we represented our first integers to the right along the line we shall call them positive integers (e.g. +2). The number represented by *A* itself we shall call zero (0), which is neither positive nor negative. And the ones represented by distances to the left we shall call negative integers (e.g. −3). Alternative notations are $^+2$ and $^-3$.

Now we need to know how to carry out operations on our new kind of numbers. Let us try adding positive and negative integers together:

$$^+4 + ^-3$$

This is 4 units to the right from *A* followed by 3 units to the left from *E*, bringing us to *B*, which is 1 unit to the right from *A*. Therefore:

$$4 - 3 = 1$$
$$\text{So } 4 - 3 \text{ is the same as } ^+4 + ^-3$$

This means we can represent subtraction by adding a negative integer. It also means that we can represent $^+7 + ^-4$ as $7 - 4$.

Examples

1. $^+15 + ^-9 = 15 - 9 = 6$
2. $^+35 + ^-23 + ^+12 = 35 - 23 + 12 = 24$
3. $^+135 + ^-96 + ^-27 = 135 - 96 - 27 = 12$

Exercise 1.10

Convert the following problems into subtractions and determine
the answers. Check your results by calculator.

1. $^+14 + ^-8$
2. $^+27 + ^-15$
3. $^+32 + ^-16$
4. $^+47 + ^-31$
5. $^+61 + ^-45$
6. $^+54 + ^-31 + ^+28$
7. $^+176 + ^-68 + ^+59$
8. $^+385 + ^-329 + ^+279$
9. $^+405 + ^-178 + ^-99$
10. $^+432 + ^-358 + ^-66$
11. $^+4 + ^-4$
12. $^+7 + ^-7$
13. $^+11 + ^-11$
14. $^+123 + ^-123$
15. $^+308 + ^-308$
16. $^+5472 + ^-5472$
17. $^-13 + ^+13$ (First write it as $^+13 + ^-13$, using Law 1.1)
18. $^-375 + ^+375$
19. $^-406 + ^+406$
20. $^-6739 + ^+6739$

The answer to all the questions from (11) onwards in the last
exercise is 0. We conclude that:

$$^+a + ^-a = 0 \quad \text{and} \quad ^-a + ^+a = 0 \qquad\qquad 1.8$$

^-a is said to be the *additive inverse* of ^+a because their sum is zero.
In fact, ^+a *and* ^-a *are each the inverse of the other under addition.*
We have discovered the following:

1. Zero is an integer (called the identity element under addition)
    such that $a + 0 = a$. No other integer has this property.
2. Every integer has an additive inverse: ^-a is the inverse of ^+a;
    ^+a is the inverse of ^-a; and 0 is the inverse of 0; i.e.
    $$^+a + ^-a = ^-a + ^+a = 0 + 0 = 0$$
3. $+$ and $-$ now have two meanings. They represent operations
    (addition and subtraction) and they also represent directions
    along a line (e.g. to the right and to the left, or up and down, or
    this way and the opposite way).

Application of negative numbers in solving equations

Suppose x is an unknown integer such that $x = 3$ (a)
In fact this equation is so simple it scarcely seems worth bothering about. It tells us all we need to know. It says x has a value $= 3$, or $x = 3$.
Next look at $x + 0 = 3$ (b)
By Law 1.7, $x + 0 = x$, so (b) becomes $x = 3$, which is (a). Thus we have the same easy answer as before. Therefore if we can convert an equation into $x + 0 = n$ we can quickly obtain the answer.
Now consider $x + 2 = 3$ (c)
We shall think of it as $(x + 2) = 3$ because that is what the instruction tells us to do.
Now write $(x + 2) + {}^-2 = 3 + {}^-2$ (d)
We have added the same thing to both sides of (c), namely $^-2$. Therefore (d) becomes:

$$x + ({}^+2 + {}^-2) = 3 + {}^-2 \qquad \text{(by Law 1.5)}$$
$$\text{and then } x + 0 = 3 + {}^-2 = 1 \qquad \text{(by Law 1.8)}$$
$$\text{Further, } x = 1 \qquad \text{(by Law 1.7)}$$

Example

Solve $x - 5 = 8$, i.e. $x + {}^-5 = 8$.

$$\begin{aligned}
&\textit{Step 1} \quad x + {}^-5 + {}^+5 = 8 + {}^+5 \\
&\textit{Step 2} \quad \quad\quad x + 0 = 8 + 5 \quad\quad\quad \text{(Law 1.8)} \\
&\textit{Step 3} \quad \quad\quad\quad\quad x = 13 \quad\quad\quad\quad \text{(Law 1.7)}
\end{aligned}$$

If we wish we can abbreviate the working as follows:

$$x - 5 + 5 = 8 + 5$$
$$x + 0 = 13$$
$$x = 13$$

Example

Solve $(y + 5) - 7 = 19$.

$$(y + 5) - 7 + 7 = 19 + 7$$
$$(y + 5) = 26$$
$$y + 5 - 5 = 26 - 5$$
$$y + 0 = 21$$
$$y = 21$$

Check this answer in the original equation: $(21 + 5) - 7 = 26 - 7 = 19$.

Exercise 1.11

Solve the following equations:

1. $x + 4 = 17$
2. $y - 3 = 5$
3. $(p + 3) + 7 = 12$
4. $(q - 15) + 32 = 58$
5. $(x + 37) - 29 = 11$
6. $(y - 82) - 93 = -58$
7. $(x + 5) - 6 = -{}^-4$

Subtraction of negative numbers

We shall be exploring the solution of equations in much more detail in a later chapter. You might have had difficulty with question (7) in the last exercise. The awkward part was probably $-{}^-4$. To see if we can make subtraction in such cases more understandable we will look at the matter more closely.

In each of the following problems the answer is 4: $6 - 2$; $7 - 3$; $8 - 4$; $9 - 5$; $10 - 6$; $5 - 1$; $4 - 0$. This means that we can always convert one subtraction sum into a different subtraction sum by adding or subtracting the same integer from each of the two numbers involved. For example, we can convert $6 - 2$ into $9 - 5$ by adding 3 to both 6 and 2.

We will now apply this idea to a more difficult problem, e.g. $0 - {}^-2$. Add $^+2$ to both 0 and $^-2$. The problem thus becomes $2 - 0$, and the answer is 2. (In fact the easiest subtraction to perform is where we subtract 0.) An alternative approach is:

$$0 - {}^-2 = 0 + {}^-({}^-2) = 0 + \text{inverse of } {}^-2$$
$$= 0 + {}^+2 = 2$$

We conclude that $\qquad 0 - ({}^-2) = 2 \text{ or } {}^+2 \text{ or } +2$
Therefore $\qquad -({}^-2) = -(-2) = +2 = {}^+2 = 2$
Now consider $0 - (+2)$. This time add $^-2$ to each number. We obtain:

$$^-2 - 0 = {}^-2 = -2$$
$$\text{This means } -(+2) = -({}^+2) = -2 = {}^-2$$

We have already discovered that adding $^-2$ is like subtracting 2. Therefore:

$$+(^-2) = +(-2) = ^-2 = -2$$

And it is obvious that adding $^+2$ is like adding 2. So:

$$+(^+2) = +(+2) = +2 = 2$$

These four results give us the following rules, where a is any integer:

$$+(^+a) = +(+a) = +a = ^+a = a$$
$$+(^-a) = +(-a) = ^-a = -a$$
$$-(^+a) = -(+a) = -a = ^-a \qquad \textit{1.9}$$
$$-(^-a) = -(-a) = ^+a = +a = a$$

These results are sometimes stated as follows: like signs give $+$, unlike signs give $-$. But that rule, as stated in those terms, can lead to errors if it is improperly applied. The results are better remembered in the form given in Law 1.9.

Examples

$$6 + (-2) = 6 - 2 = 4$$
$$6 - (-2) = 6 + 2 = 8$$
$$6 - (+2) = 6 - 2 = 4$$
$$-6 - (+2) = -6 - 2 = -8$$

Exercise 1.12

Simplify the following:

1. $5 + (-3)$
2. $7 - (+4)$
3. $18 + (-11)$
4. $43 - (-27)$
5. $-19 + (+32)$
6. $-36 + (-27)$
7. $-14 - (-15)$
8. $-23 - (-9)$
9. $106 + (-73)$
10. $325 - (-237) + (-176) - (+532)$
11. $(778 - 139) - (-586)$
12. $(165 - 93) - (24 - 45)$

1.8 Division

So far we have considered only three operations: $+$, $\times$ and $-$. We will now investigate the fourth. Looking back to Table 1.2, we can answer such questions as:

$$2 \times ? = 10$$

We look along the row level with 2 in the left-hand column until we reach number 10. This is under 5 on the top row, so the answer is 5.
   Taking another example:

$$9 \times ? = 54$$

From the table we discover that ? is 6. However, instead of asking the question, 'What number is it which, when multiplied by 9, gives an answer 54?' we invent a new operation to express the question more easily. We call this operation division. And we write the question as:

$$54 \div 9 = ?$$

In such problems the number we divide (here 54) is called the *dividend*, the number by which we divide (here 9) is called the *divisor*, and the answer is called the *quotient* (here 6).

Example

Divide 9738 by 9. Here Table 1.2 is of no use to us, since it does not extend far enough. We set out our working as follows:

$$
\begin{array}{r}
9)9738(1082 \quad or \quad 9)\underline{9738} \\
\underline{9} \qquad\qquad\qquad 1082 \\
\overline{73} \\
\underline{72} \\
\overline{18} \\
\underline{18} \\
\overline{00}
\end{array}
$$

A calculator check gives:

Step 1 insert 9738
Step 2 insert $\div$

Step 3   insert 9
Step 4   insert =

The answer checks with the above.

Example

Divide 9738 by 29. We set out the working as follows:

$$
\begin{array}{r}
29)9738(335 \\
87 \\
\hline
103 \\
87 \\
\hline
168 \\
145 \\
\hline
23
\end{array}
$$

Here the answer does not work out exactly. The quotient is 335, but there is a remainder of 23.

Example

A 2000 mm length of timber is to be cut into strips each 65 mm long. How many strips can be cut and what length is left over? We must divide 2000 by 65:

$$
\begin{array}{r}
65)2000(30 \\
195 \\
\hline
50
\end{array}
$$

There will be 30 strips and a length of 50 mm left over.

Exercise 1.13

Work out the answers to the following. Check the answers to questions 1 to 8 by calculator.

1. $93 \div 3$
2. $124 \div 4$
3. $755 \div 5$
4. $84\,864 \div 6$

5. $21\,749 \div 7$
6. $2827 \div 11$
7. $20\,757 \div 37$
8. $303\,232 \div 412$
9. $243 \div 7$
10. $409 \div 8$
11. $6872 \div 11$
12. $4896 \div 23$
13. Assuming that force, mass and acceleration of a body are connected by the relation $F = m \cdot a$, determine the acceleration produced by a force of 651 N acting on a mass of 93 kg.
14. 17 equal capacitors are in parallel, giving a total capacitance of 952 microfarads. Determine the capacitance of each. Assume the total capacitance is found by adding the separate capacitances together.
15. A hand-operated pump is used to empty a tank of water. The tank contains $7\,352\,964$ cm^3 of water. If each stroke of the pump extracts 750 cm^3 determine how many times the pump will have to be operated to almost empty the tank, leaving a volume of water less than 750 cm^3. Determine the quantity of water remaining in the tank.

1.9 Fractions

In some of the above examples our division led to a quotient together with a remainder (which is less than the divisor). We will now analyse that matter in more detail.

Suppose we ask the question $3 \div 5 = ?$ and look for the answer in Table 1.2. No matter how we search the table we cannot find an integer which corresponds with the answer. So we have to invent a new kind of number which will enable us to discover an answer. We call this new number a fraction, and we write the fraction to answer the last question as:

$$3/5 \quad \text{or} \quad \tfrac{3}{5}$$

Three is the *numerator*, and 5 is the *denominator*. In order to fit the facts this must mean that:

$$3/5 \quad \text{or} \quad \tfrac{3}{5} = 3 \div 5$$

Other examples of fractions are 4/7, 2/9, 11/13, 91/107, 1/2, 1/3 and 1/4.

To learn how to deal with fractions we will first consider Fig. 1.7. We shall be developing this idea extensively later, so it is essential to understand the basic principles. They provide a method of doing geometry by means of arithmetic and algebra.

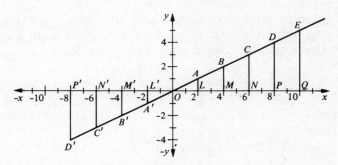

Figure 1.7

Fig. 1.7 is made up of points, lines and angles. The two lines Ox and Oy are called axes. They provide us with a method of fixing the position of every point in their plane. For example:

> A is 2 units along Ox and 1 unit along Oy
> B is 4 units along Ox and 2 units along Oy
> C is 6 units along Ox and 3 units along Oy
> D is 8 units along Ox and 4 units along Oy
> A' is -2 units along Ox and -1 units along Oy
> B' is -4 units along Ox and -2 units along Oy
> C' is -6 units along Ox and -3 units along Oy

These distances along Ox (x distance) and Oy (y distance) are called the *co-ordinates* of the point. The co-ordinates of A are $(2, 1)$ (we always quote the x distance first), the co-ordinates of B are $(4, 2)$, and the co-ordinates of C' are $(-6, -3)$.

When we draw the line OA and produce it in both directions we notice that it also passes through B, C, D, E, A', B', C' and D'. An important property of a line is that it maintains the same direction at all its points. The line $OABCDE$ slopes. The measure of its slope is called its gradient.

> The gradient of OA is defined to be $AL/OL = 1/2 = \frac{1}{2}$
> The gradient of OB is defined to be $BM/OM = 2/4 = \frac{2}{4}$
> The gradient of OC is defined to be $CN/ON = 3/6 = \frac{3}{6}$

But the gradients of all the segments of the line must be equal, because of the direction property of the line. This means that:

$$1/2 = 2/4 = 3/6 = 4/8 = 5/10 = \cdots$$
$$= -1/-2 = -2/-4 = -3/-6 \text{ etc.}$$

These are said to be equivalent fractions. Look at them carefully and note the connection.

Any fraction can be converted into an equivalent fraction by multiplying numerator and denominator (top and bottom) by the same number, positive or negative. For example:

$$\frac{1}{2} = \frac{1 \times 3}{2 \times 3} = \frac{3}{6}; \quad \frac{5}{10} = \frac{5 \times 7}{10 \times 7} = \frac{35}{70}$$

Or, again:

$$\frac{4}{8} = \frac{\cancel{4} \times 1}{\cancel{4} \times 2} = \frac{1}{2}$$

We say we have cancelled numerator and denominator by 4. This really means we may divide numerator and denominator by the same number and the resulting fraction will be equivalent. Again:

$$-1/-2 = 1/2; \; -2/-4 = 2/4; \; -3/-6 = 3/6$$

This leads us to believe that, for any a and b:

$$-a/-b = a/b = +(a/b)$$

Exercise 1.14

Draw the graph joining the points $(1, -2)$, $(2, -4)$, $(3, -6)$, $(4, -8)$, $(5, -10)$, $(-1, 2)$, $(-2, 4)$, $(-3, 6)$, $(-4, 8)$. Use the graph to discover another set of equivalent fractions.

Note that this graph slopes down to the right. We say it has a *negative gradient*. We note that $-1/2 = 1/-2$, and that each one is negative. We now note that:

$$\begin{aligned}
(+a/+b) &= +a/b \\
(+a/-b) &= -a/b \\
(-a/-b) &= +a/b \\
(-a/+b) &= -a/b
\end{aligned} \qquad 1.10$$

These rules for the combination of signs can now be added to those in Law 1.9.

Examples

1. 7/8 can be converted into $\dfrac{7 \times 9}{8 \times 9} = \dfrac{63}{72}$ (equivalent).

2. $\dfrac{16}{24}$ can be written $\dfrac{2 \times 8}{3 \times 8} = \dfrac{2}{3}$, by dividing top and bottom by 8,

    i.e. cancelling by 8, usually written as $\dfrac{\cancel{16}^{2}}{\cancel{24}_{3}} = \dfrac{2}{3}$.

3. $\dfrac{-26}{-91} = +\dfrac{26}{91}$ (rules above) $= +\dfrac{\cancel{26}^{2}}{\cancel{91}_{7}} = \dfrac{2}{7}$, cancelling down by 13.

Exercise 1.15

Write the following as equivalent fractions in their simplest form (i.e. where no more cancelling may be done):

1. 9/12
2. 12/15
3. 16/20
4. 18/24
5. 21/28
6. 32/48
7. −10/25
8. −8/−32
9. +56/−72
10. −144/−156
11. Write as an equivalent fraction with denominator 24 the fraction 3/8. (We have to multiply 8 by 3 to obtain 24. If we multiply the denominator by 3 then we must also multiply the numerator by 3.)
12. Write as equivalent fractions with denominator 144 the following:
    2/3; 3/4; 5/6; 7/8; 13/16; 19/36; 37/48.
13. Write as equivalent fractions with denominator 60 the following:
    2/3; 3/4; 3/5; 4/5; 5/6; 7/12; 11/12; 5/12; 13/15; 7/15.
14. Write as equivalent fractions with denominator 48 the following:
    2/3; 3/4; 5/8; 7/8; 5/6; 11/12; 7/12; 13/24; 19/24; 13/16; 9/16.

Operations on fractions

Now that we have encountered fractions we need to know how to deal with them when they are operated on by the four operations $+$, $-$, $\times$ and $\div$. To find out we will use the device, adapted for fractions, which we used at the very beginning to represent integers, namely distances along a line (Fig. 1.8).

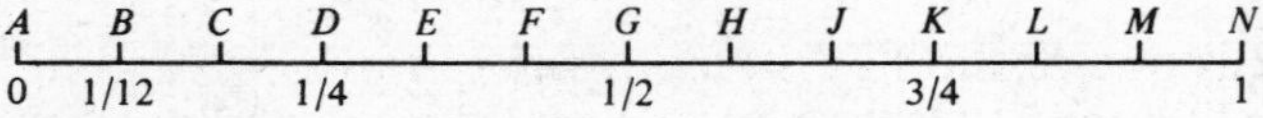

Figure 1.8

In Fig. 1.8 suppose $AN = 1$. Divide this into 12 equal parts, AB, BC, CD, etc. G is the middle point, so $AG = 1/2$, the result of dividing AN by 2. In the same way, $AD = 1/4$, because AD is the result of dividing AN by 4. From Fig. 1.8:

$$AG = 2AD$$

So $1/2 = 2 \times \frac{1}{4}$. But, by equivalent fractions, $1/2 = 2/4$. Therefore:

$$\tfrac{2}{4} = 2 \times \tfrac{1}{4}$$

Again, $AK = 9$ small units $= 3 \times 3$ small units $= 3 \times AD = 3 \times \frac{1}{4}$. But, as AK ($= 9/12$) is also, by equivalent fractions, equal to $3/4$, then:

$$\tfrac{3}{4} = 3 \times \tfrac{1}{4}$$

These results lead us to believe that, when a and b are any integers:

$$\frac{a}{b} = a \times \frac{1}{b} \quad \text{or} \quad a \times \frac{1}{b} = \frac{a}{b} \tag{i}$$

So to multiply a fraction, $\dfrac{1}{a}$, by an integer we merely multiply the numerator by that number. For example:

$$3 \times 1/7 = (3 \times 1)/7 = 3/7$$

Exercise 1.16

Express the following as single fractions:

1. $4 \times 1/5$
2. $7 \times 1/8$

3. $8 \times 1/11$
4. $21 \times 1/92$
5. $9 \times 1/17$
6. $105 \times 1/371$

Because, in Fig. 1.8, AD is divided into 3 equal parts, one of which is AB, then:

$$AB = AD/3 = \tfrac{1}{3} \times AD \text{ (by (i))} = \tfrac{1}{3} \times \tfrac{1}{4}$$

But AB is one of the 12 equal parts into which we divide AN, that is:

$$AB = AN/12 = 1/12 \quad \text{so} \quad \tfrac{1}{3} \times \tfrac{1}{4} = \tfrac{1}{12}$$

In other words, when we multiply a fraction, $\dfrac{1}{a}$, by another fraction, $\dfrac{1}{b}$, the result is the same as it would be if we multiplied the denominators together:

$$\tfrac{1}{4} \times \tfrac{1}{5} = \tfrac{1}{20}; \qquad \tfrac{1}{3} \times \tfrac{1}{7} = \tfrac{1}{21}; \qquad \tfrac{1}{11} \times \tfrac{1}{8} = \tfrac{1}{88}$$

Thus, for any integers b and c:

$$\frac{1}{c} \times \frac{1}{b} = \frac{1}{bc} \tag{ii}$$

Exercise 1.17

Express the following as single fractions:

1. $(1/4) \times (1/12)$
2. $(1/5) \times (1/17)$
3. $(1/15)(1/24)$ (here the $\times$ is omitted, but understood)
4. $(1/17)(1/31)$
5. $(1/12)(1/13)$
6. $(1/17)(1/14)$

From Fig. 1.8:

$$AF = 5 \times AB = 5 \times \tfrac{1}{12} = \tfrac{5}{12} \text{ (by (i))}$$
$$AL = 10 \times AB = 10 \times \tfrac{1}{12} = \tfrac{10}{12} \text{ (by (i))}$$

But $AL = 2AF$. Therefore $\tfrac{10}{12} = 2 \times \tfrac{5}{12}$ (similar to (i)). Again:

$$AC = 2 \times AB = 2 \times \tfrac{1}{12} = \tfrac{2}{12} \text{ (by (i))}$$
$$AG = 6 \times AB = 6 \times \tfrac{1}{12} = 6/12 \text{ (by (i))}$$

But $AG = 3AC$. So $\frac{6}{12} = 3 \times \frac{2}{12}$, again similar to (i). These results lead us to the rule:

$$n \times \frac{a}{b} = \frac{na}{b} \qquad\qquad \text{(iii)}$$

Exercise 1.18

Express the following as single fractions:

1. $6 \times (3/25)$
2. $7 \times (4/39)$
3. $8 \times (5/73)$
4. $9 \times (11/124)$
5. $11 \times (12/325)$
6. $(3/4) \times 3$ (Notice something unusual about the answer to this. We will be exploring such fractions later.)

As yet not one of (i), (ii) or (iii) has told us how to multiply two general fractions together. This is our next goal. Divide AK into 3 equal parts. We get:

$$AD = DG = GK = \tfrac{1}{3}AK \text{ or } \frac{AK}{3}$$

But $AK = \tfrac{3}{4}$. Therefore $AG = \tfrac{2}{3} \times \tfrac{3}{4} = \tfrac{6}{12}$ because $AG = 6AB$ and $AB = 1/12$. This means that:

$$\tfrac{2}{3} \times \tfrac{3}{4} \text{ is equal to } \tfrac{6}{12}$$

And that leads us to believe that, where a, b, c and d are any integers:

$$\frac{a}{b} \times \frac{c}{d} = \frac{a \times c}{b \times d} \qquad\qquad 1.11$$

This law incorporates rules (i), (ii) and (iii). It means that:

$$(3/4) \times (5/7) = (3 \times 5)/(4 \times 7) = 15/28$$

$$(5/8) \times (7/9) = \frac{5 \times 7}{8 \times 9} = \frac{35}{72}$$

Exercise 1.19

Express the following as single fractions:

1. $\frac{3}{7} \times \frac{4}{9}$
2. $\frac{5}{9} \times \frac{7}{9}$
3. $\frac{6}{11} \times \frac{3}{5}$
4. $\frac{7}{13} \times \frac{5}{6}$
5. $\frac{5}{8} \times \frac{3}{4}$
6. $\frac{6}{11} \times \frac{8}{13}$
7. $\frac{14}{15} \times \frac{16}{17}$
8. $\frac{11}{12} \times \frac{13}{14}$
9. $\frac{19}{20} \times \frac{23}{24}$
10. $\frac{29}{30} \times \frac{49}{50}$

The answer to $\frac{2}{3} \times \frac{3}{4}$ was given as $\frac{6}{12}$, but we know from equivalent fractions that 6/12 reduces to 1/2. Therefore:

$$\frac{2}{3} \times \frac{3}{4} = \frac{1}{2}$$

And we can arrive at this result by what we call cancelling, as follows:

$$\frac{2}{3} \times \frac{3}{4} = \frac{{}^1 2}{{}_1 3} \times \frac{3^1}{4_2} = \frac{1 \times 1}{1 \times 2} = \frac{1}{2}$$

Examples

1. $\dfrac{9}{10} \times \dfrac{5}{6} = \dfrac{{}^3 9}{{}_2 10} \times \dfrac{5^1}{6_2} = \dfrac{3 \times 1}{2 \times 2} = \dfrac{3}{4}$

2. $\dfrac{35}{48} \times \dfrac{32}{45} = \dfrac{{}^7 35}{{}_3 48} \times \dfrac{32^2}{45_9} = \dfrac{7 \times 2}{3 \times 9} = \dfrac{14}{27}$

Exercise 1.20

Express the following as single fractions in their lowest terms:

1. $\frac{3}{4} \times \frac{2}{5}$
2. $\frac{3}{5} \times \frac{7}{12}$
3. $\frac{3}{10} \times \frac{5}{8}$
4. $\frac{6}{7} \times \frac{14}{15}$
5. $\frac{21}{40} \times \frac{16}{55}$

6. $\frac{56}{99} \times \frac{55}{72}$

7. $\frac{42}{51} \times \frac{34}{49}$

8. $\frac{84}{105} \times \frac{65}{104}$

9. $\frac{63}{92} \times \frac{46}{147}$

Division of fractions

We can now look at the rule for dividing by a fraction. One of our problems above was:

$$\tfrac{2}{3} \times \tfrac{3}{4} = \tfrac{1}{2}$$

With that in mind, suppose we were asked the question:

$$\tfrac{2}{3} \times ? = \tfrac{1}{2}$$

Obviously we realize the answer must be $\tfrac{3}{4}$. But we also know we could have asked the question as:

$$? = \tfrac{1}{2} \div \tfrac{2}{3}$$

We know, from Law 1.11, that $\tfrac{3}{4} = \tfrac{1}{2} \times \tfrac{3}{2}$. So this means that:

$$\tfrac{1}{2} \div \tfrac{2}{3} = \tfrac{1}{2} \times \tfrac{3}{2}$$

In other words, instead of dividing by the fraction 2/3 we multiply by the fraction 3/2, i.e. the fraction 2/3 inverted. And that leads us to the rule:

$$\frac{a}{b} \div \frac{p}{q} = \frac{a}{b} \times \frac{q}{p} \qquad\qquad 1.12$$

Examples

1. $\dfrac{3}{4} \div \dfrac{8}{9} = \dfrac{3}{4} \times \dfrac{9}{8} = \dfrac{3 \times 9}{4 \times 8} = \dfrac{27}{32}$

2. $\dfrac{9}{10} \div \dfrac{9}{5} = \dfrac{{}^{1}9}{{}_{2}10} \times \dfrac{5^{1}}{9_{1}} = \dfrac{1 \times 1}{2 \times 1} = \dfrac{1}{2}$

3. $\dfrac{56}{99} \div \dfrac{72}{55} = \dfrac{{}^{7}56}{{}_{9}99} \times \dfrac{55^{5}}{72_{9}} = \dfrac{7 \times 5}{9 \times 9} = \dfrac{35}{81}$

Exercise 1.21

Express the following as single fractions in their lowest terms:

1. $\frac{3}{4} \div \frac{5}{2}$
2. $\frac{3}{5} \div \frac{12}{7}$
3. $\frac{11}{16} \div \frac{15}{16}$
4. $\frac{12}{17} \div \frac{18}{17}$
5. $\frac{32}{45} \div \frac{48}{55}$
6. $\frac{42}{51} \div \frac{49}{34}$
7. $\frac{84}{105} \div \frac{104}{65}$
8. $\frac{63}{92} \div \frac{147}{46}$
9. $\frac{16}{55} \div \frac{40}{21}$
10. $\frac{55}{72} \div \frac{99}{56}$

Further laws

When we were investigating addition we discovered that zero was the identity element, i.e. that adding zero to any integer left that integer unchanged. For example:

$$7 + 0 = 0 + 7 = 7$$

This principle still operates when we are dealing with fractions, for example:

$$3/4 + 0 = 3/4 = 0 + 3/4$$

We also discovered inverse elements under addition, i.e.

$$^+a + {}^-a = {}^-a + {}^+a = 0$$

And the same principle carries over into fractions. For instance:

$$^+\tfrac{2}{3} + {}^-\tfrac{2}{3} = {}^-\tfrac{2}{3} + {}^+\tfrac{2}{3} = 0$$

The question now is: 'Can we find similar principles to these under the operation of multiplication?'. Look back to Table 1.2. We notice along the top row, underneath the digits by which we are multiplying:

$$2 \times 1 = 2, 3 \times 1 = 3, 4 \times 1 = 4 \ldots 7 \times 1 = 7, \text{ and so on}$$

In other words $a \times 1 = a$ where a is any integer
By referring to the first column of Table 1.2 we conclude that:

$$1 \times a = a$$

That means 1 is the identity element under multiplication (multiplying any integer by 1 leaves that integer unchanged). If we examine the table in reverse order we conclude that:

$$2 \div 1 = 2, 3 \div 1 = 3 \ldots 7 \div 1 = 7, \text{ and so on}$$

Therefore: $\qquad\qquad\qquad\qquad a \div 1 = a$

However, it is not true that $1 \div a = a$.

Thus we can multiply or divide by 1 and the operation leaves the number unchanged:

$$a \times 1 = 1 \times a = 1 \qquad\qquad\qquad 1.13$$

So the question is, 'If there is an identity element under multiplication, will there be inverse elements too?'. From what we have done already on fractions, we know that

$$\frac{3}{4} \times \frac{4}{3} = \frac{{}^1\cancel{3}}{{}_1\cancel{4}} \times \frac{\cancel{4}^1}{\cancel{3}_1} = \frac{1 \times 1}{1 \times 1} = 1$$

and

$$\frac{5}{11} \times \frac{11}{5} = \frac{{}^1\cancel{5}}{{}_1\cancel{11}} \times \frac{\cancel{11}^1}{\cancel{5}_1} = \frac{1 \times 1}{1 \times 1} = 1$$

4/3 is said to be the inverse of 3/4 under multiplication, and 11/5 is said to be the inverse of 5/11 under multiplication. This leads us to believe that b/a is the inverse of a/b under multiplication. That is:

$$\frac{a}{b} \times \frac{b}{a} = 1 \qquad\qquad\qquad 1.14$$

Again, we can use these ideas to solve simple equations.

Examples

1. Solve $2x = 6$. The answer to this is obvious, but notice the method:

$$\tfrac{1}{2} \times (2x) = \tfrac{1}{2} \times 6$$

$$\left(\frac{1}{2} \times \frac{2}{1}\right) \times x = \frac{1}{{}_1\cancel{2}} \times \frac{\cancel{6}^3}{1} \qquad \text{(by Law 1.4, associative)}$$

(By Law 1.14) $\quad 1 \times x = \tfrac{3}{1} = 3$

(By Law 1.13) $\quad x = 3$

2. Solve $\dfrac{3}{5}x = \dfrac{7}{34}$.

$$\begin{aligned}
\textit{Step 1} \quad & \tfrac{5}{3} \times (\tfrac{3}{5} \times x) = \tfrac{5}{3} \times \tfrac{7}{34} \\
\textit{Step 2} \quad & (\tfrac{5}{3} \times \tfrac{3}{5}) \times x = \tfrac{35}{102} \\
\textit{Step 3} \quad & 1 \times x = 35/102 \\
\textit{Step 4} \quad & x = 35/102
\end{aligned}$$

$$\textit{Check} \quad \frac{3}{5} \times \frac{35}{102} = \frac{1 \times 7}{1 \times 34} = \frac{7}{34}$$

Exercise 1.22

Write down the inverses of the following fractions under multiplication:

1. 2/3
2. 3/4
3. 4/5
4. 7/11
5. 15/23
6. 13/8
7. 15/7
8. 23/14.

Solve the following equations:

9. $3x = 6$
10. $4x = 12$
11. $7y = 13$
12. $\tfrac{3}{4}z = \tfrac{2}{9}$
13. $\tfrac{5}{8}t = \tfrac{5}{13}$
14. $\tfrac{12}{35}x = \tfrac{9}{77}$

Addition of fractions

We still need to know how to add fractions together. Referring again to Fig. 1.8:

$$AC + CF = AF \quad \text{i.e.} \quad \tfrac{2}{12} + \tfrac{3}{12} = \tfrac{5}{12}$$
$$AF + FH = AH \quad \text{i.e.} \quad \tfrac{5}{12} + \tfrac{2}{12} = \tfrac{7}{12}$$

Adding fractions together is easy when they have the same

denominator. We simply add the numerators together:

$$\frac{a}{c} + \frac{b}{c} = \frac{a+b}{c}$$

1.15

Exercise 1.23

Add together the following pairs of fractions:

1. 3/5, 1/5
2. 2/7, 4/7
3. 3/11, 4/11
4. 7/13, 4/13
5. 8/15, 5/15.

Add together the following pairs of fractions and express the answers in their simplest forms:

6. 3/10, 1/10
7. 4/15, 8/15
8. 7/24, 13/24
9. 9/35, 6/35.

Simplify the following:

10. 1/12 + 5/12 + 1/12 + 1/12
11. 5/24 + 7/24 + 1/24 + 1/24
12. 1/60 + 7/60 + 11/60 + 13/60

But how do we calculate, e.g. $5/12 + 1/6$? We need to convert the problem into one where the two fractions have the same denominator, because we are able to answer that type of question. By equivalent fractions we know that:

$\frac{1}{6} = \frac{2}{12}$ (i.e. by multiplying numerator and denominator by 2)

$$\text{So } \frac{5}{12} + \frac{1}{6} = \frac{5}{12} + \frac{2}{12} = \frac{5+2}{12} = \frac{7}{12}$$

$$\text{Again } \frac{3}{8} + \frac{1}{4} = \frac{3}{8} + \frac{2}{8} = \frac{3+2}{8} = \frac{5}{8}$$

Exercise 1.24

Add together the following fractions:

1. 3/10, 2/5
2. 1/12, 5/6
3. 5/16, 1/4
4. 3/20, 2/5
5. 5/12, 1/4
6. 1/10, 3/5
7. 3/8, 1/2
8. 1/8, 1/4
9. 3/10, 3/20, 1/5
10. 7/20, 2/5, 1/10

In the above problems involving two fractions we changed the denominator of one fraction into that of the other. But sometimes we have to change both. For instance:

$$\frac{3}{8} + \frac{1}{3} = \frac{9}{24} + \frac{8}{24} = \frac{9+8}{24} = \frac{17}{24}$$

Twenty-four is the least number which can be found by multiplying both 8 and 3 by the same integer. It is a multiple of 8, and it is also a multiple of 3. It is, therefore, a *common multiple* of 8 and 3. In fact it is the lowest common multiple (LCM). We shall discuss the question of LCMs in more detail in Chapter 3. For the present we will consider only those cases which are relatively simple.

The LCM of 2 and 3 is 6; of 3 and 4 is 12; of 3 and 6 is 6; of 15 and 10 is 30; and of 24 and 18 is 72.

Exercise 1.25

Calculate the LCM of the following pairs of numbers:

1. 4, 6
2. 8, 12
3. 9, 12
4. 3, 5
5. 4, 7
6. 16, 24
7. 15, 20
8. 18, 24

9. 20, 30
10. 14, 21
11. 21, 28
12. 24, 32

Add together the following pairs of fractions:

13. 3/4, 1/6
14. 3/8, 7/12
15. 2/9, 5/12
16. 1/3, 2/5
17. 3/4, 1/7
18. 5/16, 7/24
19. 4/15, 3/20
20. 4/21, 5/28

Subtraction of fractions

Subtraction of fractions follows similar principles.

Examples

1. Simplify $3/10 - 2/15$.

$$\frac{3}{10} - \frac{2}{15} = \frac{9}{30} - \frac{4}{30} = \frac{9-4}{30} = \frac{\cancel{5}^{\,1}}{\cancel{30}_{6}} = \frac{1}{6}$$

2. $\dfrac{17}{36} - \dfrac{5}{24} = \dfrac{34}{72} - \dfrac{15}{72} = \dfrac{34-15}{72} = \dfrac{19}{72}$

Exercise 1.26

Simplify the following, giving your answer in the lowest terms:

1. $4/5 - 2/3$
2. $11/12 - 3/4$
3. $15/16 - 3/5$
4. $8/35 - 2/21$
5. $11/18 - 9/24$

6. $7/16 - 3/10$
7. $9/16 - 7/20$
8. $5/9 - 5/48$
9. $25/32 - 11/24$
10. $39/40 - 5/8 - 3/16$

1.10 Improper fractions and mixed numbers

A fraction means a part of a whole. $5/4$ appears, on the face of it, to be a fraction. We may write it as:

$$\frac{4+1}{4} = \frac{{}^{1}\cancel{4}}{\cancel{4}_1} + \frac{1}{4} = 1 + \frac{1}{4}, \quad \text{which we abbreviate to } 1\tfrac{1}{4}$$

In other words it is bigger than 1. It is not, therefore, a true fraction. We call it an *improper fraction*.

If in the fraction a/b, a is bigger than b, then this will always be an improper fraction, assuming both a and b are positive. For our calculations we need to be able to convert an improper fraction into a whole number and a true fraction (called a mixed number), and vice versa.

Examples

1. $15/4 = \dfrac{12+3}{4} = \dfrac{{}^{3}\cancel{12}}{\cancel{4}_1} + \dfrac{3}{4} = 3 + \dfrac{3}{4} = 3\tfrac{3}{4}$

2. $63/8$. To find out how to split up 63 we divide it by 8:

$$\frac{63}{8} = \frac{56+7}{8} = \frac{{}^{7}\cancel{56}}{\cancel{8}_1} + \frac{7}{8} = 7 + \frac{7}{8} \qquad \begin{array}{r} 8)63(7 \\ 56 \\ \hline 7 \end{array}$$

$$= 7\tfrac{7}{8}$$

3. $$\frac{394}{125} = \frac{375}{125} + \frac{19}{125} \qquad \begin{array}{r} 125)394(3 \\ 375 \\ \hline 19 \end{array}$$
$$= 3 + \frac{19}{125} = 3\tfrac{19}{125}$$

In fact we usually miss out the step $\frac{375}{125}$ because, by carrying out the above division, we know that its value is 3.

4.
$$98/16 = 6 + \frac{\overset{1}{2}}{\underset{8}{16}} = 6\tfrac{1}{8} \qquad \begin{array}{r} 16)98(6 \\ 96 \\ \hline 2 \end{array}$$

5.
$$3\tfrac{2}{3} = 3 + \frac{2}{3} = \frac{3}{1} + \frac{2}{3} = \frac{9}{3} + \frac{2}{3} = \frac{9+2}{3} = \frac{11}{3}$$

6.
$$6\tfrac{23}{51} = 6 + \frac{23}{51} = \frac{6}{1} + \frac{23}{51} = \frac{6 \times 51}{1 \times 51} + \frac{23}{51}$$

$$= \frac{306}{51} + \frac{23}{51} = \frac{306+23}{51} = 329/51$$

7.
$$4\tfrac{6}{9} = 4 + \frac{\overset{2}{6}}{\underset{3}{9}} = \frac{4}{1} + \frac{2}{3} = \frac{12}{3} + \frac{2}{3} = \frac{12+2}{3} = \frac{14}{3}$$

Exercise 1.27

Convert the following improper fractions to mixed numbers:

1. 8/5
2. 13/6
3. 17/8
4. 14/9
5. 25/7
6. 32/11
7. 54/7
8. 124/29
9. 607/30
10. 1036/25.

Convert the following mixed numbers to improper fractions:

11. $2\tfrac{1}{4}$
12. $3\tfrac{1}{2}$

13. $4\frac{3}{10}$
14. $17\frac{1}{5}$
15. $5\frac{13}{20}$
16. $7\frac{4}{11}$
17. $2\frac{135}{248}$
18. $23\frac{3}{4}$
19. $109\frac{1}{5}$
20. $43\frac{3}{17}$

Operations on mixed numbers and improper fractions

Now we can apply the following two principles in addition to those already established.

Principle one.   In addition and subtraction of fractions we always convert improper fractions into mixed numbers.

Principle two.   In multiplication and division of fractions we always convert mixed numbers into improper fractions.

Examples

1. $2\frac{1}{2} + 3\frac{1}{4} = 2 + \frac{1}{2} + 3 + \frac{1}{4}$
     $= 2 + 3 + \frac{1}{2} + \frac{1}{4}$ (by Law 1.5)
     (we can add in any order convenient to us)

   $$= 5 + \frac{2}{4} + \frac{1}{4} = 5 + \frac{2+1}{4} = 5\frac{3}{4}$$

2. $2\frac{1}{4} - 1\frac{3}{4} = 2 + \frac{1}{4} - 1 - \frac{3}{4}$
     $= 2 - 1 + \frac{1}{4} - \frac{3}{4}$ (still really Law 1.5)

   $$= 1 + \frac{1-3}{4} = 1 + \frac{-2}{4} = 1 - \frac{1}{2} = \frac{1}{2}$$

Here some people prefer to ignore principle one and to proceed:

$$\frac{9}{4} - \frac{7}{4} = \frac{9-7}{4} = \frac{2}{4} = \frac{1}{2}$$

Where small whole numbers and small denominators are involved this often provides a quicker solution, but for large numbers and large denominators the working becomes unwieldy.

3. $$3\tfrac{5}{6} + \tfrac{5}{2} - \tfrac{7}{3} = 3 + \tfrac{5}{6} + 2 + \tfrac{1}{2} - 2 - \tfrac{1}{3}$$

$$= 3 + 2 - 2 + \tfrac{5}{6} + \tfrac{1}{2} - \tfrac{1}{3} = 3 + \tfrac{5}{6} + \tfrac{3}{6} - \tfrac{2}{6}$$

$$= 3 + \frac{5 + 3 - 2}{6} = 3 + \frac{6}{6} = 3 + 1 = 4$$

4. $$4\tfrac{2}{7} + \tfrac{25}{14} - 1\tfrac{1}{6} = 4\tfrac{2}{7} + 1\tfrac{11}{14} - 1\tfrac{1}{6}$$

$$= 4 + 1 - 1 + \frac{2}{7} + \frac{11}{14} - \frac{1}{6}$$

$$= 4 + \frac{2 \times 6}{7 \times 6} + \frac{11 \times 3}{14 \times 3} - \frac{1 \times 7}{6 \times 7}$$

$$= 4 + \frac{12 + 33 - 7}{42} = 4\,\frac{\cancel{38}^{19}}{\cancel{42}_{21}} = 4\tfrac{19}{21}$$

Exercise 1.28

Express as mixed numbers the answers to:

1. $1\tfrac{1}{4} + 3\tfrac{1}{4} + 2\tfrac{1}{4}$
2. $1\tfrac{1}{5} + 2\tfrac{2}{5} + 3\tfrac{1}{5}$
3. $2\tfrac{1}{6} + 3\tfrac{5}{6}$
4. $2\tfrac{1}{4} + \tfrac{5}{4}$
5. $2\tfrac{1}{4} + \tfrac{11}{8}$
6. $3\tfrac{5}{8} + 2\tfrac{1}{4} + \tfrac{1}{2}$
7. $2\tfrac{5}{6} + \tfrac{7}{6} + 1\tfrac{2}{3}$
8. $3\tfrac{5}{8} + 2\tfrac{1}{4} - \tfrac{1}{2}$
9. $7\tfrac{7}{8} - 4\tfrac{3}{4}$
10. $7\tfrac{5}{6} - 6\tfrac{7}{12}$
11. $2\tfrac{3}{10} + \tfrac{69}{10} - \tfrac{8}{5}$
12. $3\tfrac{1}{6} - 2\tfrac{5}{6}$
13. $17\tfrac{3}{53} - 16\tfrac{50}{53}$
14. $18\tfrac{1}{8} - 17\tfrac{5}{6}$
15. $\tfrac{16}{3} + \tfrac{9}{5} - \tfrac{23}{15}$

Examples

1. $$\frac{3}{2} \times \frac{5}{4} = \frac{3 \times 5}{2 \times 4} = \frac{15}{8} = \frac{8+7}{8} = \frac{8}{8} + \frac{7}{8} = 1 + \frac{7}{8} = 1\frac{7}{8}$$

2. $$2\frac{1}{2} \times 3\frac{1}{3} = \frac{5}{{}_1\cancel{2}} \times \frac{\cancel{10}^5}{3} = \frac{5 \times 5}{1 \times 3} = \frac{25}{3} = \frac{24+1}{3} = \frac{24}{3} + \frac{1}{3} = 8\frac{1}{3}$$

3. $$3\frac{1}{5} \times 4\frac{3}{4} \div 2\frac{2}{19} = \frac{16}{5} \times \frac{19}{4} \div \frac{40}{19} = \frac{{}^1\cancel{16}}{5} \times \frac{19}{\cancel{4}_1} \times \frac{19}{\cancel{40}_{10}}$$

$$= \frac{1 \times 19 \times 19}{5 \times 1 \times 10} = \frac{361}{50} = \frac{350+11}{50} = 7\frac{11}{50}$$

Exercise 1.29

Calculate the following:

1. $\frac{3}{4} \times \frac{5}{2}$
2. $1\frac{1}{4} \times 2\frac{1}{4}$
3. $3\frac{3}{4} \times 1\frac{1}{5}$
4. $\frac{4}{5} \div 2\frac{1}{4}$
5. $\frac{4}{15} \div 1\frac{3}{5}$
6. $1\frac{1}{3} \div \frac{2}{5}$
7. $1\frac{1}{8} \div 1\frac{2}{7}$
8. $8\frac{1}{6} \times 2\frac{1}{7} \div 2\frac{4}{5}$

Many of the problems we have to deal with in practice involve more than one operation on fractions. For instance, in the motion of bodies we sometimes have to calculate $u + at$ to find the velocity, or $[(u + v)/2] \times t$ to find the distance travelled, and in electrical problems we sometimes have to calculate the value of $(V_1 - V_2) \div R$ to find the current. And we need to know the order in which to carry out those operations. There are two general principles which we follow.

Principle one. Where no brackets are mentioned in the problem then the two operations $\times$ and $\div$ take precedence over $+$ and $-$, i.e. the multiplications and divisions have to be carried out first. This means that problems such as:

$$a \pm b \times c$$
$$a \times b \pm c \times d \pm e \times f$$
$$a \pm b \div c$$
$$a \div b \pm c \div d \pm e \div f$$

(where a, b, c etc. refer to fractions or integers) require us to carry out $\times$ and/or $\div$ before we operate with $+$ and/or $-$.

Principle two.   Where brackets are mentioned then the operations inside these must be carried out before the operations outside, i.e. the operations inside take precedence over those outside. This means that problems such as:

$$(a \pm b) \times c; \qquad (a + b - c) \times d;$$

$$(a + b) \div c; \qquad \frac{a}{(b + c)};$$

$$\frac{a}{(b - c)}; \qquad \frac{(a + b)}{(c + d)}$$

require us to calculate the inside of the brackets first.

Examples

1. $a + b \times c$ *Step 1* Calculate $b \times c = B$.
                           Step 2 Calculate $a + B$.

2. $a - b \times c$ *Step 1* Calculate $b \times c = B$.
                           Step 2 Calculate $a - B$.

3. $ab + cd - ef$ *Step 1* Calculate $ab = A$, $cd = B$, $ef = C$.
                           Step 2 Calculate $A + B - C$.

4. $(a \pm b)c$ *Step 1* Calculate $a \pm b = A$.
                           Step 2 Calculate $A \times c$.

5. $(a + b - c)d$ *Step 1* Calculate $a + b - c = A$.
                           Step 2 Calculate $A \times d$.

6. $a \pm b \div c$ *Step 1* Calculate $b \div c = B$.
                           Step 2 Calculate $a \pm B$.

7. $\dfrac{a}{(b \pm c)}$ *Step 1* Calculate $b \pm c = B$.
                           Step 2 Calculate $a \div B$.

8. $\dfrac{(a \pm b)}{(c \pm d)}$ *Step 1* Calculate $a \pm b = A$.
Step 2 Calculate $c \pm d = B$.
Step 3 Calculate $A \div B$.

Even with all these rules it is still possible to be confused by a problem because sometimes a bracket is omitted when, from our point of view, it should have been inserted. For simplicity we will illustrate this with integers rather than with fractions.

The problem $\dfrac{3+2}{7}$ really means $\dfrac{(3+2)}{7}$ and that means the addition is carried out before we divide. If we think a moment we can see why this is so. A fraction a/b really means $a \div b$, so $\dfrac{3+2}{7}$ really means we have to divide $3 + 2$ by 7. But we do not write $3 + 2 \div 7$, for then $\div$ would take precedence over $+$. Instead we write $(3 + 2) \div 7$. A similar situation exists with $\dfrac{7}{3+2}$.

Therefore when we have a fraction in which the numerator or denominator itself involves an operation between two or more numbers, it helps if we insert brackets.

Examples

1.
$$\frac{4}{5} \times \frac{15}{16} + \frac{3}{4} \div \frac{9}{16} - \frac{1}{8} \times 2\tfrac{2}{7}$$

Step 1
$$\frac{{}^1\cancel{4}}{{}_{1}\cancel{5}} \times \frac{\cancel{15}^3}{\cancel{16}_4} = \frac{3}{4}$$

$$\frac{3}{4} \div \frac{9}{16} = \frac{{}^1\cancel{3}}{{}_{1}\cancel{4}} \times \frac{\cancel{16}^4}{\cancel{9}_{\,3}} = \tfrac{4}{3} = 1\tfrac{1}{3}$$

$$\tfrac{1}{8} \times 2\tfrac{2}{7} = \frac{1}{{}_{1}\cancel{8}} \times \frac{\cancel{16}^2}{7} = \tfrac{2}{7}$$

Step 2 $\tfrac{3}{4} + 1\tfrac{1}{3} - \tfrac{2}{7} = 1 + \tfrac{63}{84} + \tfrac{28}{84} - \tfrac{24}{84} = 1 + \dfrac{63 + 28 - 24}{84}$

$$= 1 + \tfrac{67}{84} = 1\tfrac{67}{84}$$

2.
$$\frac{3\frac{1}{5} + 4\frac{2}{3}}{5\frac{1}{3} - 2\frac{2}{5}} \quad \text{means} \quad \frac{(3\frac{1}{5} + 4\frac{2}{3})}{(5\frac{1}{3} - 2\frac{2}{5})}$$

Step 1
$$3\frac{1}{5} + 4\frac{2}{3} = 7 + \frac{3}{15} + \frac{10}{15} = 7\frac{13}{15}$$
$$5\frac{1}{3} - 2\frac{2}{5} = 3 + \frac{5}{15} - \frac{6}{15} = 3 - \frac{1}{15} = 2 + 1 - \frac{1}{15}$$
$$= 2 + \frac{15}{15} - \frac{1}{15}$$
$$= 2 + \frac{14}{15} = 2\frac{14}{15}$$

Step 2
$$\frac{7\frac{13}{15}}{2\frac{14}{15}} = 7\frac{13}{15} \div 2\frac{14}{15} = \frac{118}{15} \div \frac{44}{15} = \frac{{}^{59}\cancel{118}}{{}_1\cancel{15}} \times \frac{\cancel{15}^1}{\cancel{44}_{22}}$$
$$= \frac{59}{22} = 2\frac{15}{22}$$

Exercise 1.30

Simplify the following:

1. $\frac{1}{3} \times (\frac{1}{5} \times \frac{10}{11})$
2. $\frac{2}{3} \times (\frac{3}{4} \div \frac{4}{5})$
3. $\frac{2}{3} \div (\frac{3}{4} \times \frac{4}{5})$
4. $\frac{2}{3} + \frac{3}{4} \times \frac{4}{5}$
5. $(\frac{2}{3} + \frac{3}{4}) \times \frac{4}{5}$
6. $(\frac{3}{4} - \frac{2}{3}) \div \frac{5}{12}$
7. $1\frac{1}{4} \times 3\frac{1}{5} + 3\frac{1}{3} \times 1\frac{1}{5} - 2\frac{1}{5} \times 2\frac{1}{3}$
8. $\dfrac{1\frac{3}{4} + 2\frac{1}{2}}{2\frac{5}{6} - 1\frac{1}{12}}$
9. $\frac{3}{4} \times (\frac{2}{5} \div \frac{2}{3}) - \frac{11}{20}$
10. $\dfrac{3\frac{5}{12} \times 1\frac{1}{3}}{2\frac{1}{9} + 2\frac{1}{3} \times 3\frac{1}{3}}$

1.11 When division is meaningless

We have already introduced the number zero (0), and we have discovered that:
$$a + 0 = 0 + a = a$$
for every integer, or number, a.

This means that: $(a + 0) \times b = a \times b$
But, by Law 1.3: $(a + 0) \times b = a \times b + 0 \times b$
Therefore: $a \times b + 0 \times b = a \times b$
That means: $0 \times b = 0$

And this is true when b has any value we wish to give it. So when we ask the question:

$$0 \times ? = 0 \quad \text{or} \quad 0 \div 0 = ?$$

the answer is that it could be any number. In other words, it is not possible to answer the question. $0 \div 0$ is meaningless.

$0 \div 0$ can be written $\frac{0}{0}$ and if we tried to cancel out the 0 in both numerator and denominator the answer would appear to be 1. But we have shown the answer could be anything, so we must never cancel in such circumstances. Consider the following:

$$\frac{1}{1/10} = 1 \div 1/10 = 1 \times \frac{10}{1} = 10$$

$$\frac{1}{1/100} = 1 \div 1/100 = 1 \times \frac{100}{1} = 100$$

$$\frac{1}{1/1000} = 1 \div 1/1000 = 1 \times \frac{1000}{1} = 1000$$

The number by which we are dividing is getting smaller and smaller and tending to 0. The answer, on the other hand, is getting larger and larger. Therefore, the smaller our divisor (the number by which we are dividing), the larger our answer. As the divisor tends to zero the answer becomes immeasurable. We conclude that, in all cases, *division by zero is not permissible*.

1.12   Ratio

Ratio is the comparison between two quantities of the same kind. It is expressed as, for example 5 to 4, and abbreviated to $5:4$. Examples of ratio are: £15:£13; 16 kg:7 kg; 2 mm:3 mm; 62 km/h:79 km/h; 2 cm:30 mm.

When we compare them we are saying how many times bigger or smaller one is than the other. The answer is a pure number and has no dimensions. For example:

$$£10:£15 = 10:15$$

But £10 can be made up of 2 five-pound notes and £15 can be made up of 3 five-pound notes. So:

$$10:15 = 2:3$$

Compare this with:

$$\frac{10}{15} = \frac{10^2}{15_3} = \frac{2}{3}$$

We conclude that an alternative form of writing a ratio is in fraction form. So we often write:

$$3:4 = \tfrac{3}{4} \quad \text{or} \quad 3/4$$

Any ratio can be converted to a fraction.

Examples

1. $$42\,\text{g}:49\,\text{g} = 42:49 = \frac{42^6}{49_7} = \frac{6}{7}$$

2. $$84\,\text{mm}:56\,\text{cm} = 84\,\text{mm}:560\,\text{mm} = 84:560 = \frac{84^{\,3}}{560_{20}} = \frac{3}{20}$$

3. $$2\tfrac{3}{4}\,\text{kg}:16\tfrac{1}{2}\,\text{kg} = 2\tfrac{3}{4}:16\tfrac{1}{2} = \tfrac{11}{4}:\tfrac{33}{2} = \tfrac{11}{4} \div \tfrac{33}{2}$$

$$= \frac{^1 11}{_2 4} \times \frac{2^{\,1}}{33_3} = \frac{1}{6}$$

Exercise 1.31

Express the following ratios as fractions converted to lowest terms:

1. 3 kg : 5 kg
2. 70 m : 75 m
3. £24 : £32
4. 28 l : 63 l

5. 64 ohm : 36 ohm
6. 250 V : 150 V
7. $3\frac{1}{2}$ A : $2\frac{1}{4}$ A
8. $3\frac{1}{2}$ l : 4500 cm^3
9. 84 N : 144 N
10. 45 t : 35 000 kg

Proportion

When four quantities, a, b, c and d, are related so that:

$$a : b = c : d$$

we say we have a porportion. This means that when two ratios are equal they are proportional. When we know any three of the four quantities we can always find the fourth. It is obvious that:

$$6 : 8 = 3 : 4 \quad \text{or} \quad \tfrac{6}{8} = \tfrac{3}{4} \tag{i}$$

Therefore: $\qquad\qquad \tfrac{6}{8} \times 8 = \tfrac{3}{4} \times 8$

Which gives: $\qquad\qquad 6 = \tfrac{3}{4} \times 8 \tag{ii}$

Form (i) can be changed into form (ii), which is the form we shall use frequently in our calculations. More generally, when:

$$a : b = c : d \quad \text{i.e.} \quad \frac{a}{b} = \frac{c}{d}$$

Then: $\qquad\qquad \dfrac{a}{b} \times b = \dfrac{c}{d} \times b$

Therefore: $\qquad\qquad a = \dfrac{c}{d} \times b$

Examples

1. If $x : 5 = 3 : 4$ calculate x.

    Step 1 $\qquad \dfrac{x}{5} = \dfrac{3}{4}$ therefore $\dfrac{x}{5} \times 5 = \dfrac{3}{4} \times 5$

    Step 2 $\qquad\qquad x = \tfrac{15}{4} = 3\tfrac{3}{4}$

2. If $4 : y = 3 : 5$ calculate y.

  Step 1   If $\dfrac{4}{y} = \dfrac{3}{5}$ then $\dfrac{y}{4} = \dfrac{5}{3}$

  Step 2 $\dfrac{y}{4} \times 4 = \dfrac{5}{3} \times 4$

  Step 3 $y = \frac{20}{3} = 6\frac{2}{3}$

Exercise 1.32

Calculate the unknown quantities in the following proportions:

1. $x : 7 = 5 : 6$
2. $3 : y = 7 : 8$
3. $4 : 5 = p : 7$
4. $9 : 10 = 6 : q$
5. $x : \frac{3}{4} = 8 : 5$
6. $x : \frac{2}{3} = \frac{3}{8} : \frac{4}{5}$

Direct proportion

If two variables, i.e. variable quantities, a and b, are such that $a : b = 3 : 4$ this means $a/b = \frac{3}{4}$ and that leads, as we have seen, to the conclusion:

$$a = \tfrac{3}{4} \times b$$

That is, in effect, a is always b multiplied by a fixed quantity. In this case, when we know the value of b we can always find the corresponding value of a by multiplying the value of b by 3/4. When the values of b are 4, 8, 12 and 16, the values of a are 3, 6, 9 and 12. This means that when b increases so does a. And when b decreases (simply read the values of b in reverse) then again, so does a.

 In these circumstances we say that a and b are in *direct proportion*, that b is the *independent variable*, and that a is the *dependent variable*. We encounter many examples of this in practice. Some examples are: distances measured on a map compared to real distances; models built to a certain scale; weights of given volumes of a uniform substance; ratios of metals in an alloy; resistances of wires of uniform cross-section and substance; and distances travelled by objects moving at a constant speed in given times.

Examples

1. The linear speed of the rim of a wheel is proportional to the angular speed of the wheel. When the angular speed is 50 rev/s the linear speed is 600 cm/s. Calculate the linear speed when the angular speed is 70 rev/s. Determine the angular speed when the linear speed is 500 cm/s.

    Represent the unknown linear speed by v centimetres per second. Then:

    $$\frac{v}{600} = \frac{70}{50}$$

    $$\text{Therefore } v = \frac{70}{\underset{1}{\cancel{50}}} \times \cancel{600}^{12} = 840$$

    The linear speed required is therefore 840 cm/s. A rough estimate tells us this is reasonable. The angular speed has increased by less than a half from 50 to 70. The linear speed has also increased by less than a half in going from 600 to 840.

    Suppose the required angular speed is a revolutions per second. Then:

    $$\frac{a}{50} = \frac{500}{600}$$

    $$\text{Therefore } a = \frac{{}^{5}\cancel{500}}{{}_{36}\cancel{600}} \times \cancel{50}^{25} = \frac{125}{3} = 41\tfrac{2}{3}$$

    The required angular speed is therefore $41\tfrac{2}{3}$ rev/s.

2. A proposed new factory has to have a total length of 150 m and a total width of 80 m. A scale model of it has a length of 45 cm. What will the width of the model be? On the model the length of the drawing office measures 5 cm. What is the actual length of the drawing office?

    Represent the unknown width of the model by w centimetres. Then:

$$\frac{w}{45} = \frac{80}{150}$$

Therefore $w = \dfrac{\overset{8}{\cancel{80}}}{\underset{1}{\cancel{150}}} \times \cancel{45}^{3} = 8 \times 3 = 24$

The width of the model will be 24 cm.

Suppose the drawing office length measures d metres. Then:

$$\frac{d}{150} = \frac{5}{45}$$

Therefore $d = \dfrac{\overset{1}{\cancel{5}}}{\underset{3}{\cancel{45}}} \times \cancel{150}^{50} = \frac{50}{3} = 16\frac{2}{3}$

The required length of the drawing office is $16\frac{2}{3}$ m.

3. Hooke's law says that the extension of a wire which is stretched is proportional to the tension causing the extension (providing a critical value of the tension is not exceeded). Suppose that for a particular wire the extension is 15 mm when the tension is 35 N (newtons). Determine the extension when the tension is 55 N. Determine the tension when the extension is 25 mm.

Suppose the required extension is x millimetres. Then:

$$\frac{x}{15} = \frac{55}{35}$$

Therefore $x = \dfrac{\overset{11}{\cancel{55}}}{\underset{7}{\cancel{35}}} \times 15 = \frac{165}{7} = 23\frac{4}{7}$

The required extension is $23\frac{4}{7}$ mm.

Suppose the required tension is t newtons. Then:

$$\frac{t}{35} = \frac{25}{15}$$

Therefore $t = \dfrac{\overset{5}{\cancel{25}}}{\underset{3}{\cancel{15}}} \times 35 = \frac{175}{3} = 58\frac{1}{3}$

The required tension is $58\frac{1}{3}$ N.

Exercise 1.33

1. An alloy is made up of 6 parts copper to 4 parts zinc. In a casting of such an alloy there is a mass of zinc 64 kg. What is the mass of copper? In another casting there is a mass of copper 85 kg. What is the mass of zinc?

2. The weight of 56 cm³ of mercury is 763 g. What is the weight of 72 cm³ at the same temperature? What volume does a mass of 956 g occupy at that temperature?

3. The resistance of copper wire of a given cross-section is proportional to its length. If the resistance of 9 m is $2\frac{3}{4}\,\Omega$, what will be the resistance of a length 16 m? What length will be required to give a resistance of 10 Ω?

4. At a constant speed a train goes 2560 m in 64 seconds. How far will it travel, at the same speed, in 35 seconds? At the same speed again, how long will it take to travel 3240 m?

5. Where a conductor obeys Ohm's law the current passing through it is proportional to the voltage applied to the conductor. For one conductor the current is $2\frac{1}{2}$ A when the voltage is 145 V. What will the current be when the voltage is 186 V? What will the voltage be to produce a current of $1\frac{3}{4}$ A?

6. Charles's law says that when the pressure on a gas is constant then the volume is proportional to the absolute temperature. When the temperature is 310 K (kelvin) the volume is 2350 cm³. What will the volume be when the temperature is 320 K? What temperature will produce a volume of 1950 cm³?

7. For a stretched wire which obeys Hooke's law a tension of 250 N produces an extension of 14 mm. What tension will be required to extend the wire by 24 mm? When the tension is 480 N what will the extension be, assuming that the critical value of tension has not been reached?

8. The pressure law of a gas says that, when the volume remains constant, the pressure is proportional to the absolute temperature. For such a gas, when the temperature is 325 K the pressure is 200 000 Pa (pascal). What will be the pressure of that volume of the gas when the temperature is 355 K? At what temperature will the pressure be 208 000 Pa?

9. The circumference of a circle is proportional to its radius. Assuming that the circumference of a circle radius 35 cm is 220 cm, what will be the circumference of a circle radius

27 cm? What radius will a circle with a circumference of 345 cm have?

10. For a given mass acceleration is proportional to the force acting on the mass. For a particular body a force of 85 N produces an acceleration of $2\frac{1}{2}$ m/s². What will be the acceleration when the force is 123 N? What force will produce an acceleration of $3\frac{1}{4}$ m/s²?

Inverse proportion

Suppose that *a* and *b* represent two variables (variable quantities), and the following table represents pairs of corresponding values of the two.

Value of *b*:	5	10	15	20	25	30
Value of *a*:	360	180	120	90	72	60

This means that when *b* increases then *a* decreases, and when *b* decreases (read the table in reverse) then *a* increases. Because the trend for one is always opposite to the trend for the other, we call this *inverse proportion*.

Look again at the values given for *a* and *b*, and for each pair note the value of *a* × *b*. In each case you will find that the value of *a* × *b* is 1800. In other words, the value of *a* × *b* is always constant. And when that happens we say that *a* and *b* are in inverse proportion to each other. In this example:

$$a \times b = 1800$$

$$\text{Therefore } a \times b \times \frac{1}{b} = 1800 \times \frac{1}{b}$$

$$\text{That is } a = 1800 \times \frac{1}{b}$$

In fact, wherever *a* and *b* are connected by a relationship of the form:

$$a = K \times \frac{1}{b}$$

where *K* is some constant (in the example above it was 1800), then *a* and *b* vary inversely with each other, i.e. *they are in inverse proportion*.

If a_1 and b_1 represent a pair of corresponding values of a and b, and so do a_2 and b_2, then:

$$a_1 = 1800 \times \frac{1}{b_1} \quad \text{and} \quad a_2 = 1800 \times \frac{1}{b_2}$$

$$\text{Therefore } \frac{a_1}{a_2} = \left(1800 \times \frac{1}{b_1}\right) \div \left(1800 \times \frac{1}{b_2}\right)$$

$$= \cancel{1800} \times \frac{1}{b_1} \times \frac{1}{\cancel{1800}} \times \frac{b_2}{1}$$

$$= \frac{1 \times b_2}{1 \times b_1} = \frac{b_2}{b_1}$$

$$\text{Therefore } a_1 = \frac{b_2}{b_1} \times a_2$$

For example, call a_1 and a_2 120 and 72 (from the pairs of values given above). Then b_1 and b_2 will be 15 and 25. By the above formula a_1 should be:

$$\frac{{}^5\cancel{25}}{{}_1\cancel{15}} \times \cancel{72}^{24} = 5 \times 24 = 120$$

The value checks the formula.

We can also rearrange the above formula by multiplying both sides by $\dfrac{b_1}{a_1}$ and obtain:

$$a_1 \times \frac{b_1}{a_1} = \frac{b_2}{b_1} \times a_2 \times \frac{b_1}{a_1}$$

$$\text{Therefore } b_1 = \frac{a_2}{a_1} \times b_2$$

We will consider another example to illustrate the use of these formulae when, again, a and b are in inverse proportion.

b:	2	3		8	16
a:	36		12	8	

How do we find the values of a and b in the spaces which are left blank in the table?

Method 1. Since a and b are in inverse proportion, then $a \times b$ is constant, and is equal to 2×36 (in this case this is the only pair of corresponding values given). Thus:

$$a \times b = 72$$

Then $a = 72 \times \dfrac{1}{b}$ (which we use to determine a, knowing b)

and $b = 72 \times \dfrac{1}{a}$ (which we use to determine b, knowing a)

When $b = 3$, $a = {}^{24}\cancel{72} \times \dfrac{1}{\cancel{3}_1} = 24$

When $a = 12$, $b = {}^{6}\cancel{72} \times \dfrac{1}{\cancel{12}_1} = 6$

The remaining values of a and b are therefore: $a = 9$ when $b = 8$; $b = 9$ when $a = 8$; $a = 4\frac{1}{2}$ when $b = 16$. Use the above formulae to check these values.

Method 2. Using $a_1 = \dfrac{b_2}{b_1} \times a_2$ to find a and $b_1 = \dfrac{a_2}{a_1} \times b_2$ to find b:

When $b_1 = 3$, use $b_2 = 2$ and $a_2 = 36$

Then $a_1 = \dfrac{2}{3} \times 36 = 24$

When $a_1 = 12$ and a_2 and b_2 are as before

Then $b_1 = \dfrac{\cancel{36}^3}{\cancel{12}_1} \times 2 = 6$

In practice examples of inverse proportion are: speeds and times of moving objects travelling a fixed distance; angular speeds of toothed wheels meshed together and the number of teeth in the wheels; current and resistance of a conductor at a given voltage drop; length and breadth of a rectangle of given area.

Examples

1. A car travels a certain distance at a uniform speed of 52 km/h in 5 minutes. How long would the same distance take at a

uniform speed of 65 km/h? At what speed would it have to travel to cover that distance in $4\frac{1}{2}$ minutes?

Represent speed and time taken by V kilometres per hour and t minutes respectively.

$$\text{Then } V = 52 \times 5 \times \frac{1}{t}$$

When $t = 4\frac{1}{2} = 9/2$ then $V = 52 \times 5 \times \frac{2}{9} = 520/9 = 57\frac{7}{9}$

The required speed is $57\frac{7}{9}$ km/h. The time had been decreased by $1/10$; a rough estimate tells us the speed has been increased by about $1/10$. The answer therefore seems reasonable.

$$\text{When } V = 65 \text{ then } t = 52 \times 5 \times \frac{1}{V} = {}^{4}5\!\!\!/2 \times {}^{1}5\!\!\!/ \times \frac{1}{6\!\!\!/5_{13_1}} = 4.$$

The speed has been increased by $1/4$ and the time decreased by $1/5$. This seems reasonable.

An absolute check to the first answer is:

$$\frac{{}^{260}5\!\!\!/2\!\!\!/0}{9\!\!\!/ \ _1} \times \frac{9\!\!\!/^1}{2\!\!\!/_1} = 260$$

And to the second answer is:

$$65 \times 4 = 260$$

And they both agree with the product of the given pair of values:

$$52 \times 5 = 260$$

2. A gear wheel with 35 teeth revolves at a constant speed of 180 rev/min. It drives a second wheel which can be changed. When the second wheel has 30 teeth, at what speed is it rotating? How many teeth would the wheel have to have for it to revolve at 140 rev/min?

Suppose the speed at which the second wheel rotates is N revolutions per minute and the number of its teeth is n.

$$\text{Then } N = 35 \times 180 \times \frac{1}{n} \quad \text{and} \quad n = 35 \times 180 \times \frac{1}{N}$$

$$\text{When } n = 30 \text{ then } N = 35 \times {}^{6}1\!\!\!/8\!\!\!/0 \times \frac{1}{3\!\!\!/0_1} = 210$$

When $N = 140$ then $n = {}^1\cancel{35} \times {}^{45}\cancel{180} \times \dfrac{1}{\cancel{140}_{4_1}} = 45$

Check: $\quad 30 \times 210 = 6300$
$\qquad\quad 45 \times 140 = 6300$
$\qquad\quad 35 \times 180 = 6300$

3. At constant temperature, the pressure and volume of a gas are inversely proportional. At a given temperature a mass of gas occupies a volume of 645 cm^3 when the pressure is 54 units. What will the pressure be to confine the volume to 430 cm^3? When the pressure is 63 units what will the volume be?

   Suppose the pressure is p units and the volume v cubic centimetres.

   Then $p = 645 \times 54 \times \dfrac{1}{v}$ and $v = 645 \times 54 \times \dfrac{1}{p}$

   When $v = 430$, $p = {}^{3}\cancel{129}^{6}\cancel{45} \times 54^{27} \times \dfrac{1}{\cancel{430}_{86_{2_1}}} = 81$

   When $p = 63$, $v = 645 \times {}^6\cancel{54} \times \dfrac{1}{\cancel{63}_7} = 552\tfrac{6}{7}$

   Check: $\quad 430 \times 81 = 34\,830$
   $\qquad\quad 63 \times 552\tfrac{6}{7} = 34\,830$
   $\qquad\quad 645 \times 54 = 34\,830$

4. For a variable electrical conductor, when a constant voltage is applied to it, the current and resistance are inversely proportional. For a given voltage the current and resistance are $3\tfrac{1}{3}$ A and 33 Ω respectively. Determine the current through a resistor of 55 Ω and the resistance of a conductor when the current is 5 A, assuming the same voltage is applied.

   Suppose the unknown current is I amperes and the resistance is R ohms.

   Then $I = 3\tfrac{1}{3} \times 33 \times \dfrac{1}{R}$ and $R = 3\tfrac{1}{3} \times 33 \times \dfrac{1}{I}$

   When $R = 55$ then $I = \dfrac{{}^2\cancel{10}}{{}_1\cancel{3}} \times {}^{1}\cancel{14}{}^{17}\cancel{33} \times \dfrac{1}{\cancel{55}_{5_1}} = 2$

When $I = 5$ then $R = \dfrac{{}^2\cancel{10}}{\cancel{3}_1} \times {}^{11}\cancel{33} \times \dfrac{1}{\cancel{3}_1} = 22$

Check: $55 \times 2 = 110$

$\qquad\quad 22 \times 5 = 110$

$\qquad\quad 33 \times 3\tfrac{1}{3} = 110$

Exercise 1.34

1. A rectangle of given area has sides 35 cm and 24 cm. What is the length of a rectangle of the same area when its breadth is 20 cm? Determine the breadth when the length is 42 cm.

2. The current through a resistor of 560 Ω, for a certain voltage applied to it, is $\tfrac{3}{4}$ A. What will the current through a resistor of 420 Ω be and what will the resistance of a conductor be when the current through it is $\tfrac{2}{3}$ A, assuming that in each case the same voltage as before is applied.

3. The formula connecting mass, volume and density of a substance is mass = volume × density. That is, for a given mass, volume and density are in inverse proportion. A volume of a certain alloy is 12 ℓ and its density is 7 kg/ℓ. What is the density of another alloy of the same mass whose volume is 14 ℓ? The same mass of another alloy with density 4 kg/ℓ occupies a volume of V cubic centimetres. What is V?

4. A gear wheel having 45 teeth rotates at 160 rev/min. When it drives a wheel with 18 teeth, at what speed does the second wheel revolve? How many teeth must the second wheel have for its speed to be 120 rev/min?

5. The volume of a prism (V) is equal to the area of the base (A) times the height of the prism (h). The values of A and h for one prism are 144 cm^2 and 15 cm respectively. For a prism of the same volume, when $A = 90$ cm^2 what will the height be? Again for the same volume, when $h = 12$ cm determine what value the area of the base must have.

6. For a gas obeying Boyle's law pressure and volume are inversely proportional. When the pressure of a gas is $2\tfrac{1}{2}$ times the atmospheric pressure its volume is 1728 cm^3. What will the pressure of the same mass of gas occupying a volume of 1440 cm^3 be? Determine the volume of that gas when the pressure is $2\tfrac{1}{4}$ times the atmospheric pressure. Assume that atmospheric pressure remains constant and is 1 unit.

7. Where $s = v \times t$ and s is constant, we are given that for $t = 75$, $v = 32$. Determine v when $t = 60$ and find t when $v = 48$. Calculate s.

8. Where $F = m \times a$ and F is constant, we are given that $a = 3\frac{1}{4}$ when $m = 32\frac{1}{2}$. Determine a when $m = 39$ and m when $a = 2\frac{1}{2}$. Evaluate F.

9. Given that $W = I \times V$ and that W is constant, determine I when $V = 31\frac{1}{2}$ and V when $I = 1\frac{3}{4}$. It is known that $I = 1\frac{1}{5}$ when $V = 35$. Calculate W.

10. The momentum of a body, H, is given by mass $(M) \times$ velocity (v). When the momentum is constant for given bodies M and v are inversely proportional. When M is $42\frac{1}{2}$ kg, v is $3\frac{1}{5}$ m/s. Determine M when $v = 1\frac{3}{5}$ m/s and v when M is 34 kg, supposing in each case that the momentum remains constant at the original value. Determine the value of H.

Proportional parts

We will look at question (1) in Exercise 1.33 again. Suppose this time the information is slightly different. We are told that the mass of the alloy is 160 kg but we are not told the mass of the zinc. How could we tell what the masses of zinc and copper are?

If there are 6 parts of copper and 4 parts of zinc then there must be 10 parts of alloy. The ratio of copper to alloy is therefore $6:10$, and the ratio of zinc to alloy is $4:10$. Then:

$$\text{Mass of copper} = \frac{6}{10} \times 160 \text{ kg} = 96 \text{ kg}$$

$$\text{Mass of zinc} = \frac{4}{10} \times 160 \text{ kg} = 64 \text{ kg}$$

$$\text{Check: } 96 + 64 = 160 \text{ (total mass of alloy)}$$

Example

A line is divided into three parts in the ratio $3:4:5$. If the middle section is 24 cm, what is the length of each remaining section and what is the length of the whole?

Call the lengths of the sections L_1, L_2 and L_3 and total length L. Then:

$$L = L_1 + L_2 + L_3$$

And $L_1 : L_2 : L_3 : L = 3 : 4 : 5 : (3 + 4 + 5 = 12)$

$$\text{Then } L = \frac{12}{4} \times 24 = 72$$

$$L_1 = \frac{3}{4} \times 24 = 18$$

$$L_3 = \frac{5}{4} \times 24 = 30$$

Check: $18 + 24 + 30 = 72$

Exercise 1.35

1. Divide a line in the ratio $3 : 5$ when its total length is 96 mm.
2. A triangle has its sides in the ratio $5 : 6 : 7$. If the perimeter is 72 mm, calculate the length of each of its sides.
3. An alloy has a total mass of 85 kg. It is made of lead and tin in the ratio of $3 : 2$. Calculate the masses of lead and tin in the alloy.
4. A line is to be divided into three parts in the ratio $3 : 4 : 5$. If the smallest section is to be 51 mm long, calculate the lengths of the other sections and the total length.
5. A line is to be divided into three parts in the ratio $2\frac{1}{2} : 3\frac{1}{3} : 4\frac{1}{4}$. The longest section is to be 34 mm. What are the lengths of the other sections and what is the total length?

2
Decimal Fractions

2.1 Notation

We have said that 236 means 2 hundreds + 3 tens + 6 units. The digit on the extreme right, 6, takes the unit value. As we move each successive place to the left we multiply the unit value by 10. In other words, for each successive place we move to the right from a given position we divide the place value by 10, or multiply it by 1/10. So we ought to be able to move to the right from the unit place and obtain units of 1/10, 1/100, 1/1000 and so on. So we could write down a number such as:

2 units + 4 units of 1/10 + 7 units of 1/100 + 3 units of 1/1000

or   2 units + 4 tenths + 7 hundredths + 3 thousandths

But it is a very complicated way of writing a number. So we must look for an abbreviated form. We select the following:

$$2.473$$

The dot is called a decimal point. It is placed immediately after the units digit, i.e. to the right of that digit. So 2.473 means

$$2 + 4 \times 1/10 + 7 \times 1/100 + 3 \times 1/1000$$

The number 2.473 is bigger than 1, yet a part of it, .473, is less than 1, i.e. it is a fraction. So 2.473 is similar to a mixed number in fractions. Where the decimal fraction is a real fraction less than 1, such as .528, we write it as 0.528 to ensure that there is no misunderstanding about the fact that the number is less than 1.

Because a decimal fraction is in fact a fraction we must be able to convert from one form to the other easily.

Exercise 2.1

Convert the following decimal fractions into expressions involving the units 1/10, 1/100, 1/1000 etc.

1. 3.452
2. 4.564
3. 1.507
4. 6.045
5. 3.560
6. 1.005
7. 0.048
8. 3.927
9. 9.0406
10. 0.00038

2.2   Conversion from decimal fractions to fractions and vice versa

Examples

1.   0.237 means $2 \times \dfrac{1}{10} + 3 \times \dfrac{1}{100} + 7 \times \dfrac{1}{1000}$

$$= \frac{2}{10} + \frac{3}{100} + \frac{7}{1000}$$

$$= \frac{200}{1000} + \frac{30}{1000} + \frac{7}{1000}$$

$$= \frac{237}{1000} \text{ which is a proper fraction}$$

2. $0.7 = 7 \times \dfrac{1}{10} = \dfrac{7}{10}$

3. $0.83 = 8 \times \dfrac{1}{10} + 3 \times \dfrac{1}{100} = \dfrac{8}{10} + \dfrac{3}{100}$

$\qquad = \dfrac{80}{100} + \dfrac{3}{100} = \dfrac{83}{100}$

4. $0.1057 = 1 \times \dfrac{1}{10} + 0 \times \dfrac{1}{100} + 5 \times \dfrac{1}{1000} + 7 \times \dfrac{1}{10\,000}$

$\qquad = \dfrac{1000}{10\,000} + \dfrac{50}{10\,000} + \dfrac{7}{10\,000} = 1057/10\,000$

Although the detailed argument follows the steps above we naturally look for a quicker method. Notice that in each answer the numerator contains the same digits as the decimal fraction, but without the decimal point. The denominator always contains the first digit, 1, followed by as many zeros as there are decimal places in the original number. So we can write:

$$0.624 = \frac{624}{1000}; \qquad 0.6024 = \frac{6024}{10\,000}; \qquad 0.751 = \frac{751}{1000} \quad \text{etc.}$$

Sometimes the resulting fraction can be reduced to a simpler form, an equivalent fraction, by cancelling down. For example:

$$\frac{\cancel{6204}^{\,1551}}{\cancel{10\,000}_{2500}} = \frac{1551}{2500}$$

Exercise 2.2

Convert the following decimal fractions into fractions expressed in their lowest terms:

1. 0.6
2. 0.25
3. 0.35
4. 0.75
5. 0.125
6. 0.375
7. 0.625

8. 0.875
9. 0.24
10. 0.16
11. 0.32
12. 0.96
13. 0.153
14. 0.719
15. 0.853
16. 0.705
17. 0.02
18. 0.05
19. 0.025
20. 0.003
21. 0.1003
22. 0.0307
23. 0.00205

How do we carry out the reverse process, that is, convert a fraction into a decimal fraction? First of all notice that in the above process, before we cancelled down our fraction to the lowest terms we always obtained a fraction with a denominator of 10, 100, 1000, or 10 000 – what we call powers of ten. First of all, then, let us aim for that:

$$\frac{4}{5} = \frac{4 \times 2}{5 \times 2} = \frac{8}{10} = 8 \times \frac{1}{10} = 0.8$$

$$\frac{18}{25} = \frac{18 \times 4}{25 \times 4} = \frac{72}{100} = \frac{70}{100} + \frac{2}{100} = \frac{7}{10} + \frac{2}{100} = 0.72$$

In the above examples we made use of the facts that:

$$\frac{8}{10} = 0.8 \quad \text{or} \quad \frac{8.0}{10} = 0.8$$

and
$$\frac{72}{100} = 0.72 \quad \text{or} \quad \frac{72.0}{100} = 0.72$$

Once we obtain a fraction whose denominator is a power of ten we can easily convert it into a decimal. For example:

$$\frac{63}{100} = \frac{63.0}{100} = 0.63 \qquad \frac{302}{1000} = \frac{302.0}{1000} = 0.302$$

The digits of the decimal are the same as those in the numerator of the fraction. We can then move the decimal point to the left the same number of places as there are zeros in the denominator, or, alternatively, move the digits an equivalent number of places to the right of the decimal point.

Exercise 2.3

Convert the following into decimal form:

1. 31/100
2. 27/100
3. 306/1000
4. 717/1000
5. 82/1000
6. 7/100
7. 803/100 000

First convert the following into equivalent fractions whose denominators are powers of ten and then convert them into decimal form:

8. 3/5
9. 11/20
10. 19/20
11. 17/20
12. 4/25
13. 7/50
14. 29/50
15. 56/125
16. 37/40
17. 93/250
18. 87/200
19. 107/400
20. 718/8000

It often helps to remember certain basic fractions and their decimal equivalents. For instance:

$0.5 = 1/2;$ $0.05 = 1/20;$ $0.15 = 3/20;$ $0.25 = 5/20 = 1/4;$

$0.35 = 7/20;$ $0.45 = 9/20;$ $0.125 = 1/8;$ $0.375 = 3/8;$

$0.625 = 5/8;$ $0.75 = 3/4;$ $0.875 = 7/8$

It is not always possible to determine easily an equivalent fraction with a denominator which is a power of ten, and therefore we need a method which can be applied in all circumstances. From the above we know that:

$$\frac{18}{25} \quad \text{means} \quad 18 \div 25 \quad \text{or} \quad 18.0000 \div 25$$

By the previous method we know the answer must be:

$$\frac{18 \times 4}{25 \times 4} = \frac{72}{100} = 0.72$$

So we arrange our working as follows:

$$\begin{array}{r} 00. \\ \hline 25\overline{)18.0000000000000} \end{array}$$

In other words, we carry out a normal long division, and place the answer above 18.000000 with the decimal point of the answer immediately above the decimal point of the 18.000000. We know that the first digit in the answer must come immediately to the right of that point, so we go on:

$$\begin{array}{r} 00.72 \\ \hline 25\overline{)18.000000000000} \\ 17\ 5 \\ \hline 50 \\ 50 \\ \hline \cdot\ \cdot \end{array}$$

Example

Convert 112/125 to its decimal equivalent.

Step 1   Write fraction as $\dfrac{112.0000}{125}$

Step 2   Put the decimal point of answer immediately above the decimal point in 112.0000.

Step 3   Proceed with the division as though there were no decimal points.

$$\begin{array}{r} 000.896 \\ \hline 125\overline{)112.0000} \\ 100\ 0 \\ \hline 1200 \\ 1125 \\ \hline 750 \\ 750 \\ \hline \cdot\ \cdot\ \cdot \end{array}$$

Therefore 112/125 = 0.896.

Exercise 2.4

Convert the following fractions to their decimal equivalents by the division method:

1. 7/8
2. 9/16
3. 13/16
4. 21/25
5. 17/25
6. 25/32
7. 29/64
8. 53/64
9. 86/125
10. 105/125

In each case check the accuracy of your answer by using your calculator; e.g. step 1 insert 13; step 2 insert ÷; step 3 insert 16; step 4 insert =.

2.3 Recurring and non-terminating decimals

Let us now apply the above method to try to convert 1/3 to a decimal:

$$
\begin{array}{r}
0.33333 \\
3\overline{)1.00000000000000} \\
9 \\
\overline{10} \\
9 \\
\overline{10} \\
9 \\
\overline{10} \\
9 \\
\overline{10} \\
9 \\
\overline{10}
\end{array}
$$

We shall never be able to end the process. There will always be a remainder, no matter how many times we carry out the division operation, and all the digits in the answer will be 3. This is said to be a *recurring decimal*, and we write it as follows: 0.33̇3 or 0.3̇. A check by calculator gives the answer 0.3333333. This appears to terminate because the calculator rounds off the answer to a given number of places, in this case 8 (not decimal places).

Exercise 2.5

Work out the following and express them as recurring decimals. (Check the results by calculator.)

1. 2/3
2. 1/6
3. 4/9
4. 11/18
5. 5/12
6. 17/24
7. 23/36

Example

We will now try to convert 1/7 to a decimal:

$$
\begin{array}{r}
0.142857142857 \\
7\overline{)1.000000000000000} \\
\underline{7} \\
30 \\
\underline{28} \\
20 \\
\underline{14} \\
60 \\
\underline{56} \\
40 \\
\underline{35} \\
50 \\
\underline{49} \\
1
\end{array}
$$

The remainder at the bottom of the working is the same as the number we started with, so if we went on with the division we would merely repeat the digits we already have in the answer, and we would obtain a cycle of digits over and over again. There would again be recurrence, but this time the recurrence would be of a sequence of digits, namely 142857. So we write 1/7 as 0.$\dot{1}$42857$\dot{7}$, i.e. we put two dots, one to show the start of the sequence and the other to show its end.

A decimal such as 0.375 terminates at the third decimal place. *A recurring decimal never terminates.*

There are other numbers which, when converted into decimal form, neither terminate nor are recurring. They are *non-terminating decimals.* Examples are: π; $\sqrt{2}$, $\sqrt{3}$ and $\sqrt{5}$ (which we have not yet defined but will deal with later); and e and ln (1.5) (which are beyond the scope of this text).

Exercise 2.6

Evaluate as recurring decimals:

1. 2/7
2. 3/11
3. 5/13
4. 12/17

2.4 Degrees of accuracy

Most calculators give the decimal value of 2/3 as 0.6666667, which is the rounded-off answer for 0.$\dot{6}$, and is much more accurate than we require for most normal purposes.

It is essential that we be able to give any value to the particular degree of accuracy which is needed. Fig. 2.1 represents a line of length *AB* and part of a ruler which we are using to measure the line. *AB* is a length greater than 2 + 5/10, i.e. greater than 2.5 and less than 2 + 6/10, i.e. less than 2.6. How would we estimate the length of *AB*? It seems closer to 2.6 than to 2.5, and so we would probably estimate it to be 2.57, i.e. 7/10 of the way from 2.5 to 2.6.

Figure 2.1

Or we might estimate it to be 2.56, or even 2.58, because we could never rely absolutely on our judgement about the digit following the 5. For this reason we might be satisfied to give an answer as being nearer 2.6 than 2.5, and say that 2.6 is near enough the value we are looking for. In that case we would say we were giving a reading correct to one decimal place.

In other words, if *AB* were nearer to 2.6 than 2.5 we would give the length as 2.6, and if *AB* were nearer to 2.5 we would give the length as 2.5. Consequently, 2.51, 2.52, 2.53 and 2.54 will all be given, correct to one decimal place, as 2.5, and 2.56, 2.57, 2.58 and 2.59 will all be given, correct to one decimal place, as 2.6. What shall we do about 2.55? This number is exactly half-way between 2.5 and 2.6, so we might give the answer as either of these. But it is better to have a rule to which we can always adhere.

One rule which has long been in operation is always to add 1 to the digit before the 5, which in this example would produce the result 2.6. However, the principle advanced in BS 1957 is that:

> 2.45 correct to one decimal place is 2.4
> 2.55 correct to one decimal place is 2.6
> 2.65 correct to one decimal place is 2.6
> 2.75 correct to one decimal place is 2.8

That is, where the digit of the decimal place to which we wish to give our answer is even, and followed by 5 only, we leave that digit unchanged. Where the digit is odd and followed by 5 only, we add 1 to that digit.

Examples

1. 3.4527 correct to one decimal place is 3.5.
2. 3.55016 is 3.6 to one decimal place.
3. 1.412 correct to two decimal places is 1.41.
4. 6.293 correct to one decimal place is 6.3; correct to two decimal places is 6.29.
5. 5.067 correct to two decimal places is 5.07; correct to one decimal place is 5.1.
6. 3.1416 correct to two decimal places is 3.14; correct to three decimal places is 3.142; correct to one decimal place is 3.1.
7. 11.0984 correct to two decimal places is 11.10 (note: not 11.1); correct to one decimal place is 11.1; correct to three decimal places is 11.098.

Exercise 2.7

Express the following decimals correct to the degree of accuracy indicated.

To one decimal place:

1. 3.14
2. 5.74
3. 10.33
4. 10.83
5. 4.28
6. 6.79
7. 17.67
8. 16.01
9. 23.05
10. 48.55
11. 62.14566
12. 13.8542
13. 41.753
14. 16.252

To two decimal places:

15. 9.138
16. 7.463
17. 19.054689
18. 102.5978
19. 63.6054
20. 0.0556

Sometimes, instead of referring to decimal places, to distinguish the position of a digit in a number we talk about significant figures.

Examples

1. In 1035 the first significant figure is 1; correct to three significant figures is 1040.
2. In 2005 the first significant figure is 2; correct to three significant figures is 2000.
3. In 52 094 the first significant figure is 5; correct to four significant figures is 52 090.
4. In 1.472 the first significant figure is 1; correct to three significant figures is 1.47.

5. In 0.234 the first significant figure is 2; correct to two significant figures is 0.23.
6. In 0.008071 the first significant figure is 8; correct to two significant figures is 0.0081.
7. 1035 correct to two significant figures is 1000; 52 094 correct to three significant figures is 52 100.

When we say that 0.008071 correct to two significant figures is 0.0081 we are really saying, to the degree of accuracy we can depend on, that 0.008071 is nearer to 0.0081 than it is to 0.0080.

Exercise 2.8

Express the following decimals first correct to three decimal places and then correct to two significant figures.

1. 0.6584
2. 0.32765
3. 4.0257
4. 18.823
5. 421.0658
6. 305.267
7. 1458.005
8. 6053.256
9. 714.352
10. 0.00452
11. 0.1035
12. 3.0045
13. 10.451
14. 16.075

2.5 Percentages

Frequently we encounter and use fractions of a special kind, where the denominator is an easily manageable number, 100; e.g. 6/100, 11/100, 50/100. We call these percentages (6 per cent, 11 per cent, 50 per cent), cent being an abbreviation for 100.

Therefore when we say 4 per cent the 4 refers to the numerator of the fraction and 'per cent' to the denominator, so 4 per cent = $\frac{4}{100}$. Per cent is frequently abbreviated to the symbol %. Using that notation we have $4\% = \frac{4}{100}$.

Examples

$$50\% = \frac{50}{100} = \frac{50^{\;1}}{100_2} = \frac{1}{2}$$

$$25\% = \frac{25}{100} = \frac{25^{\;1}}{100_4} = \frac{1}{4}$$

$$35\% = \frac{35}{100} = \frac{35^{\;7}}{100_{20}} = \frac{7}{20}$$

To convert a percentage to a fraction we merely divide the percentage by 100 and then reduce the fraction to its lowest terms.

Exercise 2.9

Convert the following percentages to fractions and express the answers in their lowest terms:

1. 15%
2. 45%
3. 12%
4. 32%
5. 66%
6. 84%
7. 4%
8. 6%
9. 14%
10. 34%
11. 20%
12. 25%

Consider now the converse problem, converting a fraction into a percentage. Remember that a percentage is a special fraction with a denominator 100.

$$\frac{3}{4} = \frac{3 \div 4}{4 \div 4} = \frac{3/4}{1} = \frac{(3/4) \times 100}{100} = \frac{3}{4} \times 100\%$$

To convert a fraction into a percentage we merely multiply the fraction by 100.

Examples

1. $\dfrac{7}{20} = \dfrac{7}{20} \times 100\% = \dfrac{\cancel{700}^{35}}{\cancel{20}_{1}} \% = 35\%$

2. $\dfrac{3}{8} = \dfrac{3}{8} \times 100\% = \dfrac{\cancel{300}^{75}}{\cancel{8}_{2}} \% = \dfrac{75}{2}\% = 37\tfrac{1}{2}\%$

3. $\dfrac{1}{3} = \dfrac{1}{3} \times 100\% = \dfrac{100}{3}\% = 33\tfrac{1}{3}\%$

Exercise 2.10

Convert the following fractions to percentages:

1. 3/5
2. 7/10
3. 1/4
4. 5/8
5. 11/20
6. 19/40
7. 1/6
8. 2/3
9. 2/7
10. 5/16
11. 4/9
12. 17/32

A decimal fraction is merely a fraction in a different form, so to convert it to a percentage we use the same method as above:

$$65\% = 65.0\% = \frac{65.0}{100} = 0.65$$

$$\left(\text{or, in full} = \frac{6}{10} + \frac{5}{100} = \left(6 \times \frac{1}{10} \right) + \left(5 \times \frac{1}{100} \right) \right)$$

$$= 0.6 + 0.05 = 0.65$$

Therefore, to convert a percentage into a decimal fraction, we merely move the decimal point two places to the left, or move the digits two places to the right.

Examples

1. $23.4\% = 0.234$
2. $50.1\% = 0.501$
3. $34\frac{1}{2}\% = 34.5\% = 0.345$
4. $23\frac{1}{3}\% = 23.33\dot{3}\% = 0.2333\dot{3}$

5. $3\frac{1}{8}\% = \frac{25}{8}\% = \frac{\overset{1}{\cancel{25}}}{\underset{32}{\cancel{800}}} = \frac{1}{32} = 0.03125$ (by calculator). If we

   did not have the use of a calculator we would have to divide 1 by 32 in long division, or $3\frac{1}{8}\% = 3.125\% = 0.03125$.

To convert a decimal into a percentage we move the decimal point two places to the right, or move the digits two places to the left.

Examples

1. $0.108 = 10.8\%$
2. $1.063 = 106.3\%$
3. $0.0546 = 5.46\%$
4. $0.0074 = 0.74\%$

Exercise 2.11

Convert the following percentages into decimal fractions:

1. 62.5%
2. 37.5%
3. 12.5%

4. 87.5%
5. 8.5%
6. 5.5%
7. 11.2%
8. 90.7%
9. 124.6%
10. 102.4%
11. 0.58%
12. 0.25%
13. 0.043%
14. 0.0025%

Convert the following decimal fractions into percentages:

15. 0.25
16. 0.60
17. 0.126
18. 0.054
19. 0.582
20. 0.167
21. 0.203
22. 0.007

2.6 Operations on decimal fractions

When we add or subtract integers we arrange one underneath the other so that the digits of corresponding units are in the same vertical column. For example, $23\,859 \pm 9427$ is arranged:

$$23\,859$$
$$9\,427$$

We use the same principle when carrying out these operations with decimals. For example:

23.859	23.859	180.23	180.23
+ 19.427	− 19.427	+ 71.5	− 71.5
43.286	4.432	251.73	108.73

Exercise 2.12

Calculate the following:

1. $18.3 + 11.5$
2. $24.8 + 15.3$
3. $82.75 + 11.12$
4. $82.75 + 11.1$
5. $601.5 + 34.27$
6. $8.7 - 4.5$
7. $19.5 - 11.1$
8. $26.3 - 14.5$
9. $58.37 - 14.2$
10. $92.6 - 21.36$
11. $160.2 - 35.38$
12. $64.09 + 23.2 - 58.35$

Consider now 2.1×1.6:

$$\left(2 + \frac{1}{10}\right)\left(1 + \frac{6}{10}\right) = \left(\frac{20}{10} + \frac{1}{10}\right)\left(\frac{10}{10} + \frac{6}{10}\right)$$

$$= \frac{21}{10} \times \frac{16}{10} = \frac{21 \times 16}{100} = \frac{336}{100}$$

$$= \frac{336.0}{100} = 3.36 \quad \text{(by calculator)}$$

$$or \quad \frac{300}{100} + \frac{30}{100} + \frac{6}{100} = 3 + 3 \times \frac{1}{10} + 6 \times \frac{1}{100} = 3.36$$

But 21×16, by long multiplication, is:

$$\begin{array}{r} 21 \\ 16 \\ \hline 126 \\ 21 \\ \hline 336 \end{array} = 336.0$$

So the rule is: ignore decimal points in the numbers to be multiplied together and write down the answer for the multiplication of the digits. Now count up the number of decimal places in the two original numbers (in this case the numbers were 2.1 and 1.6, so altogether we have two decimal places). Now place the decimal point in the answer so that two decimal places are obtained in the result. For example:

8.3 × 2.4   (two decimal places altogether)

= 19.92

$$\begin{array}{r} 83 \\ 24 \\ \hline 332 \\ 166 \\ \hline 1992 \end{array}$$

An alternative method is: as before obtain 83 × 24 = 1992. The real problem was 8.3 × 2.4, i.e. (8+)(2+), so the answer must be bigger than 8 × 2 = 16. The only way we can obtain a number just bigger than 16 from 1992 is by placing the decimal point between 9 and 9, so the answer is 19.92.

Example

In 20.6 × 39.8, the answer is approximately 20 × 40 = 800.

$$\begin{array}{r} 206 \\ 398 \\ \hline 1648 \\ 1854 \\ 618 \\ \hline 81988 \end{array}$$

So the true answer is 819.88.

Exercise 2.13

Calculate the following:

1. 3.2 × 2.3
2. 4.1 × 3.4
3. 18.2 × 7.5
4. 207.8 × 37.2
5. 2.35 × 5.6
6. 2.35 × 4.85
7. 16.09 × 14.62
8. 58.72 × 15.2

9. 33.45×0.672
10. 0.045×0.0023
11. 150.2×0.0078
12. 506.1×403.8

For division of decimals we need to consider an example such as $2.1 \div 1.6$:

$$\frac{2.1}{1.6} = \frac{2.1 \times 10}{1.6 \times 10} = \frac{21}{16} = \frac{16 + 5}{16} = \frac{16}{16} + \frac{5}{16}$$

$$= 1 + \frac{4}{16} + \frac{1}{16} = 1 + \frac{1}{4} + \frac{1}{16}$$

$$= 1 + 0.25 + 0.0625 = 1.3125$$

But the normal way of arriving at this result is by long division. In the above working we showed that $2.1/1.6 = 21/16$. So we divide 21 by 16:

$$
\begin{array}{r}
1.3125 \\
16\overline{)21.0000000000} \\
\underline{16} \\
5\,0 \\
\underline{4\,8} \\
20 \\
\underline{16} \\
40 \\
\underline{32} \\
80 \\
\underline{80} \\
\cdot\cdot
\end{array}
$$

We may use either of two rules:

1. Move the decimal point in the divisor (the number by which we are dividing, here 16) to the right of the last significant figure and move the decimal point to the right in the dividend (the number we are dividing, here 21) by exactly the same number of decimal places. Then place the decimal point in the quotient (the answer, here 1.3125) immediately above that. Proceed to divide, ignoring decimal points.
2. Completely ignore the decimal points in both divisor and dividend. Work out the answer by the normal long-division

technique. Then obtain an approximate answer to the question by estimation and place the decimal point in the answer to fit that estimate.

Example

Using the second method, for $82.075 \div 16.3$:

Step 1   Calculate $82075/163$. We obtain $5035 \ldots$
Step 2   A rough estimate of the answer gives $80/16 = 5$.
Step 3   The real answer, therefore, must be $5.035 = 5.04$ correct to two decimal places.

Exercise 2.14

Give the answers to the following correct to one decimal place:

1. $6.3/2.5$
2. $9.4/4.3$
3. $16.8 \div 8.5$
4. $149.8 \div 71.3$
5. $11.8 \div 22.7$
6. $76.4 \div 150.3$

Give the answers to the following correct to two decimal places:

7. $35.06 \div 4.56$
8. $79.82 \div 14.05$
9. $0.0045 \div 0.083$
10. $5.007 \div 42.38$
11. $809.37 \div 67.42$
12. $5056 \div 300.24$

2.7   Miscellaneous examples on decimals and percentages

1.   During 20 days of a harvest period 65 per cent of the days are fine. How many fine days are there?

$$\text{No. of fine days} = 20 \times 65\% = {}^{1}20 \times \frac{65^{\,13}}{100_{1}} = 1 \times 13 = 13$$

2. A sample specimen of brass, of mass 12.3 kg, is an amalgam of copper and zinc, with 61.4 per cent copper and 38.6 per cent zinc. Calculate the masses of copper and zinc in the alloy.

Mass of copper $= 12.3 \times 61.4\% = 12.3 \times \dfrac{61.4}{100}$

$$= \frac{12.3 \times 61.4}{100} = \frac{755.22}{100} = 7.5522 \approx 7.6,$$

i.e. 7.6 kg of copper

Mass of zinc $= 12.3 \times 38.6\% = 12.3 \times 38.6/100$

$$= \frac{12.3 \times 38.6}{100} = 4.7478 \approx 4.7,$$

i.e. 4.7 kg of zinc

Note: The second answer might have been found merely by subtracting 7.6 from 12.3, giving 4.7. Alternatively, should the amount of zinc be found by the method shown above, a check on the results can be obtained by adding the amounts of copper and zinc together; the result should be 12.3.

3. On a summer day the temperature at 9 a.m. was 21°C. By midday the temperature had risen by 30%. What was the temperature at midday?
The temperature rose by:

$$21 \times 30\% = 21 \times \frac{3}{10} = \frac{63}{10} = 6.3$$

The temperature at midday, therefore, was $21 + 6.3 = 27.3$°C.
Alternatively: the temperature at midday was 130 per cent of that at 9 a.m. Therefore:

$$130\% \times 21 = \frac{130}{100} \times 21 = 27.3 \quad \text{(by calculator)}$$

4. When an electrical power source is put on load the effective voltage to the load is reduced by 14.3 per cent. If the reduction in the voltage is 35.2 V, what is the off-load voltage?

The off-load voltage is represented by 100 per cent, and the actual value of the 14.3 per cent reduction is 35.2 V. Therefore 1 per cent is represented by 35.2/14.3. Therefore the off-load voltage is:

$$\frac{35.2}{14.3} \times 100 = 246.2$$

correct to one decimal place (by calculator).

Exercise 2.15

1. An alloy is composed of 1.5 kg tin, 4.3 kg copper and 0.2 kg antimony. Calculate the percentage of each metal in the alloy.

2. The power consumption, W, in an electrical circuit is given by $W = I \cdot V$, where I and V represent current and voltage. If there is a percentage increase of 10 per cent in V and a 5 per cent decrease in I, calculate the percentage change in W. (*Hint*: Represent the original V by 100 and the original I by 300.)

3. The area of a circle (A) equals πr^2, where r is the radius. If there is a 5 per cent decrease in the radius calculate the percentage change in the area.

4. A brick of mass 2.4 kg is left to soak in water. After absorbing water for some time its mass becomes 3.15 kg. What is the percentage increase in the apparent mass of the brick? That is, what percentage is the mass of the water absorbed of the original mass of the brick?

5. A sample of mineral ore weighing 155 kg yields 18 per cent mineral. Calculate the mass of mineral yielded from the sample.

6. 1000 tonnes of crude oil produces 26.7 tonnes of lubricating high-grade oil, 14.4 tonnes of bitumen and 36 tonnes of kerosene. Calculate the percentage yields of lubricating oil, of bitumen and of kerosene.

7. Density is defined as mass/volume. If the mass of a liquid remains constant while the volume increases by 3 per cent due to a rise in temperature, calculate the percentage change in density.

8. A large tank contains water, oil and air under pressure. The total pressure at the bottom of the tank is the sum of those

due to (a) the depth of water, (b) the depth of oil floating on the water, and (c) the depth of the air above them. If *H* represents the unit of atmospheric pressure (standardized), the pressures due to the air, the oil and the water respectively are 2.5 *H*, 1.8 *H* and 3.2 *H*. Determine the percentage contribution to the total pressure at the bottom of the tank of each of the air, oil and water.

9. The volume of a box is length × breadth × height. If the length is increased by 10 per cent, the breadth by 15 per cent and the height by 5 per cent, determine the percentage increase in the volume.

10. The momentum of a body is mass × velocity. If the mass of a body increases by 25 per cent and the momentum by 15 per cent, what must the percentage change in the velocity be?

3
Indices

Before we embark on this chapter it is essential that we understand two basic principles and ideas:

1. Multiples. The numbers 8, 12, 16, 20, etc. are all multiples of 4 because they can be written as 2×4, 3×4, 4×4, 5×4, etc. In general, any number which can be written in the form $m \times n$, where m and n are integers, is a multiple both of m and n. For example: 28 is a multiple of 2, 4, 7, and 14; and 36 is a multiple of 2, 3, 4, 6, 9, 12 and 18.
2. Factors. Because 28 is a multiple of 2, 4, 7 and 14, each of 2, 4, 7 and 14 is said to be a factor of 28. Similarly, 2, 3, 4, 6, 9, 12 and 18 are said to be factors of 36. A factor of a given number is another number which divides exactly into the given number (i.e., with no remainder). For example: factors of 12 are 2, 3, 4 and 6; factors of 16 are 2, 4 and 8; factors of 24 are 2, 3, 4, 6, 8 and 12; factors of 32 are 2, 4, 8 and 16; and factors of 42 are 2, 3, 6, 7, 14 and 21.

Exercise 3.1

In each question select, from the numbers given, those which are multiples of either of those in brackets:

1. (2, 3)   4, 6, 5, 8, 9, 7, 10, 11, 12
2. (4, 5)   6, 8, 10, 9, 14, 15, 18
3. (14, 12)   7, 6, 4, 8, 24, 18, 21, 28, 35, 36
4. (16, 15)   32, 8, 3, 5, 20, 48, 30, 45, 64

Write down all possible factors of the following:

5. 15
6. 20
7. 21
8. 27
9. 36
10. 48
11. 40

In each question select, from the numbers given, those which are multiples of *both* of those in brackets:

12. (2, 3) 4, 6, 5, 8, 9, 7, 10, 11, 12
13. (4, 5) 6, 8, 10, 9, 14, 15, 18, 20, 30, 100
14. (14, 12) 24, 18, 21, 28, 42, 84, 96, 168
15. (8, 12) 16, 32, 24, 36, 48, 96, 108, 288

3.1 Prime factors: HCF and LCM

In Chapter 1 we considered briefly the LCM (lowest common multiple) of two or more numbers when we had to add fractions. For example, the LCM of 6 and 4 is 12. There are, of course, other multiples, but 12 is the lowest of them all.

Sometimes we are interested in a number which is called the highest common factor (HCF). The HCF of 6 and 4 is the largest number which is a factor of both. This is 2.

These answers are easily obtained, but it is not nearly so easy to find the LCM and the HCF of, for example, 48, 54 and 102. One method of obtaining these is to write the given numbers in factor form, using prime factors (i.e., numbers which cannot be divided exactly by any number other than themselves and 1). Examples of prime numbers are 2, 3, 5, 7, 11, 13, 17, 19, 23, 29 and 31. Other than 2, no prime number can be even, because all even numbers are divisible by 2. To find the LCM and HCF of 48, 54 and 102, then, we write:

$$48 = 2 \times 24 = 2 \times 2 \times 12 = 2 \times 2 \times 2 \times 6$$
$$= 2 \times 2 \times 2 \times 2 \times 3 \tag{i}$$

$$54 = 2 \times 27 = 2 \times 3 \times 9 = 2 \times 3 \times 3 \times 3 \tag{ii}$$

$$102 = 2 \times 51 = 2 \times 3 \times 17 \tag{iii}$$

The LCM must be a multiple of $2 \times 2 \times 2 \times 2$ from (i), also a multiple of $3 \times 3 \times 3$ from (ii) and a multiple of 17 from (iii). So the LCM must be:

$$(2 \times 2 \times 2 \times 2) \times (3 \times 3 \times 3) \times 17 = 16 \times 27 \times 17 = 7344$$

In the three different numbers, 48, 54 and 102, only three prime factors occur: 2, 3 and 17. And each prime factor occurs in the LCM the greatest number of times it appears in any one of the three numbers. 2 occurs four times in (i); 3 appears three times in (ii); and 17 occurs once in (iii).

The HCF $= 2 \times 3 = 6$; 6 is the greatest number which will divide exactly into all three of 48, 54 and 102. The rule for writing down the factors of the HCF is: each prime factor occurs in the HCF the least number of times it appears in any of the three numbers. Two appears once in (ii) and (iii); 3 occurs once in (i) and (iii); and 17 does not occur at all in (i) and (ii).

In (i), (ii) and (iii) it is quite a lengthy process to write down the prime factors, so we must look for a shorter method. For instance, we need an abbreviation for numbers such as $2 \times 2 \times 2 \times 2 \times 2 \times 2 \times 2$. Here 2 occurs as a factor 7 times. So we write it as 2^7. Similarly, we write $3 \times 3 \times 3 \times 3$ as 3^4, 5×5 as 5^2, $7 \times 7 \times 7$ as 7^3, and $10 \times 10 \times 10 \times 10$ as 10^4. Using this idea the example above becomes:

$$48 = 2^4 \times 3$$
$$54 = 2 \times 3^3$$
$$102 = 2 \times 3 \times 17$$
$$\text{LCM} = 2^4 \times 3^3 \times 17$$
$$\text{HCF} = 2 \times 3$$

Exercise 3.2

Express the following numbers in prime factor form:

1. 12
2. 18
3. 24
4. 20
5. 25
6. 30
7. 36
8. 42

9. 48
10. 54
11. 50
12. 8
13. 16
14. 32
15. 72
16. 81
17. 98
18. 108
19. 200
20. 750

Find the LCM and HCF of the following sets of numbers:

21. 18, 20, 24
22. 20, 25, 30
23. 36, 42, 54
24. 28, 42, 98
25. 72, 81, 108

3.2   Bases, powers and indices

Consider the following numbers and how they can be expressed using the principles discussed in Section 3.1.

$$2 = 2^1 \qquad\qquad (i)$$
$$4 = 2 \times 2 = 2^2$$
$$8 = 2 \times 2 \times 2 = 2^3$$
$$16 = 2 \times 2 \times 2 \times 2 = 2^4$$
$$32 = 2 \times 2 \times 2 \times 2 \times 2 = 2^5$$
$$64 = 2 \times 2 \times 2 \times 2 \times 2 \times 2 = 2^6$$

Here the calculations are based on the number 2, called the *base*.

$$3 = 3^1 \qquad\qquad (ii)$$
$$9 = 3 \times 3 = 3^2$$
$$27 = 3 \times 3 \times 3 = 3^3$$
$$81 = 3 \times 3 \times 3 \times 3 = 3^4$$
$$243 = 3 \times 3 \times 3 \times 3 \times 3 = 3^5$$
$$729 = 3 \times 3 \times 3 \times 3 \times 3 \times 3 = 3^6$$

Here the base is 3.

$$4 = 4^1 \qquad \text{(iii)}$$
$$16 = 4 \times 4 = 4^2$$
$$64 = 4 \times 4 \times 4 = 4^3$$
$$256 = 4 \times 4 \times 4 \times 4 = 4^4$$
$$1024 = 4 \times 4 \times 4 \times 4 \times 4 = 4^5$$

The base is 4.

$$5 = 5^1 \qquad \text{(iv)}$$
$$25 = 5 \times 5 = 5^2$$
$$125 = 5 \times 5 \times 5 = 5^3$$
$$625 = 5 \times 5 \times 5 \times 5 = 5^4$$
$$3125 = 5 \times 5 \times 5 \times 5 \times 5 = 5^5$$

The base is 5.

$$6 = 6^1 \qquad \text{(v)}$$
$$36 = 6 \times 6 = 6^2$$
$$216 = 6 \times 6 \times 6 = 6^3$$
$$1296 = 6 \times 6 \times 6 \times 6 = 6^4$$

The base is 6.

The terms on the right are called powers; for example, 2^4 is the fourth power of 2. The small numbers above and to the right of the bases 2, 3, 4, 5 and 6 are called *indices*. For example, in (ii) 81 is the fourth power of 3 (index 4).

We have discovered the rules governing integers under addition, subtraction, multiplication and division. What are the rules governing powers? For a moment let us consider only base 2:

We know that $4 \times 8 = 32$
From (i), $4 \times 8 = 2^2 \times 2^3$
But $32 = 2^5$ (from (i))
Therefore $2^2 \times 2^3 = 2^5$
Again from (i), $4 \times 16 = 2^2 \times 2^4$
But $4 \times 16 = 64 = 2^6$
Therefore $2^2 \times 2^4 = 2^6$

Exercise 3.3

Use (i) above to obtain similar results by considering the following:

1. 2×4
2. 2×8
3. 2×16

4. 8×8
5. 4×4
6. 2×32

Use (ii) above to obtain similar results, using base 3 instead of base 2, by considering the following:

7. 3×9
8. 3×27
9. 3×81
10. 3×243
11. 9×9
12. 9×27
13. 9×81
14. 27×27

By looking carefully at the results we detect a common pattern. Although we shall not extend (i) to find the value of $2^{11} \times 2^{9}$, we would conclude from the above results that it was 2^{20}. And that:

$$3^{7} \times 3^{6} = 3^{13}$$

In general, we may conclude that:

$$2^{p} \times 2^{q} = 2^{p+q} \qquad 3^{x} \times 3^{y} = 3^{x+y}$$

All these results are covered by the rule:

$$a^{m} \times a^{n} = a^{m+n} \qquad\qquad 3.1$$

where a represents any base and m and n are (positive) integers.

Examples

1. $(3^{4} \times 3^{3}) \times 3^{5} = 3^{7} \times 3^{5} = 3^{12}$
2. $(a^{p} \times a^{q}) \times a^{r} = a^{p+q} \times a^{r} = a^{p+q+r}$
3. $(b^{x} \times b^{x}) \times b^{y} = b^{2x} \times b^{y} = b^{2x+y}$

Exercise 3.4

Use Law 3.1 to simplify the following:

1. $2^{2} \times 2^{5}$
2. $3^{4} \times 3^{2}$

3. $4^2 \times 4^4$
4. $5^2 \times 5^3$
5. $(2^2 \times 2^3) \times 2^2$
6. $6^2 \times 6^2$
7. $(3^3 \times 3^2) \times 3^3$
8. $(a^2 \times a^3) \times a^4$
9. $6^p \times 6^q$
10. $(p \times p^2) \times p^4$
11. $a^b \times a^c$
12. $a^b \times a^b$
13. $b^a \times b^c$
14. $(a^p \times a^p) \times a^p$
15. $(a^p \times a^p) \times a^q$
16. $a^p \times a^q \times a^r$

By using (i), from the beginning of this section, we obtain:

$$16 \div 8 = 2^4 \div 2^3$$
$$\text{But } 16 \div 8 = 2 = 2^1$$
$$\text{So } 2^4 \div 2^3 = 2^1$$

From (ii) at the beginning of this section:

$$243 \div 9 = 3^5 \div 3^2$$
$$\text{But } 243 \div 9 = 27 = 3^3$$
$$\text{So } 3^5 \div 3^2 = 3^3$$

Exercise 3.5

Use (i) to (v) at the beginning of the section to obtain similar results by considering:

1. $625 \div 125$
2. $256 \div 64$
3. $1024 \div 16$
4. $625 \div 25$
5. $3125 \div 5$
6. $1296 \div 6$

7. $216 \div 36$
8. $1024 \div 64$
9. $729 \div 9$
10. $729 \div 3$

By looking carefully at your results try to arrive at a rule similar to Law 3.1, but where division is substituted for multiplication. Now give answers to:

11. $3^7 \div 3^3$
12. $5^{10} \div 5^7$
13. $7^8 \div 7^2$
14. $8^5 \div 8^2$
15. $3^7/3^3$
16. $5^{10}/5^7$
17. $7^8/7^2$
18. $8^5/8^2$
19. $35^6/35^3$
20. $409^{11}/409^3$

The results above point to:

$$2^p \div 2^q = 2^p/2^q = 2^{p-q}$$

and $\quad 5^x \div 5^y = 5^x/5^y = 5^{x-y}$

The law which covers all cases is:

$$a^m \div a^n = a^m/a^n = a^{m-n} \qquad\qquad 3.2$$

where a is any base and m and n are positive integers.

Exercise 3.6

Use Law 3.2 to simplify the following:

1. $2^5 \div 2^2$
2. $2^6 \div 2^4$
3. $3^7 \div 3^2$
4. $4^3/4$
5. $5^4/5^2$
6. $(2^5 \div 2^2) \div 2^2$

7. $(3^6 \div 3^2) \div 3^2$
8. $a^4 \div a^3$
9. b^5/b^2
10. $(a^p \div a^q) \div a^q$
11. $(b^{2p} \div b^p) \div b$
12. $(a^p \times a^p) \div a^p$

To obtain the next rule we shall consider:

$8^2 = (2^3)^2$
However, $8^2 = 8 \times 8 = 2^3 \times 2^3 = 2^{3+3} = 2^6$
So $(2^3)^2 = 2^6$
Similarly, $9^3 = (3^2)^3$
But $9^3 = 9 \times 9 \times 9 = 3^2 \times 3^2 \times 3^2 = 3^6$ (by Law 3.1)
So $(3^2)^3 = 3^6$
Again, $(5^2)^4 = 25^4 = 25 \times 25 \times 25 \times 25$
$= 5^2 \times 5^2 \times 5^2 \times 5^2$
$= 5^{2+2+2+2} = 5^8$ (by Law 3.1)
So $(5^2)^4 = 5^8$

By looking at these results we would conclude that:

$$(7^3)^5 = 7^{15}$$

The pattern would be:

$$(2^p)^q = 2^{p \times q} = 2^{pq}$$
$$(3^x)^y = 3^{x \times y} = 3^{xy}$$

And, in general:

$$(a^m)^n = a^{mn} \qquad\qquad 3.3$$

Exercise 3.7

Use Law 3.3 to simplify the following:

1. $(2^2)^2$
2. $(2^2)^3$
3. $(2^3)^2$
4. $(3^2)^4$
5. $(3^3)^2$

6. $(4^4)^3$
7. $(3^2)^4$
8. $[(2^2)^2]^3$
9. $(a^3)^2$
10. $(a^4)^2$
11. $(a^p)^q$
12. $(a^p)^2$
13. $(a^3)^q$
14. $(b^p)^q$
15. $[(a^p)^q]^r$

Summary

$$2^p = 2 \times 2 \times 2 \times 2 \times \cdots \times 2 \quad \text{(2 written as a factor } p \text{ times)}$$

$$a^m \times a^n = a^{m+n} \qquad \text{(Law 3.1)}$$

$$a^m/a^n = a^m \div a^n = a^{m-n} \qquad \text{(Law 3.2)}$$

$$(a^m)^n = a^{mn} \qquad \text{(Law 3.3)}$$

In all these cases the power is taken to be a positive integer. From these rules we are able to deduce others. First:

$$(a \times b)^2 = (a \times b) \times (a \times b) = (a \times a) \times (b \times b) \; Associative \; law$$
$$= a^2 \times b^2 = a^2 b^2$$

Leading, in general, to:

$$(a \times b \times c \times \cdots)^p = (abc \cdots)^p = a^p b^p c^p \cdots \qquad 3.4$$

Second:

$$(a \div b)^3 = (a/b)^3 = (a/b) \times (a/b) \times (a/b)$$
$$= \frac{a}{b} \times \frac{a}{b} \times \frac{a}{b} = \frac{a^3}{b^3}$$

Leading, in general, to:

$$(a \div b)^p = (a/b)^p = a^p/b^p \qquad 3.5$$

Zero index or power

Up to now all powers have been positive integers, but the above laws lead us to cases where the powers may take other values. In particular, Law 3.2 is fruitful. By that law $2^3/2^3$, $3^4 \div 3^4$, $4^3 \div 4^3$ and a^p/a^p all lead to the same result. For example:

$$2^3/2^3 = 2^{3-3} = 2^0$$

But, since $2^3 = 8$, then $2^3/2^3 = 8/8 = 1$

Further, $\quad 1 = 3^4 \div 3^4 = 3^{4-4} = 3^0$

$$1 = 4^3 \div 4^3 = 4^{3-3} = 4^0$$

and $\quad 1 = a^p/a^p = a^{p-p} = a^0$

Giving $\quad a^0 = 1$ $\hfill 3.6$

Note: a^0 cannot mean a written down as a factor zero times. It is merely an alternative way of writing 1. It is a necessary consequence of the previous laws.

Negative powers or indices

$1/2 = 2^0/2^1$ (by Law 3.6) $= 2^{0-1}$ (by Law 3.2) $= 2^{-1}$
Therefore $2^{-1} = \frac{1}{2}$ (1/2 is called the reciprocal of 2)
$1/3 = 3^0/3^1 = 3^{0-1} = 3^{-1}$
Therefore $3^{-1} = \frac{1}{3}$ (the reciprocal of 3)

Exercise 3.8

Express the following in index form, i.e. with suitable bases to the appropriate power:

1. $1/4$ (base 4)
2. $1/5$ (base 5)
3. $1/6$ (base 6)
4. $1/7$
5. $1/11$
6. $1/31$
7. $1/a$ (base a)

The answer to (7) above is a^{-1}, and $4^{-1}, 5^{-1}, 6^{-1}, 7^{-1}, 11^{-1}$ and 31^{-1} are the answers to the previous questions. We conclude that:

$$a^{-1} = 1/a \text{ (reciprocal of } a) \hfill 3.7$$

We take this a stage further:

$$1/2^n = 2^0/2^n = 2^{0-n} = 2^{-n}$$
$$1/3^p = 3^0/3^p = 3^{0-p} = 3^{-p}$$

Exercise 3.9

In similar fashion arrive at corresponding results for the following:

1. $1/4^n$
2. $1/5^x$
3. $1/6^a$
4. $1/7^m$
5. $1/8^p$
6. $1/9^n$
7. $1/10^p$
8. $1/a^n$

The next rule, then, is:

$$a^{-n} = 1/a^n \text{ (reciprocal of } a^n)$$ *3.8*

In the examples of negative powers we have chosen, the powers have been negative integers. So far we have not encountered a power which is fractional.

Fractional indices

The terms 'power' and 'index' are often used as though they had exactly the same meaning, but for many the term 'power' is restricted to positive integral values of the index. So far we have found no meaning for fractional indices. From (i) at the beginning of this section, $2^2 = 4$, i.e. $4 = 2$ to the power of 2, more usually called 2 squared.

This relationship between 2 and 4 tells us how to calculate 4 starting from 2. Suppose we wished to proceed in the reverse direction, i.e., to calculate 2 starting from 4. We have said that $4 = 2$ squared, or the square of 2. In reverse we say that $2 =$ the square root of 4. It is written:

$$2 = \sqrt{4}$$

Similarly:

$$9 = 3^2 \text{ therefore } 3 = \sqrt{9}$$
$$16 = 4^2 \text{ therefore } 4 = \sqrt{16}$$
$$25 = 5^2 \text{ therefore } 5 = \sqrt{25}$$
$$36 = 6^2 \text{ therefore } 6 = \sqrt{36}$$

And, because $7^2 = 49, 8^2 = 64, 9^2 = 81, 10^2 = 100, 11^2 = 121$ and $12^2 = 144$, then $\sqrt{49} = 7, \sqrt{64} = 8, \sqrt{81} = 9, \sqrt{100} = 10, \sqrt{121} = 11$ and $\sqrt{144} = 12$.

Consequently, since $\sqrt{4} = 2$, then:

$$(\sqrt{4})^2 = 2^2 = 4 = 4^1$$

Now, suppose that $\sqrt{4}$ may be written as 4^x, where x is unknown. Then:

$(\sqrt{4})^2 = (4^x)^2 = 4^{2x}$ (assuming Law 3.3 applies)

Then $4^{2x} = 4^1$ (see above)

This means that $2x = 1$ and therefore $x = \frac{1}{2}$

Therefore $\sqrt{4}$ means $4^{\frac{1}{2}}$

Similarly, $\sqrt{9} = 3$ so $(\sqrt{9})^2 = 3^2 = 9 = 9^1$

Put $\sqrt{9} = 9^y$ $(9^y)^2 = 9^1$, giving $9^{2y} = 9^1$

Leading to $2y = 1$ or $y = \frac{1}{2}$

Consequently $\sqrt{9} = 9^{\frac{1}{2}}$

Exercise 3.10

By considering similarly the square roots of 16, 25, 36, 49 and 64 show that $\sqrt{16} = 16^{\frac{1}{2}}$, $\sqrt{25} = 25^{\frac{1}{2}}$, $\sqrt{36} = 36^{\frac{1}{2}}$, $\sqrt{49} = 49^{\frac{1}{2}}$ and $\sqrt{64} = 64^{\frac{1}{2}}$.

The next rule, therefore, is:

$$\sqrt{a} = a^{\frac{1}{2}} \qquad\qquad 3.9$$

Here a must be positive.

Thus we have introduced indices which are positive integers, zero, negative integers, and now positive fractions. In fact an index can have any real value. Just as we showed that the index $\frac{1}{2}$ is related to the square root, so we are able to show that:

$$a^{\frac{1}{3}} = \sqrt[3]{a} \text{ (i.e., the cube root of } a)$$

(A cube root is the number that, when cubed, gives us the original value.) Similarly:

$$a^{\frac{1}{4}} = \sqrt[4]{a} \text{ (the fourth root of } a)$$

In general, where n is a positive integer:

$$a^{\frac{1}{n}} = \sqrt[n]{a} \text{ (the } n\text{th root of } a)$$

Examples

1. $625^{\frac{1}{2}} = \sqrt{625} = 25$
2. $27^{\frac{1}{3}} = \sqrt[3]{27} = 3$
3. $16^{\frac{1}{4}} = \sqrt[4]{16} = 2$
4. $243^{\frac{1}{5}} = \sqrt[5]{243} = 3$

Exercise 3.11

Simplify the following:

1. $81^{\frac{1}{2}}$
2. $64^{\frac{1}{3}}$
3. $125^{\frac{1}{3}}$
4. $625^{\frac{1}{4}}$
5. $121^{\frac{1}{2}}$
6. $169^{\frac{1}{2}}$
7. $216^{\frac{1}{3}}$
8. $343^{\frac{1}{3}}$
9. $32^{\frac{1}{5}}$
10. $64^{\frac{1}{6}}$
11. $128^{\frac{1}{7}}$
12. $3125^{\frac{1}{5}}$
13. $10\,000^{\frac{1}{4}} \times 3\,200\,000^{\frac{1}{5}}$
14. $49^{\frac{1}{2}} \times 27^{\frac{1}{3}} \times 16^{\frac{1}{4}}$
15. $(49^{\frac{1}{2}})^2$
16. $(49^2)^{\frac{1}{2}}$
17. $(27^{\frac{1}{3}})^3$
18. $(27^3)^{\frac{1}{3}}$
19. $(4^{\frac{1}{2}})^3$
20. $(4^3)^{\frac{1}{2}}$

Note: The answer to (17) is 27, just as if $(27^{\frac{1}{3}})^3$ followed Law 3.3, i.e. the indices $\frac{1}{3}$ and 3 could be multiplied together. And similarly with (18). In fact, we shall assume that all the rules we have discovered so far for positive integral indices apply equally when the indices take any real values, including both positive and negative fractions.

This means that (19) and (20) in Exercise 3.11 are each equal to $4^{\frac{3}{2}}$. Thus the index $\frac{3}{2}$ means either the cube of the square root or the square root of the cube, i.e. $a^{\frac{3}{2}}$ can be written as:

$$(\sqrt{a})^3 \quad \text{or} \quad \sqrt{a^3}$$

If we wish to evaluate the result arithmetically it is usually easier to express it in the first form, because a^3 might turn out to be very large, making the resulting square root difficult to determine. For example, $(\sqrt{625})^3$ is fairly easy to work out because $\sqrt{625} = 25$, and $25^3 = 15\,625$, whereas 625^3 is a very large number, and the next step, i.e. to find its square root, is difficult. Not even a calculator helps us here because it gives us a rounded-off value of 625^3.

Examples

1. $16^{\frac{3}{4}}$ means $(16^{\frac{1}{4}})^3 = 2^3 = 8$; or $(16^3)^{\frac{1}{4}}$, which is difficult to work out.

2. $27^{\frac{2}{3}}$ means $(27^{\frac{1}{3}})^2 = 3^2 = 9$; or $(27^2)^{\frac{1}{3}}$.

3. $4^{-\frac{1}{2}} = \dfrac{1}{4^{\frac{1}{2}}}$, assuming Law 3.8 applies $= \frac{1}{2}$.

4. $64^{-\frac{5}{6}} = \dfrac{1}{64^{\frac{5}{6}}} = \dfrac{1}{(64^{\frac{1}{6}})^5} = \dfrac{1}{2^5} = \dfrac{1}{32}$

5. $\sqrt{4xy} = (4xy)^{\frac{1}{2}} = 4^{\frac{1}{2}} \cdot x^{\frac{1}{2}} \cdot y^{\frac{1}{2}}$ (by Law 3.4) $= 2x^{\frac{1}{2}}y^{\frac{1}{2}}$

6. $(9a^3b^2c^{-1})^{\frac{1}{2}} \times (\frac{16}{27}a^{-2}b^3c^4)^{\frac{1}{3}} = 3a^{\frac{3}{2}}bc^{-\frac{1}{2}} \times \dfrac{2^{\frac{4}{3}}}{3}a^{-\frac{2}{3}}bc^{\frac{4}{3}}$

$$= 2^{\frac{4}{3}} \cdot a^{\frac{3}{2}-\frac{2}{3}} \cdot b^2 \cdot c^{\frac{4}{3}-\frac{1}{2}}$$

$$= 2^{\frac{4}{3}} \cdot a^{\frac{5}{6}} \cdot b^2 \cdot c^{\frac{5}{6}}$$

because we may multiply the factors in any convenient order (the associative law).

Exercise 3.12

Simplify the following, giving answers in positive indices:

1. $3p^2q^3 \times 2p^3q^4$
2. $(16x)^{\frac{3}{4}}$
3. $(27y)^{\frac{2}{3}}$
4. $(25xy^{-1})^{\frac{1}{2}}$
5. $(243x^3y^2)^{\frac{1}{5}}$
6. $(\frac{4}{9}a^4b^{-3})^{-\frac{1}{2}}$
7. $49x^4y^3 \div 14x^2y^2$
8. $5a^{-2}b^3 \div 15a^3b^{-1}$
9. $(ab)^3$
10. $(2x^2y^3)^2$
11. $\left(\dfrac{ax^2y^3}{z^4}\right)^p$
12. $\sqrt{9x^2}$
13. $\sqrt{\dfrac{16x^{-2}y^4}{z^3}}$
14. $\sqrt[3]{\dfrac{27x^{-6}y^{-3}}{8z^{-4}}}$
15. $\sqrt{1.44x^2y^{-4}}$
16. $\sqrt{\dfrac{49}{a^3b^{-4}}}$
17. $\dfrac{2xy^2}{3xz} \times \dfrac{6yz^2}{8zx^2}$
18. $\dfrac{10x^3y^4}{21x^2z^2} \times \dfrac{14y^5z^3}{25x^2y^3z^4}$
19. $4a^2b^2c^3 \times 6ab^2c^3$
20. $3ab^{-1}c^2 \times 5a^2b^3c^4$
21. $6a^2b^3c^{-2} \div 3ab^2c^3$
22. $16p^{-1}q^{-2}r^2 \div 12p^2qr^{-1}$
23. $\sqrt{25a^2b^4}$
24. $\sqrt{144x^3y}$
25. $\sqrt{225p^6q^{-2}r^4}$
26. $(2xy^2)^2$

27. $(3a^{-1}b)^3$
28. $(6pq^2)^{-2}$
29. $(64a^{-1}b^{-2})^{-\frac{1}{2}}$
30. $(81p^{\frac{1}{2}}q^2)^{\frac{1}{2}}$
31. $(121x^{-\frac{1}{2}}y^{-\frac{3}{2}}z^{\frac{1}{4}})^2$
32. $\sqrt{\dfrac{48a^6b^{-3}}{3a^{-2}b}}$

4

Standard Form and Binary Form

4.1 Standard form

A number such as 58 231 means $50\,000 + 8000 + 200 + 30 + 1$, or:

$$5 \times 10^4 + 8 \times 10^3 + 2 \times 10^2 + 3 \times 10 + 1$$

The number 19 may be written as:

$$\tfrac{19}{10} \times 10 = 1.9 \times 10 = 1.9 \times 10^1$$

Similarly: $254.3 = \tfrac{254.3}{100} \times 100 = 2.543 \times 100 = 2.543 \times 10^2$
And: $0.487 = (0.487 \times 10) \times \tfrac{1}{10} = 4.87 \times \tfrac{1}{10} = 4.87 \times 10^{-1}$

We have converted each of the three numbers above into what is called standard form. A number expressed in standard form is written as:

$$a \times 10^n$$

where $1 \leq a < 10$ and n is an integer (positive or negative). Why do we need to express numbers in this way?

First, we can compare roughly the magnitudes of numbers very quickly, e.g. 2×10^3 and 3×10^5. The second number is roughly 100 (10^2) times the first. (We ignore the 3 and the 2 and look only at 10^5 and 10^3.) Similarly, 6×10^{-7} and 4.2×10^{-3}. The first is roughly 10^{-4} times the second, i.e. $1/10^4$ of it, or $1/10\,000$ of it.

100

Second, we can handle the standard forms better when using a slide rule. For example:

$$\frac{(6.35 \times 10^3) \times (3.19 \times 10^{-2})}{(4.78 \times 10^4)}$$

$$= \frac{6.35 \times 3.19}{4.78} \times \frac{10^3 \times 10^{-2}}{10^4} \approx 4.24 \times 10^{-3}$$

Third, the standard form helps us to understand the use of logarithms better and helps us to appreciate the display on our calculators. From the above we conclude that the rule for conversion from decimal to standard form is: shift the decimal point to the position immediately to the right of the first significant figure. If we have moved the point x places to the left we multiply the resulting decimal by 10^x. If we have moved the decimal point y units to the right we multiply the resulting decimal by 10^{-y}.

Exercise 4.1

Convert the following to standard form:

1. 83.2
2. 64.5
3. 123.6
4. 101.5
5. 6049.7
6. 3051
7. 8140
8. 6200
9. 0.146
10. 0.902
11. 0.043
12. 0.0065
13. 0.0000205
14. 1 300 000
15. 250 000
16. 23.5×10^2
17. 0.48×10^{-6}
18. $\frac{75}{2} \times 10^2$

4.2 Conversion from standard form to decimal form

Examples

1. $2.74 \times 10^3 = 2.74 \times 1000 = 2740$

2. $4.52 \times 10^{-4} = 4.52 \times \dfrac{1}{10\,000} = \dfrac{4.52}{10\,000} = 0.000452$

3. $6.027 \times 10^7 = 6.027 \times 10\,000\,000 = 60\,270\,000$

4. $3.0502 \times 10^{-3} = 3.0502 \times \dfrac{1}{1000} = \dfrac{3.0502}{1000} = 0.0030502$

In case (1) the decimal point was moved 3 places to the right. In (2) it was moved 4 places to the left. In (3) it was moved 7 places to the right. In (4) it was moved 3 places to the left. Therefore we can conclude that the rule is: to convert a number in standard form $a \times 10^x$ into decimal form, move the decimal point in a x places to the right if x is positive and x places to the left if x is negative.

Exercise 4.2

Convert to denary, or decimal form, the following:

1. 2.3×10^2
2. 4.8×10^4
3. 2.01×10^1
4. 6.06×10^{-1}
5. 1.2×10^{-2}
6. 3.5×10^{-4}
7. 8.62×10^7
8. 1.08×10^{-6}
9. 7.5×10^{-5}

4.3 Addition and subtraction of numbers in standard form

Examples

1. $2.5 \times 10^3 + 3.2 \times 10^3 = 2500 + 3200 = 5700 = 5.7 \times 10^3$
    This is exactly the same as if we had said:

$$2.5 \times 10^3 + 3.2 \times 10^3 = (2.5 + 3.2) \times 10^3 \text{ (distributive law)}$$
$$= 5.7 \times 10^3$$

2. $3.2 \times 10^3 - 2.5 \times 10^3 = (3.2 - 2.5) \times 10^3 = 0.7 \times 10^3$
$$= (7 \times 10^{-1}) \times 10^3 = 7 \times 10^{3-1} = 7 \times 10^2$$

3. $2.5 \times 10^3 + 3.2 \times 10^2 = 2500 + 320 = 2820 = 2.82 \times 10^3$
Or: $\quad 2.5 \times 10^3 + 3.2 \times 10^2 = 2.5 \times 10^3 + 0.32 \times 10^3$
$$= (2.5 + 0.32) \times 10^3 = 2.82 \times 10^3$$

We can use either of two methods:

1. Convert each number to normal decimal form, add or subtract by rules for decimals, and then convert the answer to standard form.
2. The numbers will be, say, $a_1 \times 10^{n_1}$ and $a_2 \times 10^{n_2}$. Alter the second number by changing the position of the decimal point in a_2 and the value of n_2 to n_1 so that the value of the number is unchanged. Then proceed as in example 1 above.

Exercise 4.3

Calculate the following and give answers in standard form:

1. $4.6 \times 10^2 + 2.3 \times 10^2$
2. $8.2 \times 10^3 + 1.7 \times 10^3$
3. $5.3 \times 10^4 + 3.2 \times 10^4$
4. $4.6 \times 10^2 + 2.3 \times 10$
5. $4.6 \times 10^2 + 2.3 \times 10^3$
6. $1.4 \times 10^4 + 1.4 \times 10^3$
7. $8.2 \times 10^2 + 1.1 \times 10^4$
8. $8.1 \times 10 + 9.1 \times 10^{-1}$
9. $7.5 \times 10^0 + 6.5 \times 10^{-1}$
10. $1.6 \times 10^{-1} + 1.6 \times 10^{-2}$
11. $2.3 \times 10^{-1} + 8.4 \times 10^{-3}$
12. $5.8 \times 10^2 - 3.6 \times 10^2$
13. $6.7 \times 10^3 - 1.02 \times 10^2$
14. $7.2 \times 10^4 - 8.8 \times 10^3$
15. $1.05 \times 10^6 - 1.02 \times 10^5$

16. $5.8 \times 10 - 3.6 \times 10^0$
17. $5.8 \times 10^{-1} - 3.6 \times 10^{-1}$
18. $4.9 \times 10^{-2} - 3.6 \times 10^{-2}$
19. $6.1 \times 10^{-3} - 1.5 \times 10^{-3}$
20. $3.8 \times 10^{-6} - 2.9 \times 10^{-6}$
21. $3.8 \times 10^{-5} - 2.9 \times 10^{-6}$
22. $4.5 \times 10^2 + 5.8 \times 10^2 - 6.3 \times 10^2$
23. $6.03 \times 10^3 + 3.07 \times 10^5 - 9.09 \times 10 + 4.46$
    $\times 10^{-2} - 9.89 \times 10^{-1}$

4.4 Binary numbers

The number 2843 is really $2 \times 10^3 + 8 \times 10^2 + 4 \times 10 + 3 \times 1$. It is called a denary number because it is written using the base number 10. We may write numbers in forms using any base. When we use the base 10 the digits of the number (in shortened form) are never more than 9. In denary all digits range from 0 to 9 inclusive. If the base were 4 then all digits would range from 0 to 3 inclusive; e.g. 31021_4 (where the suffix 4 indicates that we are employing the base number 4) means $3 \times 4^4 + 1 \times 4^3 + 0 \times 4^2 + 2 \times 4 + 1 \times 1$.

Because electronic calculators depend basically on the principle of one or other circuits being switched on or off (i.e., two possibilities only), and for other reasons, we sometimes wish to consider a number system with base 2, which means the only digits employed are 0 and 1. This is called a binary system, and the numbers used in this system are binary numbers. For example, in binary, 101101 means:

$$1 \times 2^5 + 0 \times 2^4 + 1 \times 2^3 + 1 \times 2^2 + 0 \times 2 + 1 \times 1$$

Its value in denary is:

$$1 \times 32 + 1 \times 8 + 1 \times 4 + 1 \times 1 = 32 + 8 + 4 + 1 = 45$$

Conversion from denary to binary

One method of converting from denary to binary is to remember successive powers of 2, e.g. $2^1 = 2$; $2^2 = 4$; $2^3 = 8$; $2^4 = 16$; $2^5 = 32$; $2^6 = 64$ and so on.

Examples

Convert the following to binary:

1. 64.

$$64 = 1 \times 2^6 + 0 = 1 \times 2^6 + 0 \times 2^5 + 0 \times 2^4 + 0 \times 2^3 + 0 \times 2^2$$
$$+ 0 \times 2 + 0 \times 1$$
$$= 1000000_2 = 1000000$$

2. 43. Here we look for the highest power of 2 which is less than 43. So:

$$
\begin{aligned}
43 &= 32 + 11 \quad \text{It is 32, which is } 2^5.\\
&= 32 + 8 + 3 \quad \text{Again, } 8 = 2^3. \text{ This is the highest}\\
&\qquad\text{power of 2 less than 11.}\\
&= 32 + 8 + 2 + 1 \quad 2 = 2^1, \text{ and this is the highest}\\
&\qquad\text{power of 2 less than 3.}\\
&= 2^5 + 2^3 + 2^1 + 1\\
&= 1 \times 2^5 + 0 \times 2^4 + 1 \times 2^3 + 0 \times 2^2 + 1 \times 2 + 1 \times 1\\
&= 101011
\end{aligned}
$$

Therefore $43 = 101011$.

Alternatively, to find the binary equivalent of 43 divide the number successively by 2:

$$
\begin{array}{l}
2\underline{)43}\\
2\underline{)21} \ \text{r. } \underline{1}\\
2\underline{)10} \ \text{r. } \underline{1}\\
2\underline{)5} \ \text{r. } \underline{0}\\
2\underline{)2} \ \text{r. } \underline{1}\\
2\underline{)1} \ \text{r. } \underline{0}
\end{array}
$$

To obtain the answer from the working take the underlined digits in order from the bottom to the top of the right-hand column of remainders.

Exercise 4.4

Convert the following denary numbers into binary form:

1. 5
2. 7

3. 8
4. 10
5. 13
6. 16
7. 20
8. 23
9. 29
10. 31
11. 32
12. 37
13. 41
14. 48
15. 51
16. 55
17. 59
18. 63
19. 64

Conversion from binary to denary

Example

Convert 110111 into denary.

$$110111 = 1 \times 2^5 + 1 \times 2^4 + 0 \times 2^3 + 1 \times 2^2 + 1 \times 2 + 1 \times 1$$
$$= 32 + 16 + 0 + 4 + 2 + 1 = 55$$

Exercise 4.5

Convert the following binary numbers into denary:

1. 11
2. 101
3. 100
4. 1010
5. 1011
6. 10011
7. 11001
8. 11000
9. 111000

10.	101010
11.	101110
12.	101111
13.	111100
14.	111111

Addition of two binary numbers

The basic rules for addition in binary are:

$$0 + 0 = 0$$
$$0 + 1 = 1$$
$$1 + 0 = 1$$
$$1 + 1 = 0 \quad \text{carry } 1$$

Examples

1. 101 + 11

```
        101
         11
Carry line   11
       1000
```

Check by conversion to denary: 101 = 5
                                  11 = 3
                              Add = 8
                                  = 8

2. 11011 + 10100 + 1101

```
            11011
            10100
             1101
Carry line  11111
           111100
```

Check: 11011 = 27
         10100 = 20
          1101 = 13
          Add = 60
              = 32 + 16 + 8 + 4
              = 111100

Exercise 4.6

Perform the following calculations:

 1. $11 + 1$
 2. $11 + 10$
 3. $100 + 11$
 4. $110 + 11$
 5. $101 + 10$
 6. $1010 + 11$
 7. $1010 + 10$
 8. $11011 + 1111$
 9. $11100 + 110 + 101$
10. $11111 + 1111 + 11$
11. $101010 + 1010 + 1010 + 10$
12. $111011 + 1101 + 11$

Conversion from decimals to binary and vice versa

To convert a denary integer to binary we divided successively by 2 and, as a result, obtained the successive terms in *increasing* powers of 2 (positive powers: the terms move progressively to the left). In converting a decimal to binary we shall obtain successive terms in *decreasing* powers of 2 (negative powers: the terms move progressively to the right).

To convert a decimal to binary, then, we multiply successively by 2, and each time we end up with a digit (0 or 1) in the partial result, that digit becomes the coefficient of the appropriate power of 2.

Examples

1. 0.5 (decimal) becomes:

$$0.5 \times 2 = 1.0 = 1 \times 2^{-1} = 0.1_2$$

2. 0.75 becomes:

$$0.75 \times 2 = 1.50 \qquad 1 \times 2^{-1}$$
$$0.50 \times 2 = 1.00 \qquad 1 \times 2^{-2}$$

Therefore 0.75 (decimal) $= 0.11_2$.

3. 0.3492 becomes:

$$
\begin{array}{ll}
0.3492 & \\
\underline{\quad 2 \quad} & \\
0.6984 & 0 \times 2^{-1} \\
\underline{\quad 2 \quad} & \\
1.3968 & 1 \times 2^{-2} \\
\underline{\quad 2 \quad} & \\
0.7936 & 0 \times 2^{-3} \\
\underline{\quad 2 \quad} & \\
1.5872 & 1 \times 2^{-4} \\
\underline{\quad 2 \quad} & \\
1.1744 & 1 \times 2^{-5} \\
\underline{\quad 2 \quad} & \\
0.3488 & 0 \times 2^{-6} \\
\underline{\quad 2 \quad} & \\
0.6976 & 0 \times 2^{-7} \\
\underline{\quad 2 \quad} & \\
1.3952 & 1 \times 2^{-8}
\end{array}
$$

Therefore $0.3492 \approx 0.01011001_2$.

4. Convert 101.1011_2 to decimal.

$$
\begin{aligned}
101.1011_2 &= 1 \times 2^2 + 0 \times 2 + 1 \times 1 + 1 \times 2^{-1} + 0 \times 2^{-2} \\
&\quad + 1 \times 2^{-3} + 1 \times 2^{-4} \\
&= 4 + 0 + 1 + 0.5 + 0 + 0.125 + 0.0625 \\
&= 5.6875
\end{aligned}
$$

Exercise 4.7

Convert the following decimals into binary:

1. 0.25
2. 0.125
3. 0.0625
4. 0.03125
5. 0.0150625
6. 0.875
7. 0.375
8. 0.625
9. 0.28125
10. 0.09375
11. 0.434
12. 0.52
13. 0.67
14. 1.5
15. 14.5
16. 3.875
17. 9.125
18. 7.0625
19. 11.03125
20. 7.434

Convert the following binary numbers to decimals:

21. 0.10
22. 0.01
23. 0.001
24. 0.111
25. 0.101
26. 0.1011
27. 0.100101
28. 11.11
29. 111.101
30. 100.001

Where the decimal number is large the method of conversion into binary is lengthy and tedious, because we have to divide successively by 2. This is where numbers to base 8 (octal) prove useful.

Conversion from decimal numbers to binary via octal and vice versa

In the octal system no digit is greater than 7: they range from 0 to 7 inclusive. 3207.14_8 means:

$$3 \times 8^3 + 2 \times 8^2 + 0 \times 8 + 7 \times 1 + 1 \times 8^{-1} + 4 \times 8^{-2}$$

Examples

1. Convert 3207 (denary) to octal.

$$
\begin{array}{rl}
8\overline{)3207} & \\
8\overline{)400} & \text{r. } 7 \\
8\overline{)50} & \text{r. } 0 \\
8\overline{)6} & \text{r. } 2 \\
8\overline{)0} & \text{r. } 6 \\
\end{array}
$$

Therefore $3207_{10} = 6207_8$
Check:
$$
\begin{aligned}
6207_8 &= 6 \times 8^3 + 2 \times 8^2 + 7 \times 1 \\
&= 6 \times 512 + 2 \times 64 + 7 \\
&= 3072 + 128 + 7 = 3207_{10}
\end{aligned}
$$

2. Convert from octal to denary 75306_8.
    Here we follow the procedure outlined in the check above:

$$
\begin{aligned}
75306_8 &= 7 \times 8^4 + 5 \times 8^3 + 3 \times 8^2 + 0 \times 8 + 6 \times 1 \\
&= 7 \times 4096 + 5 \times 512 + 3 \times 64 + 6 \\
&= 28\,672 + 2560 + 192 + 6 = 31\,430_{10}
\end{aligned}
$$

Check:
$$
\begin{array}{rl}
8\overline{)31430} & \\
8\overline{)3928} & \text{r. } 6 \\
8\overline{)491} & \text{r. } 0 \\
8\overline{)61} & \text{r. } 3 \\
7 & \text{r. } 5 \\
\end{array}
$$

3. Convert 3207_{10} to binary via octal.
    From (1) above:

$$3207_{10} = 6207_8 = 6 \times 8^3 + 2 \times 8^2 + 0 \times 8 + 7 \times 1$$
$$= (110)(1000)^3 + (10)(1000)^2 + (111)$$
(since $8 = 1000_2$; $6 = 110_2$; $2 = 10_2$; $7 = 111_2$
i.e. $2^3 = 1000$; $6 = 2^2 + 2$)
$$\doteq 110000000000 + 10000000 + 111$$
(Further, $8^2 = (2^3)^2 = 1000^2$; $8^3 = 1000^3$ etc.)
$$= 110010000111_2$$

4. Convert 101101_2 to denary via octal.

$$101101_2 = 2^5 + 2^3 + 2^2 + 1 = 2^2 \times 2^3 + 1 \times 2^3 + 4 + 1$$
$$= (4 + 1) \times 2^3 + 5 = 5 \times 2^3 + 5 = 55_8 = 45_{10}$$

Or: $101101_2 = 100000 + 1000 + 101$
$$= (100)(1000) + 1000 + 101$$
$$= 4 \times 8 + 8 + 5 = 32 + 8 + 5 = 45_{10}$$

Exercise 4.8

Convert the following from decimal to binary via octal:

1. 43
2. 57
3. 95
4. 536
5. 1062
6. 3429
7. 5053
8. 6247
9. 7178
10. 7485

Convert the following to decimal from binary via octal:

11. 11011
12. 11111
13. 1001000
14. 1001001000
15. 1000110011
16. 1111111111

Addition of octal numbers

Here the basic rules are:

$1 + 0 = 1$; $1 + 1 = 2$; $1 + 2 = 3$; $1 + 3 = 4$;
$1 + 4 = 5$; $1 + 5 = 6$; $1 + 6 = 7$; $1 + 7 = 0$ carry 1;
$2 + 3 = 5$; $2 + 6 = 0$ carry 1;
$4 + 5 = 1$ carry 1;   and so on

Examples

1. $321_8 + 434_8$
    $= 755_8$

$$
\begin{array}{r}
321 \\
434 \\
\hline
755 \\
\hline
\end{array}
$$

2. $6207_8 + 3152_8 + 2041_8$
    $= 13422_8$

$$
\begin{array}{r}
6207 \\
3152 \\
2041 \\
\text{Carry line} \quad 1 \ \ 11 \\
\hline
13422 \\
\hline
\end{array}
$$

3. $352.73_8 + 140.65_8 + 46.23_8$
    $= 562.03_8$

$$
\begin{array}{r}
352.73 \\
140.65 \\
46.23 \\
\text{Carry line} \quad 112 \ 1 \\
\hline
562.03 \\
\hline
\end{array}
$$

Exercise 4.9

Add the following sets of octal numbers together:

1. $134 + 322$
2. $435 + 532$
3. $134 + 322 + 435$
4. $532 + 435 + 322$
5. $134 + 322 + 435 + 532$

6. $7026 + 2513 + 1402$
7. $5656 + 37462$
8. $37756 + 65645 + 23305$

Subtraction of binary numbers

The basic rules are:

$$0 - 0 = 0$$
$$1 - 0 = 1$$
$$1 - 1 = 0$$
$$0 - 1 = 1 \quad \text{carry } 1$$

Examples

1. $100 - 10$.

$$
\begin{array}{r}
100 \\
10 \\
\text{Carry line} \quad 1 \\
\hline
10
\end{array}
$$

Check: in denary $4 - 2 = 2$
$2 = 10_2$

2. $1011 - 101$.

$$
\begin{array}{r}
1011 \\
101 \\
\text{Carry line} \quad 1 \\
\hline
110
\end{array}
$$

Check: in denary $(8 + 2 + 1) - (4 + 1)$
$= 11 - 5 = 6 = 110_2$

3. $101011 - 101001$.

$$
\begin{array}{r}
101011 \\
101001 \\
\hline
10
\end{array}
$$

Check: in denary $(32 + 8 + 2 + 1) - (32 + 8 + 1)$
$= 43 - 41 = 2 = 10_2$

Exercise 4.10

Perform the following subtractions in binary:

1. $110 - 10$
2. $111 - 11$
3. $1010 - 10$
4. $1011 - 10$
5. $1011 - 111$
6. $11111 - 1011$
7. $10101 - 111$
8. $10000001 - 111111$

Subtraction of octal numbers

The basic rules are:

$7 - 6 = 1; 7 - 5 = 2; 7 - 4 = 3; \ldots 7 - 1 = 6, 7 - 0 = 7;$
$6 - 7 = 5 - 6 = 4 - 5 = 3 - 4 = 2 - 3 = 1 - 2 = 0 - 1 = 7$ carry 1
$5 - 7 = 4 - 6 = 3 - 5 = 2 - 4 = 1 - 3 = 0 - 2 = 6$ carry 1
$4 - 7 = 3 - 6 = 2 - 5 = 1 - 4 = 0 - 3 = 5$ carry 1
etc. to $1 - 7 = 0 - 6 = 2$ carry 1

Examples

1. $563_8 - 342_8.$

$$\begin{array}{r} 563 \\ 342 \\ \hline 221 \end{array}$$

Check: in denary $371 - 226 = 145$
$= 221_8$

2. $563_8 - 344_8.$

$$\begin{array}{r} 563 \\ 344 \\ \text{Carry line} \quad 1 \\ \hline 217 \end{array}$$

Check: in denary $371 - 228 = 143$
$= 217_8$

3. $4302_8 - 3625_8.$

$$
\begin{array}{r}
4302 \\
3625 \\
\text{Carry line} \quad 111 \\
\hline
455
\end{array}
$$

Check: in denary $2242 - 1941 = 301$
$$= 455_8$$

4. $7130.21_8 - 4653.73_8.$

$$
\begin{array}{r}
7130.21 \\
4653.73 \\
\text{Carry line} \quad 1111\ 1 \\
\hline
2254.26
\end{array}
$$

Exercise 4.11

Perform the following subtractions in octal:

1. $15 - 7$
2. $16 - 7$
3. $25 - 17$
4. $32 - 23$
5. $45 - 36$
6. $325 - 126$
7. $453 - 221$
8. $675 - 432$
9. $401 - 263$
10. $3045 - 2301$
11. $7123 - 4607$

Alternative methods of subtraction in binary and octal

Here we perform an addition instead of a subtraction. For example:

$$
\begin{array}{r}
100 \\
10 \\
\hline
cba
\end{array}
$$

We need to find *cba* which, when added to 10, produces the top line, 100. So we need to solve:

$$a + 0 = 0 \quad \text{(first column)}$$
$$b + 1 = 0 \quad \text{(second column; here this can be true only if we carry 1)}$$
$$c + 1 \text{ (carried)} = 1 \quad \text{(third column)}$$

In binary the only digits which can appear in the top row are 0 and 1. We know that:

$$0 = 0 + 0$$
$$0 = 1 + 1 \quad \text{(when 1 is carried)}$$
$$1 = 1 + 0$$
$$1 = 0 + 1$$

The pairs of numbers on the right of these equations are complementary to the numbers on the left. So in the above problem $a = 0$, $b = 1$ and $c = 0$. And our answer is:

$$
\begin{array}{r}
100 \\
10 \\
\hline
10 \\
\hline
\end{array}
$$

This agrees with the answer obtained by direct subtraction.

Examples

1. $1011 - 111$.

$$
\begin{array}{r}
1011 \\
111 \\
\text{Carry line} \quad 1 \\
\hline
0100 \\
\hline
\end{array}
$$

Add these two lines.

$0100 = 100$

2. $1001.010 - 110.101$.

$$
\begin{array}{r}
1001.010 \\
110.101 \\
\text{Carry line} \quad 11 \ 1 \ \ 1 \\
\hline
0010.101 \\
\hline
\end{array}
$$

Add these two lines.

$0010.101 = 10.101$

Exercise 4.12

Repeat Exercise 4.10 by this addition method.
For subtraction in octal performed by the above method the complementary pairs of numbers are obtained from the following relationships:

$$0 = 0 + 0 = (7 + 1 = 6 + 2 = 5 + 3 = 4 + 4 \text{ etc.;}$$
$$\text{in each case carry 1)}$$
$$1 = 1 + 0 = (7 + 2 = 6 + 3 = 5 + 4 \text{ etc.;}$$
$$\text{in each case carry 1)}$$
$$2 = 2 + 0 = 1 + 1 = (7 + 3 = 6 + 4 = 5 + 5 \text{ etc.;}$$
$$\text{in each case carry 1) and so on until:}$$
$$6 = 6 + 0 = 5 + 1 = 4 + 2 = 3 + 3 = (7 + 7 \text{ carry 1)}$$
$$7 = 7 + 0 = 6 + 1 = 5 + 2 = 4 + 3 \text{ etc.}$$

Examples

1. $74_8 - 43_8$.

$$
\begin{array}{r}
74 \\
43 \\
\hline
31
\end{array}
$$
Column 1: since $3 + 1 = 4$
Column 2: since $3 + 4 = 7$

2. $563_8 - 345_8$.

$$
\begin{array}{r}
563 \\
345 \\
1 \\
\hline
216
\end{array}
$$
Carry line

Column 1: $6 + 5$ carry $1 = 3$
Column 2: $1 + 4 + 1 = 6$
Column 3: $2 + 3 = 5$

3. $3204.61_8 - 753.74_8$.

$$
\begin{array}{r}
3204.61 \\
753.74 \\
11 \ 1 \ 1 \\
\hline
2230.65
\end{array}
$$
Carry line

Column 1: $5 + 4$ carry $1 = 1$
Column 2: $6 + 7 + 1$ carry $1 = 6$
Column 3: $0 + 3 + 1 = 4$
Column 4: $3 + 5$ carry $1 = 0$
Column 5: $2 + 7 + 1$ carry $1 = 2$
Column 6: $2 + 1 = 3$

Exercise 4.13

Repeat Exercise 4.11 using the addition method.

5

The Use of Four-figure Tables

In Chapter 3 we said that a^2 was a to the power of 2, or a squared. The term 'squared' is used because, when we draw a square, side a (Fig. 5.1), the formula to find the area (A) of the square is:

$$A = a \times a = a^2 \qquad\qquad 5.1$$

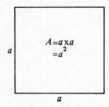

Figure 5.1

Consequently the square of a number is the number multiplied by itself. The relationship in Law 5.1 relates A to a while, at the same time, making A the subject of the formula. To reverse the relationship, making a the subject of the formula, we write, by indices:

$$(a^2)^{\frac{1}{2}} = A^{\frac{1}{2}}$$

i.e., $a = A^{\frac{1}{2}} = \sqrt{A}$ (from Chapter 3)

Consequently a is the square root of A. (The square root of a given number is that number which, when squared, produces the given number.)

5.1 Tables of squares

Examples

1. Using tables of squares find 32.45^2.
    First we ignore the decimal point altogether and look up 32 in the left-hand column in the tables of squares. Looking along that row we stop under 4 to locate 1050. Then we look at the extreme right-hand set of columns under 5 and see the number 3. This is added to 1050 to give 1053. Now, since 32.45 is rather more than 30, and $30^2 = 900$, our answer must be more than 900, but not much more. The answer, therefore, must be 1053.0, or 1053.

2. Find from the tables 509.2^2.
    Following a similar procedure, first find 50, then look along that row and stop under 9, and finally look at the extreme right under 2. We obtain 2593. And 509.2 is rather more than 500, and $500^2 = 250\,000$, so our answer must be slightly more than that, in other words 259 300.0, or 259 300.

3. Find 0.1496^2.
    1496 from the tables gives 2237. And 0.1496^2 is bigger than $0.1^2 = 0.1 \times 0.1 = 0.01$. Therefore our answer must be 0.02237.

Alternatively we may use standard form:

2. $$509.2^2 = (5.092 \times 10^2)^2 = (5.092)^2 \times 10^4$$

Now we know that 5.092^2 must be slightly bigger than 5^2, which is 25. So, from the tables, $5.092^2 = 25.93$. Therefore:

$$509.2^2 = 25.93 \times 10^4 = 259\,300$$

3. $$0.1496^2 = (1.496 \times 10^{-1})^2 = 1.496^2 \times 10^{-2}$$

1.496^2 must lie between 1^2 and 2^2, i.e., between 1 and 4. The tables give $1.496^2 = 2.237$. Then:

$$0.1496^2 = 2.237 \times 10^{-2} = 0.02237$$

Exercise 5.1

Using tables of squares calculate the squares of the following numbers:

1. 4.231
2. 6.052
3. 9.007
4. 11.25
5. 16.39
6. 25.80
7. 77.6
8. 328.7
9. 1057
10. 0.1234
11. 0.2062
12. 0.8147
13. 0.03051
14. 0.09124
15. 0.00362

5.2 Tables of square roots

Finding square roots is slightly more complicated. Suppose we wish to find the square root of 32.45, i.e. $\sqrt{32.45}$. There are two sets of figures or, in some cases, two sets of tables (one for numbers between 1 and 10 and another for numbers between 10 and 100). Before we decide which set to use we work out a rough answer to the question. We know that $\sqrt{25} = 5$ and $\sqrt{36} = 6$, so our answer must lie between 5 and 6 (because 32 lies between 25 and 36). We then use that row of digits in the one table, or that set of tables, which would give us such an answer. The two possible sets of digits are 1801 and 5696. We cannot place the decimal point anywhere in 1801 to give an answer between 5 and 6, but we can in 5696. The answer, therefore, must be 5.696.

Example

Find $\sqrt{3245}$.
Here:

$$\sqrt{3245} = \sqrt{32.45 \times 100} = (32.45 \times 100)^{\frac{1}{2}}$$
$$= 32.45^{\frac{1}{2}} \times 100^{\frac{1}{2}} = \sqrt{32.45} \times \sqrt{100}$$
$$= 5.696 \times 10 = 56.96$$

Rule: When we wish to work out the square root of a number we express the number in the form $b \times 10^{2n}$, where b is a number between 1 and 10, or is a number between 10 and 100, not an integer but a decimal, and n is an integer which may be either positive or negative. We then look up b in the appropriate tables. The square root of 10^{2n} is 10^{n}. The final answer is the product of the result in the tables and 10^{n}.

Examples

1. $\sqrt{378.6} = \sqrt{3.786 \times 10^2} = \sqrt{3.786} \times 10^1 = 1.946 \times 10^1$
    $= 19.46$

2. $\sqrt{52\ 960} = \sqrt{5.296 \times 10^4} = \sqrt{5.296} \times 10^2 = 2.301 \times 10^2$
    $= 230.1$

3. $\sqrt{4343} = \sqrt{43.43 \times 10^2} = \sqrt{43.43} \times 10 = 6.590 \times 10 = 65.90$

4. $\sqrt{0.2035} = \sqrt{20.35 \times 10^{-2}} = \sqrt{20.35} \times 10^{-1} = 4.511 \times 10^{-1}$
    $= 0.4511$

5. $\sqrt{0.09026} = \sqrt{9.026 \times 10^{-2}} = \sqrt{9.026} \times 10^{-1} = 3.004 \times 10^{-1}$
    $= 0.3004$

6. $\sqrt{0.00035} = \sqrt{3.5 \times 10^{-4}} = \sqrt{3.5} \times 10^{-2} = 1.871 \times 10^{-2}$
    $= 0.01871$

An alternative method is shown below. Although the effect is the same the principle appears to be different. In fact it is not. Here the digits are paired off on each side of the decimal point.

1. $\sqrt{3|78.60|} = \sqrt{3.78} \times 10$ and then as above.

2. $\sqrt{5|29|60} = \sqrt{5.296} \times 10 \times 10$ etc.

3. $\sqrt{43|43} = \sqrt{43.43} \times 10$ etc.

4. $\sqrt{0.20|35|} = \sqrt{20.35} \div 10$ etc.

5. $\sqrt{0.09|26|} = \sqrt{9.26} \div 10$ etc.

6. $\sqrt{0.00|03|5} = \sqrt{3.5} \div 100$ etc.

Exercise 5.2

Using tables of square roots calculate the square roots of the following numbers:

1. 5
2. 91 324
3. 17.83
4. 76.07
5. 123.9
6. 905.2
7. 1005
8. 21 942
9. 8 261 000
10. 0.5
11. 0.9324
12. 0.1239
13. 0.04236
14. 0.0852
15. 0.002163
16. 0.0001145
17. 0.01029
18. 0.0000165

5.3 Reciprocal tables

In Chapter 3 we defined the reciprocal of 15 as 1/15. It is obvious that 1/2 is greater than 1/3 and that 1/3, in turn, is greater than 1/4. And 1/4 > 1/5 > 1/6 and so on. In other words, the larger the denominator the smaller the fraction (i.e., the reciprocal). This means that $1/2.36 > 1/2.361$. For this reason we find that the digits in the differences column of the reciprocal tables must be subtracted, not added.

Examples

1. Find $1/3.754$.
    Look for 37 down the left-hand column and go along that row to the number under 5. It is 0.2667. The final 4 in the differences column at the end gives a digit 3, which must be subtracted from 2667 as follows: $0.2667 - 0.0003 = 0.2664$.
2. Find $1/6.003$.
    Here the steps are $0.1667 - 0.0001 = 0.1666$.
3. Find $1/8.209$.
    The working is $0.1220 - 0.0001 = 0.1219$.
4. Find $1/40.52$.
    First step: rearrange to

$$1/(4.052 \times 10) = (1/4.052) \times (1/10)$$
$$= 0.2468 \div 10 = 0.02468.$$

Check the above answers:

1. $1/3.754 \approx 1/3 \approx 0.3$; 0.2664 is reasonable.
2. $1/6.003 \approx 1/6 \approx 0.16$; 0.1666 seems reasonable.
3. $1/8.209 \approx 1/8 = 0.125$; 0.1219 seems reasonable.
4. $1/40.52 \approx 1/40 = 1/4 \times 1/10 = 0.25 \div 10 = 0.025$; 0.02468 seems reasonable.

Alternative method

5. Find $1/0.00269$.
    Here we would completely ignore the decimal point at first and merely look up the reciprocal of 2.69. The table gives this as 0.3717. Still ignoring decimal points, we would look upon our preliminary answer as 3717. We fix the decimal point by asking ourselves what the approximate value of $1/0.00269$ is. It is, very approximately, $1/0.002$, that is, $1 \div \frac{2}{1000}$, which must be equal to $1 \times \frac{1000}{2} = 1 \times 500 = 500$. This means the answer must be in the hundreds. In other words, the answer must be 371.7.

Exercise 5.3

Using reciprocal tables, calculate the reciprocals of the following numbers:

1. 2.165
2. 4.297
3. 6.452
4. 10.98
5. 22.75
6. 152.8
7. 6329
8. 0.2165
9. 0.4297
10. 0.03874
11. 0.00623
12. 0.000448

5.4 The use of logarithm tables

To determine what a logarithm is, we will consider the following table:

$$1000 = 10^3$$
$$100 = 10^2$$
$$10 = 10^1$$
$$1 = 10^0$$
$$0.1 = 1/10 = 10^{-1}$$
$$0.01 = 1/100 = 10^{-2}$$
$$0.001 = 1/1000 = 10^{-3}$$

Each number on the extreme left can, therefore, be written as 10^n, where n is an integer, either positive or negative, or zero, i.e., $N = 10^n$.

If we multiply a number on the left by 10 it becomes the number above, and, on the right, the power of 10 is increased by 1 when that happens. If we divide a number on the left by 10 it becomes the number below and, at the same time, the power of 10 is decreased by 1. Consequently a few more lines can be filled in:

$$10\,000 = 10^4; \ 100\,000 = 10^5; \ 0.0001 = 10^{-4}; \ 0.00001 = 10^{-5};$$

and so on. So far all the powers have been integers. We will now fill in some more spaces, this time between the lines above.

By the square root tables: $\sqrt{10} \approx 3.162$
We also know that $\sqrt{10} = 10^{\frac{1}{2}}$; therefore $3.162 \approx 10^{\frac{1}{2}}$
Further: $31.62 = 3.162 \times 10 \approx 10^{\frac{1}{2}} \times 10^1 = 10^{1.5}$
And $316.2 = 3.162 \times 10^2 \approx 10^{\frac{1}{2}} \times 10^2 = 10^{2.5}$
We could go further: $\sqrt{3.162} \approx \sqrt{10^{\frac{1}{2}}} = (10^{\frac{1}{2}})^{\frac{1}{2}} = 10^{\frac{1}{4}}$;
$$\sqrt{3.162} \approx 1.779$$
Giving: $1.779 \approx 10^{0.25}$
And: $17.79 \approx 10^{0.25} \times 10 = 10^{1.25}$
And: $177.9 \approx 10^{0.25} \times 10^2 = 10^{2.25}$
Again: $\sqrt{1.779} \approx 1.333 \approx \sqrt{10^{\frac{1}{4}}} = (10^{\frac{1}{4}})^{\frac{1}{2}} = 10^{\frac{1}{8}} = 10^{0.125}$

In this way we can fill in the numbers on the left between 1 and 10, between 10 and 100, and so on. For each number we would discover an index, and we would find that, for any number, N, there was just one index, x, such that:

$$N = 10^x \qquad\qquad 5.2$$

where x is the logarithm of N. It is important to note that, for x to be real, N must be positive. As N increases from 0 to ∞, x increases from $-\infty$ to $+\infty$. The table at the beginning of this section implies that as N increases from 0 to 1, x increases from $-\infty$ to 0; as N increases from 1 to 10, x changes by 1; as N increases from 10 to 100, x changes by 1 again; and as N increases from 100 to 1000, x changes by 1 again.

When we try to draw a graph showing the relationship between N and x the problem of choosing suitable scales arises. If we choose a scale suitable to N between 1 and 10 it becomes too extended for the ranges 10 to 100, 100 to 1000 etc. If we select a scale suitable to the range 10 to 100, that is too cramped for the range 1 to 10. However, it is possible, by calculation, to construct one set of tables which tells us how to determine x when we know N (logarithm tables) and another set of tables which tells us how to determine N when we know x (antilogarithm tables).

Look at the logarithm tables (they operate on a principle similar to that for squares and square root tables). They tell us that:

$$\log 2 \qquad\qquad = \log 2.000 = 0.3010$$

This means that: $\quad 2 = 10^{0.3010}$

Therefore: $\qquad 20 = 2 \times 10 = 10^{0.3010} \times 10 = 10^{1.3010}$

Again: $\qquad\quad 200 = 2 \times 100 = 10^{0.3010} \times 10^2 = 10^{2.3010}$

Further: $\qquad\;\, 2000 = 2 \times 1000 = 10^{0.3010} \times 10^3 = 10^{3.3010}$

The numbers 2, 20, 200 and 2000 all have the same decimal part of their logarithms, namely 0.3010.

Similarly, the tables tell us that:

$$\log 3.256 \qquad\qquad = 0.5127$$

Meaning: $\qquad 3.256 = 10^{0.5127}$

Leading to: $\quad 32.56 = 3.256 \times 10 = 10^{0.5127} \times 10 = 10^{1.5127}$

Again: $\qquad\quad 325.6 = 3.256 \times 10^2 = 10^{0.5127} \times 10^2 = 10^{2.5127}$

Further: $\qquad\;\, 3256 = 3.256 \times 10^3 = 10^{0.5127} \times 10^3 = 10^{3.5127}$

The numbers 3.256, 32.56, 325.6 and 3256 all have logarithms with the same decimal part, 0.5127.

The decimal part of a logarithm, then, has nothing to do with the position of the decimal point in the original number. This *decimal* part of the logarithm is called the *mantissa*, and we use the logarithm tables to find its value. The *whole number* part of the logarithm is called the *characteristic*, and we will now discover how to determine this. Notice that:

> when the number was 3.256 the characteristic was 0
> when the number was 32.56 the characteristic was 1
> when the number was 325.6 the characteristic was 2
> when the number was 3256 the characteristic was 3

For each place the decimal point is moved to the right from its position in the top line the characteristic increases by 1. Now consider:

$$0.3256 = 3.256 \times \tfrac{1}{10} = 3.256 \times 10^{-1} = 10^{0.5127} \times 10^{-1}$$
$$= 10^{-1+0.5127}$$

We could write 0.3256 as $10^{-0.4873}$, but then the decimal part would be different from the decimal parts above, and we want them all to be the same so that we can use the same set of tables for the one sequence of digits irrespective of where the decimal point in the original number lies. So we write:

$$0.3256 = 10^{-1+0.5127}$$
$$0.03256 = 10^{-2+0.5127}$$
$$0.003256 = 10^{-3+0.5127}$$

Thus the mantissa is still obtained from the sequence of digits 3256. Now, for each place the decimal point is moved to the left from its position in 3.256 the characteristic decreases by 1.

In summary, then, the logarithm of a number is made up of two parts:

1. the mantissa;
2. the characteristic.

To determine the mantissa look up the sequence of digits of the number in the tables.

The following shows how to proceed to find the characteristic:

	Number	*Characteristic*
(a)	6.205	0
	62.05	1
	620.5	2
	6205.0	3
	0.6205	−1
	0.06205	−2
	0.006205	−3

Take the decimal point in (a) as a reference point. The characteristic here is 0. Every place the decimal point moves to the right the characteristic increases by 1. Every place the decimal point moves to the left the characteristic decreases by 1. Now go back to:

$$0.003256 = 10^{-3+0.5127}$$

The index is −3 + 0.5127. The mantissa is positive and the characteristic is negative. In fact, only characteristics can be negative: the mantissa is always positive. Yet the above notation looks very complicated, so we abbreviate it and write it as $\bar{3}.5127$, to indicate that only 3 is negative. $\bar{3}$ is called *bar three*. In future we shall write:

$$0.003256 = 10^{\bar{3}.5127}$$

$$\text{or} \quad \log{(0.003256)} = \bar{3}.5127$$

Exercise 5.4

Use logarithm tables to calculate the logarithms of the following numbers:

1. 4.921
2. 8.476
3. 18.29
4. 63.74
5. 334.7
6. 528.6
7. 4827
8. 7979
9. 30 410
10. 6 213 000
11. 0.3428
12. 0.8787
13. 0.06249
14. 0.09023
15. 0.002527
16. 0.007468

Just as we must be able to use tables to discover the logarithm of a number, so we must also be able, given a logarithm, to find the number corresponding to it. We either use antilogarithm tables or use logarithm tables in reverse. When finding a number from its logarithm, the mantissa alone determines the sequence of digits, and the characteristic alone determines the position of the decimal point.

Examples

	Logarithm	*Number*
(a)	0.4771	3.000
	1.4771	30.00
	2.4771	300.0
	3.4771	3000.0
	$\bar{1}$.4771	0.3000
	$\bar{2}$.4771	0.03000
	$\bar{3}$.4771	0.003000

Note:

When the characteristic is 0 the decimal point goes after the first significant figure.
When the characteristic increases by 1 the decimal point moves one place to the right.
When the characteristic decreases by 1 the decimal point moves one place to the left.

So the rule for determining the position of the decimal point by observation of the characteristic is: move the decimal point from the standard position (a) by the same number of places as the value of the characteristic; to the right if the characteristic is positive, and to the left if it is negative.

Exercise 5.5

Use antilogarithm tables (or logarithm tables in reverse) to calculate the numbers whose logarithms are:

1. 0.3214
2. 0.8617
3. 0.12428
4. 1.8125
5. 2.6643
6. 2.8219
7. 3.4123
8. 3.4136
9. 3.2615
10. 1.0265
11. 0.1649
12. $\bar{1}$.2498
13. $\bar{1}$.3693
14. $\bar{2}$.8649
15. $\bar{2}$.0106
16. $\bar{3}$.7748
17. 0.0045
18. 0.0004
19. $\bar{1}$.0098
20. 2.0705

5.5 Calculations using logarithms

Consider now $2 = 10^{0.3010}$; $3 = 10^{0.4771}$.

$$2 \times 3 = 10^{0.3010} \times 10^{0.4771} = 10^{0.3010+0.4771} = 10^{0.7781}$$

$$= 5.999 \text{ by antilogarithm tables}$$

The answer obtained by logarithms agrees roughly with that obtained by simple multiplication, i.e. $2 \times 3 = 6$, although it does indicate that the fourth digit, using four-figure tables, cannot always be relied on. Similarly:

$$3/2 = 10^{0.4771}/10^{0.3010} = 10^{0.4771-0.3010}$$

$$= 10^{0.1761} = 1.500 \text{ by antilogarithm tables}$$

In this case the answer obtained by logs does agree with that obtained by simple calculation.

Multiplication

Suppose a number $M = 10^x$, i.e. $\log M = x$, and a number $N = 10^y$, i.e. $\log N = y$. Then:

$$M \times N = 10^x \times 10^y = 10^{x+y}$$

That is: $\log (M \times N) = x + y = \log M + \log N$ *5.3*

Examples

1. Calculate 6.723×4.984.
    By the above:

    $$\log (6.723 \times 4.984) = \log 6.723 + \log 4.984$$

    $$= 0.8276 + 0.6976 = 1.5252$$

    By antilogs, the digits of the answer are 3352. The characteristic is 1, and the decimal point goes one place right from the standard position. Answer: 33.52. Rough check: $6 \times 4 = 24$.

2. Calculate 67.23×0.4984. (To simplify the working and the setting out we adopt a two-column method of arranging the working.)

Number	Logarithm
67.23	1.8276
0.4984	$\bar{1}$.6976
33.52	1.5252
	e dcba

Col. (a): $6 + 6 = 12 = 2$ carry 1
Col. (b): $1 + 7 + 7 = 15 = 5$ carry 1
Col. (c): $1 + 9 + 2 = 12 = 2$ carry 1
Col. (d): $1 + 6 + 8 = 15 = 5$ carry 1 (and this 1 is positive)
Col. (e): $1 + (-1) + 1 = 1$
Answer: 33.52
Rough check: $60 \times 0.5 = 30$

3. Calculate 0.9357×0.002135.

Number	Logarithm
0.9357	$\bar{1}$.9711
0.002135	$\bar{3}$.3294
0.001997	$\bar{3}$.3005
	j ihgf

Col. (f): $4 + 1 = 5$
Col. (g): $9 + 1 = 10 = 0$ carry 1
Col. (h): $1 + 2 + 7 = 10 = 0$ carry 1
Col. (i): $1 + 3 + 9 = 13 = 3$ carry 1 (positive)
Col. (j): $1 + (-3) + (-1) = -3 = \bar{3}$
Answer: 0.001997
Rough check: $1 \times 0.002 = 0.002$

Exercise 5.6

Add the following pairs of logarithms. (Some answers have been entered; fill in the rest.)

1. 4.0
    <u>1.0</u>
    3.0

2. 3.0
    <u>2.0</u>
    1.0

3. 2.0
    <u>1.0</u>
    1.0

4. 4.0
    <u>2.0</u>
    ——

5. 5.0
    <u>2.0</u>
    ——

6. 3.0
    <u>1.0</u>
    ——

7. 2.4
    <u>1.1</u>
    1.5

8. 3.7
    <u>1.4</u>
    3.1

9. 4.3
    <u>2.5</u>
    ——

10. 0.1
     1.3
     ───

     ───

11. 0.5
     $\bar{1}$.2
     ───

     ───

12. 0.8
     $\bar{1}$.3
     ───

     ───

13. $\bar{1}$.5
     $\bar{1}$.8
     ───

     ───

14. $\bar{2}$.6
     1.7
     ───

     ───

15. $\bar{1}$.3
     1.8
     ───

     ───

16. $\bar{1}$.9
     $\bar{2}$.8
     ───

     ───

Exercise 5.7

Using logarithm tables calculate the following (check your answers by rough estimates):

1. 6.294×4.827
2. 3.028×9.807
3. 63.85×3.549
4. 82.94×38.72
5. 10.25×90.07

6. 453.2×74.61
7. 736.2×358.7
8. 4293×8.652
9. 2345×5432
10. 2.076×0.4239
11. 0.6352×11.27
12. 0.5246×603.7
13. 0.4713×0.3714
14. 0.02495×0.8629
15. 0.04561×0.0715
16. 0.002803×0.07145

Division

For the same M and N as before:

$$M/N = 10^x/10^y = 10^{x-y}$$

$$\text{Therefore } \log(M/N) = x - y = \log M - \log N \qquad 5.4$$

Examples

1. Calculate $6.723/4.984$

Number	Logarithm
6.723	0.8276
4.984	0.6976
1.349	0.1300

Answer: 1.349
Rough check: $6/4 = 1.5$

2. Calculate $67.23/0.4984$.

Number	Logarithm
67.23	1.8276
0.4984	$\bar{1}$.6976
134.9	2.1300
	e dcba

Col. (a): $6 - 6 = 0$
Col. (b): $7 - 7 = 0$
Col. (c): $2 - 9 = 3$ carry 1
Col. (d): $8 - 6 - 1 = 1$
Col. (e): $1 - (-1) = 1 + 1 = 2$
Answer: 134.9
Rough check: $60/0.5 = 60 \times 2 = 120$

3. Calculate 0.002135/0.9357.

Number	Logarithm
0.002135	$\bar{3}.3294$
0.9357	$\bar{1}.9711$
0.002282	$\bar{3}.3583$
	t s r q p

Col. (p): $4 - 1 = 3$
Col. (q): $9 - 1 = 8$
Col. (r): $2 - 7 = 5$ carry 1
Col. (s): $3 - 9 - 1 = 3$ carry 1 (positive)
Col. (t): $-3 - (-1) - 1 = -3 - 0 = -3 = \bar{3}$
Answer: 0.002282
Rough check: $0.002/1 = 0.002$

Exercise 5.8

Subtract the lower from the upper logarithms. (Some answers have been completed; fill in the rest.)

1. 1.0
    0.0
    ───
    1.0
    ───

2. 3.4
    1.2
    ───
    2.2
    ───

3.   1.5
     0.3
     ———

     ———

4.   1.5
     0.8
     ———
     0.7

5.   1.4
     0.7
     ———

6.   2.2
     1.6
     ———

7.   0.2
     $\overline{1}$.2
     ———
     1.0

8.   0.6
     $\overline{1}$.6
     ———
     1.0

9.   0.6
     $\overline{1}$.5
     ———
     1.1

10. 0.4
     $\overline{1}$.5
     ———
     0.9

11. $\overline{1}$.6
     0.5
     ———
     $\overline{1}$.1

12. $\overline{2}.8$
     $\overline{1}.4$
     ____
     $\overline{1}.4$
     ____

13. $\overline{2}.4$
     $\overline{1}.8$
     ____
     $\overline{2}.6$
     ____

14. $\overline{1}.4$
     $\overline{2}.8$
     ____
     0.6
     ____

15. $\overline{3}.7$
     $\overline{5}.9$
     ____
     1.8
     ____

Exercise 5.9

Use logarithm tables to calculate the following (check your answers by a rough estimate):

1. 7.254/5.386
2. 86.49/38.27
3. 74.86/5.729
4. 429.7/15.62
5. 9248/6462
6. 0.8126/0.6128
7. 0.03425/0.02534
8. 0.00853/0.005265
9. 4.219/9.164
10. 10.35/31.62
11. 602.7/754.8
12. 1258/6109
13. 0.4155/0.7428
14. 0.0314/0.0628
15. 0.0724/0.926
16. 0.000448/3.86

Other operations using logarithms

By using logarithms for calculation we have turned problems involving multiplication and division into ones involving addition and subtraction, which are much easier to handle.

We will now apply our knowledge of logarithms to solve problems on reciprocals, squares and square roots, and check our answers with the ones we got when we used the special tables for those purposes.

Referring back to our original set of values when we set out to discover logarithms to base 10, we wrote:

$$1 = 10^0; \text{ meaning } \log 1 = 0 \qquad\qquad 5.5$$

Reciprocals

Example

Evaluate by logs 1/62.59.

Number	Log
1	0.0000
62.59	1.7965
0.01598	$\bar{2}.2035$

1/62.59 = 0.01598
Rough check: 1/60 ≈ 1/50 = 0.02
Our answer is of the right order of magnitude. Reciprocal tables give 0.01598.

Exercise 5.10

Repeat Exercise 5.3, but this time calculating the reciprocals using logs. Check the answers by a rough estimate and also by comparison with the answers you obtained using reciprocal tables.

Powers, squares and square roots

Consider 2.104^3. By log tables:

$2.104 = 10^{0.3230}$; $\log 2.104 = 0.3230$
Then $(2.104)^3 = (10^{0.3230})^3 = 10^{0.3230 \times 3} = 10^{0.9690}$
That is $\log 2.104^3 = 0.9690 = 3 \times 0.3230 = 3 \times \log 2.104$

If that is typical then it appears that:

$$\log N^p = p \log N$$

Let us see if we can prove this.

Suppose $N = 10^y$, i.e. $y = \log N$
Therefore $N^p = (10^y)^p = 10^{py}$
Giving $\log N^p = py = p \log N$ 5.6

Examples

1. Finishing off the problem above, $2.104^3 = 9.311$

Number	Log
2.104	0.3230
2.104^3	$3 \times 0.3230 = 0.9690$

Rough check: $2^3 = 8$

2. $46.71^2 = 2182$

Number	Log
46.71	1.6694
46.71^2	$2 \times 1.6694 = 3.3388$

Rough check: $50^2 = 2500$

3. $0.2758^4 = 0.005786$

Number	Log
0.2758	$\bar{1}.4406$
0.2758^4	$4 \times \bar{1}.4406 = \bar{3}.7624$

Rough check: $0.2^4 = 0.0016$

Exercise 5.11

Using Law 5.6 and log tables, calculate the values of the following (check where possible by normal calculation or estimation, and also by tables of squares where appropriate):

1. 4^2
2. 5^2
3. 8^2
4. 13^2
5. 17^2
6. 2^3
7. 5^3
8. 11^3
9. 2^4
10. 3^4
11. 5.25^2
12. 8.045^2
13. 16.4^3
14. 0.2^2
15. 0.5^2
16. 0.4^3
17. 0.623^2
18. 0.0714^3
19. 0.0102^4
20. 0.0041^3

We shall assume that Law 5.6 applies not only when p is an integer but also when it is a fraction, and apply it to calculate the square root of 32.54:

$$\sqrt{32.54} = (32.54)^{\frac{1}{2}} = (10^{1.5124})^{\frac{1}{2}} = 10^{1.5124 \times \frac{1}{2}} = 10^{0.7562}$$
$$= 5.705$$

By square root tables: $\sqrt{32.54} = 5.704$

This illustrates again that the fourth digit in four-figure tables is not always reliable. A rough check tells us that the answer lies between the square root of 25 and the square root of 36, i.e., between 5 and 6.

Examples

1. The square root of $459.3 = 21.43$

Number	Log
459.3	2.6621
$459.3^{\frac{1}{2}}$	$\frac{1}{2} \times 2.6621 = 1.3311$
21.43	1.3311

Rough check: $\sqrt{441} = 21$.
Square root tables give 21.43.

2. $\sqrt{0.6587}$

Number	Log
0.6587	$\bar{1}.8187 = \bar{2} + 1.8187$
$0.6587^{\frac{1}{2}}$	$\bar{1} + 0.9094 = \bar{1}.9094$
0.8117	$\bar{1}.9094$

In this case we have a problem in dividing $\bar{1}.8187$ by 2 because the logarithm really means $-1 + 0.8187$, and if we divide that by 2 as it stands we shall obtain $-0.5 + 0.4094$. (The last 4 is a rounded-off figure.) Yet the negative part of a logarithm must be an integer, so we rearrange $\bar{1}.8187$ as $\bar{2} + 1.8187$ and then divide by 2. We obtain 0.8117.
Rough check: $\sqrt{0.64} = 0.8$.
Square root tables give 0.8116.

Exercise 5.12

Repeat Exercise 5.2, but this time using logarithm tables to calculate the square roots. Compare your answers with those obtained by the square root table method. Also check by rough estimate.

Application to calculations using standard formulae

Examples

1. Using the acceleration under gravity formula, $s = \frac{1}{2}gt^2$, calculate s where $g = 9.807$ and $t = 3.5$.

Number		Log
0.5		$\bar{1}.6990$
9.807		0.9915
3.5	0.5441	
3.5^2		1.0882
60.08		1.7787

$s = 0.5 \times 9.807 \times 3.5^2 = 60.08 \approx 60.1$, since the fourth digit is not reliable.
Rough check: $\frac{1}{2} \times 10 \times 3^2 = 45$.
Note that in this problem we found it useful to use a three-column method of setting down the working: two columns for logs and one for numbers.

2. The formula for the diameter of a circle whose area is A is $d = 2\sqrt{A/\pi}$. Calculate d when $A = 64.37$ and $\pi = 3.142$.

Number		Log
2		0.3010
64.37	1.8087	
3.142	0.4972	
	1.3115	
	divide by 2	0.6558
9.053		0.9568

$$d = 2\sqrt{\frac{64.37}{3.142}} = 9.053$$
Rough check: $2 \times \sqrt{20} \approx 2 \times \sqrt{16} = 8$.

Exercise 5.13

Calculate the values, by logarithms, of the unknown letters, using the following formulae:

1. $V = I \cdot R$: $I = 3.52$; $R = 16.95$; $V = ?$
2. $V = L \cdot B \cdot H$: $L = 23.05$; $B = 19.76$; $H = 11.54$; $V = ?$
3. $F = M \cdot a$: $M = 108.7$; $a = 0.652$; $F = ?$
4. $E = M \cdot g \cdot h$: $M = 73.62$; $g = 9.807$; $h = 23.48$; $E = ?$

5. $T = k \cdot \dfrac{X}{L}$: $k = 4385$; $X = 2.394$; $L = 105.6$; $T = ?$

6. $E = \frac{1}{2} \cdot M \cdot V^2$: $M = 42.95$; $V = 13.03$; $E = ?$

7. $F = G \cdot \dfrac{M_1 \cdot M_2}{d^2}$: $G = 6.673 \times 10^{-11}$; $M_1 = 79.5 \times 10^8$;

   $M_2 = 46.3 \times 10^9$; $d = 3.5 \times 10^{-1}$; $F = ?$
8. $A = \pi r^2$: $\pi = 3.142$; $r = 9.547$; $A = ?$
9. $V = \pi r^2 \cdot h$: $\pi = 3.142$; $r = 6.075$; $h = 31.52$; $V = ?$
10. $V = \frac{4}{3} \pi r^3$: $\pi = 3.142$; $r = 8.496$; $V = ?$
11. $T = 2\pi \sqrt{L/g}$: $\pi = 3.142$; $g = 9.807$; $L = 14.25$; $T = ?$

6
Calculators

There are many models of electronic calculator on the market today. Their construction, operation and capabilities differ widely. Each year new models, incorporating new ideas, are introduced and some older ones are taken out of production. The books of instructions issued with calculators are not always clear about the full capabilities of the models, and the purchaser often has to discover for himself, by trial and error, the best procedures to adopt.

We shall explain only the very basic elements in this chapter, restricting ourselves to the key C, for clearing any numbers remaining after a previous calculation, the ten number keys, from 0 to 9 inclusive, the four operations keys, $+$, $-$, $\times$ and $\div$, the $=$ key and the decimal point key. These keys might well be arranged in an order similar to that in Fig. 6.1.

In Fig. 6.1 the key CE clears only the last entry in working out a problem. This is useful, for instance, when it is realized that the last entry was wrong and all the previous entries were correct. It saves clearing everything and having to start the calculation from the beginning. Some calculators have a key, AC, which does what the C key in Fig. 6.1 does (clears everything) and a key, C, which performs the same function as the CE key in Fig. 6.1.

In Fig. 6.1 spaces have been left because other basic models have keys MC, M$-$, M$+$, MR (memory keys), $+/-$, %, $\sqrt{x}$, $1/x$, x^2 and so on.

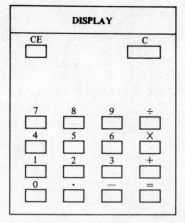

Figure 6.1

6.1 The four basic operations

We shall now illustrate the operation of our basic model by working through a few simple examples.

Example

Calculate 15 + 23 + 46.

Sequence	1	2	3	4	5	6
Key in	15	+	23	+	46	=
Display	15	15	23	38	46	84

A simple calculation checks this. If you need more practice in this very simple kind of problem make up similar problems yourself, and check the answers by ordinary addition to reassure yourself that you have got the method correct.

Examples

1. Calculate 65 + 23 − 47.

Sequence	1	2	3	4	5	6
Key in	65	+	23	−	47	=
Display	65	65	23	88	47	41

2. Calculate $28 + 46 - 93$.

Sequence	1	2	3	4	5	6
Key in	28	+	46	−	93	=
Display	28	28	46	74	93	−19

Simple checks show that these are correct.

Exercise 6.1

Calculate:

1. $32 + 41 + 19$
2. $17 + 27 + 36 + 29$
3. $82 + 19 - 38$
4. $135 + 208 - 96$

Again, devise similar problems if more practice is needed.

Example

Calculate $82.09 + 372.65 - 140.74$.

Sequence	1	2	3
Key in	82.09	+	372.65
Display	82.09	82.09	372.65

Sequence	4	5	6
Key in	−	140.74	=
Display	454.74	140.74	314

Rough check: $80 + 370 - 140 = 450 - 140 = 310$

Exercise 6.2

Calculate:

1. $63.75 + 825.49 - 362.24$
2. $200.26 + 356.48 - 140.81 - 223.29$
3. $2148.6 + 139.58 + 0.012345 - 832.04$
4. $0.9082 + 0.06153 - 0.1349 - 0.9925$

Example

Calculate $25 \times 4 \times 7$.

Sequence	1	2	3	4	5	6
Key in	25	$\times$	4	$\times$	7	$=$
Display	25	25	4	100	7	700

A simple calculation shows that answer to be correct.

Exercise 6.3

Calculate:

1. $15 \times 6 \times 40$
2. $75 \times 8 \times 70$

Again, make up more of a similar kind if you think you need more practice.

Example

Calculate $600 \times 30 \div 18$.

Sequence	1	2	3	4	5	6
Key in	600	$\times$	30	$\div$	18	$=$
Display	600	600	30	18 000	18	1000

A simple calculation shows this answer to be correct.

Exercise 6.4

Calculate:

1. $125 \times 8 \div 10$
2. $144 \times 16 \div 8$

Examples

1. Calculate $\dfrac{153.29 \times 18.06}{74.53 \times 20.81}$.

Sequence	1	2	3	4
Key in	153.29	×	18.06	÷
Display	153.29	153.29	18.06	2768.4174

Sequence	5	6	7	8
Key in	74.53	÷	20.81	=
Display	74.53	37.145007	20.81	1.7849594

The answer is approximately 1.785.

Rough check: $\dfrac{150 \times 20}{70 \times 20} \approx 2.0$.

2. Calculate $\dfrac{0.00583 \times 0.725}{0.0815 \times 0.0321}$.

Sequence	1	2	3	4
Key in	0.00583	×	0.725	÷
Display	0.00583	0.00583	0.725	0.0042267

Sequence	5	6	7	8
Key in	0.0815	÷	0.0321	=
Display	0.0815	0.0518619	0.0321	1.6156374

The answer is approximately 1.616.

Rough check: $\dfrac{0.006 \times 0.7}{0.08 \times 0.03} = \dfrac{6 \times 7}{8 \times 3} = \dfrac{42}{24} \approx 1.75$.

Exercise 6.5

Calculate:

1. $\dfrac{248.67 \times 31.07}{58.83 \times 19.66}$

2. $\dfrac{4.826 \times 3.719}{2.645 \times 7.902}$

3. $\dfrac{0.502 \times 0.205}{0.363 \times 0.318}$

4. $\dfrac{0.00209 \times 0.0516}{0.000417 \times 0.375}$

Now repeat the problems in Exercises 5.7 and 5.9. Check your answers with the ones you obtained using logarithm tables.

6.2 Numbers in standard form

By this stage you should be confident about using your calculator to perform a series of calculations involving + and − or a series involving × and ÷. However, there can still be some difficulties, especially with × and ÷ operations. The reason for this is that most basic calculators have an eight-digit display. If an answer goes into more than eight digits the calculator will either give the answer correct to the eighth digit or just chop the answer off short at the eighth digit. An even greater difficulty is when the decimal point in the answer is to the right of the eighth digit. Here our calculator will respond in one of two ways.

We will illustrate this with an example. Suppose the true answer, correct to eight digits, is 5 091 274 600.0. Some calculators give the answer in standard form, i.e., 5.0912746×10^9. But the display cannot show 10^9 because that requires two rows of figures, one above the other. Instead it gives just 9, i.e. the power of 10. The display would then be 5.0912746 :09 with a space to separate the index, 09, from the rest.

Others do not incorporate this principle and would register 50.912746 and give some indication that the true position of the decimal point was not as read in the display. Often the digits flash on and off, and when that happens we always take the true position of the decimal point to be eight places further to the right than in the display. With calculators of the latter kind, if the answer were, for example, 0.00000000065, then the calculator would merely register 0.

To avoid problems of this nature we can convert all numbers in such calculations into standard form.

Examples

1. Calculate
$$58\ 234.6 \times 9473.2 = 5.82346 \times 10^4 \times 9.4732 \times 10^3$$
$$= 5.82346 \times 9.4732 \times 10^7$$

Sequence	1	2	3	4
Key in	5.82346	$\times$	9.4732	$=$
Display	5.82346	5.82346	9.4732	55.166801

Answer $= 55.166801 \times 10^7 = 5.5166801 \times 10^8$
$\approx 5.5167 \times 10^8$.

2. Calculate $\dfrac{54.29 \times 0.0007162}{95\,480\,000} = \dfrac{5.429 \times 10^1 \times 7.162 \times 10^{-4}}{9.548 \times 10^7}$

$$= \frac{5.429 \times 7.162}{9.548} \times \frac{10^{-3}}{10^7}$$

$$= \frac{5.429 \times 7.162}{9.548} \times 10^{-10}$$

Sequence	1	2	3
Key in	5.429	$\times$	7.162
Display	5.429	5.429	7.162

Sequence	4	5	6
Key in	$\div$	9.548	$=$
Display	38.882498	9.548	4.0723186

Answer $= 4.0723186 \times 10^{-10} \approx 4.072 \times 10^{-10}$
$= 0.0000000004072$

Rough check: $\dfrac{5 \times 7}{9} = \dfrac{35}{9} \approx 4 \times 10^{-10}$

Exercise 6.6

Calculate:

1. $\dfrac{2486.7 \times 31\,070}{0.5883 \times 0.01966}$

2. $\dfrac{48\,260 \times 371\,900}{26.45 \times 0.0007902}$

3. $\dfrac{0.000502 \times 0.00205}{3630 \times 31.8}$

4. $\dfrac{0.0209 \times 0.00516}{41.7 \times 37\,500}$

When we wish to add or subtract very large numbers or very small numbers which would mean the decimal point's being too far to the right or to the left of the eight digits, we again convert the numbers to standard form.

Examples

1. $8 \times 10^9 + 5 \times 10^9 - 4 \times 10^9 = (8 + 5 - 4) \times 10^9$
   (by the distributive law) $= 9 \times 10^9$

2. $6.23 \times 10^{-11} + 7.09 \times 10^{-11} - 5.54 \times 10^{-11}$
   $= (6.23 + 7.09 - 5.54) \times 10^{-11}$
   $= 7.78 \times 10^{-11}$

Sequence	1	2	3	4	5	6
Key in	6.23	+	7.09	−	5.54	=
Display	6.23	6.23	7.09	13.32	5.54	7.78

Exercise 6.7

Calculate:

1. $4 \times 10^{10} + 7 \times 10^{10} - 6 \times 10^{10} + 3 \times 10^{10}$
2. $1.95 \times 10^{10} + 8.07 \times 10^{10} - 4.68 \times 10^{10}$
3. $6.26 \times 10^{-10} + 9.01 \times 10^{-10} - 8.55 \times 10^{-10}$

As we have seen, where each number written in standard form contains 10 to the same power, the calculation is very easy. But suppose we had to cope with:

$$8 \times 10^9 + 7 \times 10^8$$

We modify the second number so that it is written as 0.7×10^9. The problem becomes:

$$8 \times 10^9 + 0.7 \times 10^9 = (8 + 0.7) \times 10^9$$
$$= 8.7 \times 10^9$$

And the answer is already in standard form. We might have

changed the first number to produce:

$$80 \times 10^8 + 7 \times 10^8 = (80 + 7) \times 10^8 = 87 \times 10^8$$

But now we have to convert back to standard form:

$$(8.7 \times 10^1) \times 10^8 = 8.7 \times 10^9$$

So it is more convenient to convert the number with the smaller index into a form in which its power equals that of the larger index.

Examples

1. Calculate

$$3\ 741\ 200\ 000 + 612\ 900\ 000 + 30\ 560\ 000$$
$$= 3.7412 \times 10^9 + 6.129 \times 10^8 + 3.056 \times 10^7$$
$$= 3.7412 \times 10^9 + 0.6129 \times 10^9 + 0.03056 \times 10^9$$
$$= (3.7412 + 0.6129 + 0.03056) \times 10^9$$
$$= 4.38466 \times 10^9 = 4\ 384\ 660\ 000 \approx 4\ 385\ 000\ 000$$

2. Calculate

$$0.00000000206 + 0.000000000194 - 0.0000000000728$$
$$= 2.06 \times 10^{-9} + 0.194 \times 10^{-9} - 0.0728 \times 10^{-9}$$
$$= (2.06 + 0.194 - 0.0728) \times 10^{-9} = 2.1812 \times 10^{-9}$$
$$\approx 2.18 \times 10^{-9} = 0.00000000218$$

Exercise 6.8

Calculate:

1. $492\ 300\ 000 + 32\ 740\ 000 + 8\ 051\ 000$
2. $1\ 012\ 000\ 000 + 516\ 100\ 000 - 39\ 970\ 000$
3. $0.0000000723 + 0.00000000545 - 0.000000000934$
4. $0.00000000526 + 0.000000000913 - 0.0000000996$

6.3 Powers

If your calculator has a key y^x it is simple to discover the power of a number whether or not the number is integral, and whether the power is positive or negative, and integral or otherwise. Here, however, we shall work on the assumption that we do not possess such a calculator. We are able to calculate the positive integral power of a number with some basic calculators.

Examples

1. Calculate 3^5

Sequence	1	2	3	4	5	6
Key in	3	×	=	=	=	=
Display	3	3	9	27	81	243

Note: Power 5. Number of = keyed in is four.

2. Calculate 4.23^3

Sequence	1	2	3	4
Key in	4.23	×	=	=
Display	4.23	4.23	17.8929	75.686967

Note: Power 3. Number of = keyed in is two. Rough check: $4^3 = 64$.

3. Calculate 0.75^4

Sequence	1	2	3	4	5
Key in	0.75	×	=	=	=
Display	0.75	0.75	0.5625	0.421875	0.3164062

$0.75^4 \approx 0.32$
Note: Power 4. Number of = keyed in is three. Rough check:
$$0.7^4 = (0.7^2)^2 = 0.49^2 \approx 0.5^2 = 0.25$$

4. The rough check in the last example gives us the method of approaching the calculation 1.02^{12}. We write it as $(1.02^3)^4$ because if we left it as originally expressed we would need to press the = key 11 times.

Sequence	1	2	3	4
Key in	1.02	×	=	=
Display	1.02	1.02	1.0404	1.061208

Sequence	5	6	7	8
Key in	×	=	=	=
Display	1.061208	1.1261624	1.1950925	1.2682417

$1.02^{12} \approx 1.27$

5. Calculate $\left(\frac{2}{3}\right)^3$

Sequence	1	2	3	4
Key in	2	÷	3	=
Display	2	2	3	0.6666666

Sequence	5	6	7
Key in	×	=	=
Display	0.6666666	0.4444443	0.2962961

Check: $\left(\frac{2}{3}\right)^3 = \frac{8}{27} \approx \frac{8}{24} = \frac{1}{3} \approx 0.3$; calculator value ≈ 0.296.

Exercise 6.9

Calculate:

1. 4^2
2. 7^2
3. 11^2
4. 16^2
5. 31^2
6. 2.38^2
7. 0.52^2
8. 0.0349^2
9. 8.27^3
10. 23.5^3
11. 0.0734^3
12. 1.02^{10}
13. 1.03^{20}
14. 1.04^{50}
15. $\left(\frac{4}{7}\right)^3$

6.4 Reciprocals

If your calculator has a key $1/x$ then it is easy to find the reciprocal of a number. Suppose, however, there is no such key. We will begin by looking at an easy example to which we already know the answer. For example, the reciprocal of 4 is $\frac{1}{4}$, which is 0.25.

Method one

Sequence	1	2	3	4
Key in	1	÷	4	=
Display	1	1	4	0.25

Method two

Sequence	1	2	3	4
Key in	4	÷	=	=
Display	4	4	1	0.25

Method two operates only if the calculator has what is called a division constant. The same number of sequences is required in the two cases. Method one might appear to be the more obvious choice, but in certain problems method two has an advantage. Suppose we wanted the reciprocal of $\frac{3}{4}$, i.e. $1/\frac{3}{4}$. Method two would be:

Sequence	1	2	3	4	5	6	7
Key in	3	÷	4	=	÷	=	=
Display	3	3	4	0.75	0.75	1	1.3333333

Examples

1. Find the reciprocal of 135.07.

Sequence	1	2	3	4
Key in	135.07	÷	=	=
Display	135.07	135.07	1	0.0074035

Rough check: $\dfrac{1}{135.07} \approx \dfrac{1}{100} = 0.01$

2. Find the reciprocal of 0.02038.

Sequence	1	2	3	4
Key in	0.02038	÷	=	=
Display	0.02038	0.02038	1	49.067713

Rough check: $\dfrac{1}{0.02038} \approx \dfrac{1}{0.02} = 50$

3. Find the reciprocal of 3.25^4.

Sequence	1	2	3	4
Key in	3.25	×	=	=
Display	3.25	3.25	10.5625	34.328125

Sequence	5	6	7	8
Key in	=	÷	=	=
Display	111.5664	111.5664	1	0.0089632

Rough check: $3.25^4 \approx 3^4 = 81 \approx 100$ $\quad \frac{1}{100} = 0.01$

Look again at the last example, the reciprocal of 3.25^4:

$$= \frac{1}{3.25^4} = 3.25^{-4}$$

It means we have discovered a routine for working out negative integral powers of a number.

Example

Find the reciprocal of 4^{-7}.

Sequence	1	2	3	4	5	6
Key in	4	×	=	=	=	=
Display	4	4	16	64	256	1024

Sequence	7	8	9	10	11
Key in	=	=	÷	=	=
Display	4096	16 384	16 384	1	0.0000616

Exercise 6.10

Calculate the reciprocals of:

1. 59.46
2. 13.062
3. 40 906.2
4. 0.2099
5. 0.0007503
6. 5/3
7. 4/7

8. $1\frac{2}{3}$
9. 2^3
10. 5^3
11. 4.5^2
12. 93.26^3
13. 0.527^2
14. 0.08364^3

Calculate:

15. 3^{-4}
16. 8^{-3}
17. 5^{-4}
18. 6.32^{-2}
19. 0.407^{-3}
20. $\left(\frac{3}{4}\right)^{-2}$

6.5 Square roots

If you have a square root key on your calculator then the calculation of square roots is a simple process. If, however, you have only the very basic machine you can use the following method to obtain square roots quite quickly.

Example

Suppose we wish to calculate $\sqrt{5}$. First of all we make a rough estimate; call it e. For instance, we might say:

$$\sqrt{5} \approx \sqrt{4} = 2$$

Then we use a formula to get a better estimate; call this e_1.

$$e_1 = \frac{1}{2}\left(\frac{5}{e} + e\right)$$

First attempt:

Sequence	1	2	3	4	5	6	7	8
Key in	5	÷	2	+	2	÷	2	=
Display	5	5	2	2.5	2	4.5	2	2.25

Second attempt: $e_2 = \frac{1}{2}\left(\frac{5}{2.25} + 2.25\right)$

Sequence	1	2	3	4
Key in	5	÷	2.25	+
Display	5	5	2.25	2.2222222

Sequence	5	6	7	8
Key in	2.25	÷	2	=
Display	2.25	4.4722222	2	2.2361111

Third attempt: $e_3 = \frac{1}{2}\left(\frac{5}{2.2361111} + 2.2361111\right)$

Sequence	1	2	3	4
Key in	5	÷	2.2361111	+
Display	5	5	2.2361111	2.2360248

Sequence	5	6	7	8
Key in	2.2361111	÷	2	=
Display	2.2361111	4.4721358	2	2.2360679

Fourth attempt: $e_4 = \frac{1}{2}\left(\frac{5}{2.2360679} + 2.2360679\right)$

Sequence	1	2	3	4
Key in	5	÷	2.2360679	+
Display	5	5	2.2360679	2.236068

Sequence	5	6	7	8
Key in	2.2360679	÷	2	=
Display	2.2360679	4.4721359	2	2.2360679

When two successive estimates are the same we take that to be the square root of the number we are looking for, to the degree of accuracy of our calculator. In four attempts, then, we were able to establish that:

$$\sqrt{5} \approx 2.2360679$$

In other words, our formula for calculating the square roots of numbers (let us call them n) is:

$$\text{New estimate} = \frac{1}{2}\left(\frac{n}{\text{old estimate}} + \text{old estimate}\right)$$

Now repeat Exercise 5.2 using the above method, or the special key if you have one on your calculator. Check the answers obtained previously against those you obtain using the calculator.

Difficulties arise when we come to do problems involving + and − on the one hand and × and ÷ on the other. For example, try to calculate $3 + (2 \times 5)$:

Sequence	1	2	3	4	5	6
Key in	3	+	2	×	5	=
Display	3	3	2	5	5	25

Our calculator did the problem as $(3 + 2) \times 5$, and if we have no keys other than the very basic and our calculator does not use techniques which avoid this difficulty, then we have to note down intermediate answers on paper. With the above problem we can get out of the difficulty by rearranging the calculation as:

$$2 \times 5 + 3$$

Then our calculator will give us the correct answer. In a problem such as:

$$(53.2 \times 16.9 \times 3.08) + (19.25 \times 43.61 \times 2.96)$$
$$- (25.73 \times 35.42 \times 3.11)$$

we write down the intermediate answers:

$$2769.1664 + 2484.8978 - 2834.319 = 2419.7452$$

However, some calculators have memory keys – MC, M+, M−, MR – and then we are able to solve the problem without writing anything down. MC is the key we press when we wish to cancel everything left in the memory. M+ puts a number we have keyed in or calculated into the memory with a + sign attached to it. M− performs a similar function, but attaches a − sign. MR is the key we press when we wish to recall all the entries we have put in the memory. We will use such a calculator to work out the problem above:

$$(53.2 \times 16.9 \times 3.08) + (19.25 \times 43.61 \times 2.96)$$
$$- (25.73 \times 35.42 \times 3.11)$$

Sequence	1	2	3	4
Key in	MC	53.2	×	16.9
Display	0	53.2	53.2	16.9

Sequence	5	6	7	8
Key in	×	3.08	=	M+
Display	899.08	3.08	2769.1664	2769.1664

Sequence	9	10	11	12
Key in	19.25	×	43.61	×
Display	19.25	19.25	43.61	839.4925

Sequence	13	14	15	16
Key in	2.96	=	M+	25.73
Display	2.96	2484.8978	2484.8978	25.73

Sequence	17	18	19	20
Key in	×	35.42	×	3.11
Display	25.73	35.42	911.3566	3.11

Sequence	21	22	23
Key in	=	M−	MR
Display	2834.319	2834.319	2419.7452

Exercise 6.11

Calculate the following:

1. $(2 \times 3 \times 4) + (5 \times 6 \times 7) + (3 \times 5 \times 8)$
2. $(8 \times 9 \times 10) + (11 \times 12 \times 7) - (6 \times 8 \times 4)$
3. $(3 \times 4 \div 2) + (4 \times 5 \div 10)$
4. $(19.2 \times 37.5) + (42.3 \times 88.1)$
5. $(61.7 \div 2.45) - (81.3 \div 5.6)$
6. $(51.8 \times 43.9 \times 86.7) - (93.7 \times 76.9 \times 102.6)$
7. $(101.5 \times 57.2 \div 13.8) + (58.9 \div 2.35 \times 762.1)$
   $- (523.6 \times 104.3)$

7

Introduction to Algebra

In the earlier chapters we encountered the following laws which we saw applied readily to integers and which we extended to fractions. We shall extend them further in this chapter. For easy reference the laws are given again here.

$$\left.\begin{array}{l} a + (b + c) = (a + b) + c \\ a \times (b \times c) = (a \times b) \times c \end{array}\right\} \text{Associative laws}$$

$$\left.\begin{array}{l} a + b = b + a \\ a \times b = b \times a \end{array}\right\} \text{Commutative laws}$$

$$\left.\begin{array}{l} a \times (b + c) = a \times b + a \times c \\ (b + c) \times a = a \times (b + c) \\ \qquad\qquad = a \times b + a \times c \end{array}\right\} \text{Distributive laws}$$

$$\left.\begin{array}{c} a^m \times a^n = a^{m+n} \\ a^m/a^n = a^{m-n} \\ (a^m)^n = a^{mn} \\ a^0 = 1 \\ a^{-1} = \dfrac{1}{a} \\ a^{-n} = \dfrac{1}{a^n} \end{array}\right\} \text{Laws of indices}$$

We may add to the laws of indices as follows:

Consider:
$$(2 \times 3)^2 = 6^2 = 36 = 4 \times 9 = 2^2 \times 3^2$$

Similarly:
$$(3 \times 5)^3 = 15^3 = 15 \times 15 \times 15 = 3375 = 27 \times 125 = 3^3 \times 5^3$$

Both of these are examples of the general law:
$$(a \times b)^p = a^p \times b^p$$

We may add yet another law:
$$\left(\frac{a}{b}\right)^p = \frac{a^p}{b^p}$$

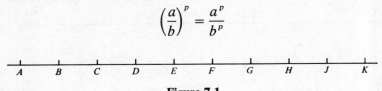

Figure 7.1

Fig. 7.1 shows a line which is divided into equal lengths so that $AB = BC = CD = DE$, etc. Represent each length by the letter x, of no fixed value. Now:
$$AC = 2AB = 2x$$

What do we mean by $2x$? AC is twice the length of AB, i.e. $2 \times AB$, i.e. $2 \times x$. So $2x$ means $2 \times x$, and $3x$ means $3 \times x$ and $\frac{1}{2}x$ means $\frac{1}{2} \times x$, and so on. But we know that $1 \times$ any number equals that number, so $1 \times x = x$, or x means $1 \times x$ or, shortened, $1x$.

Now: $\qquad\qquad AC = AB + BC = x + x$

Therefore: $\qquad\qquad x + x = 2x,$

or $\qquad\qquad\qquad 1x + 1x = 2x$

Similarly: $\qquad AD = AC + CD = 2x + x = 2x + 1x$

But: $\qquad\qquad\qquad AD = 3AB = 3x$

Then: $\qquad\qquad\qquad 2x + 1x = 3x$

Also: $\qquad\qquad AF = AD + DF = 3x + 2x$

But: $\qquad\qquad\qquad AF = 5AB = 5x$

Then: $\qquad\qquad\qquad 3x + 2x = 5x$

From these examples we see how to add together different multiples of an unspecified number, x. We would expect that:
$$7x + 5x = 12x$$

Using Fig. 7.1 again: $AE - AD = 4x - 3x$

But: $\qquad\qquad AE - AD = DE = AB = x$

So: $$4x - 3x = x$$
Similarly, by considering $AF - AD$, we obtain:

$$5x - 3x = 2x$$

And thus we can see how to subtract one multiple of x from another multiple of x.

Examples

1. $4x + 3x + 5x + 2x = (4x + 3x) + 5x + 2x = (7x + 5x) + 2x$
    $$= 12x + 2x = 14x$$

2. $4x + 3x - 5x + 2x - 3x = 7x - 5x + 2x - 3x$
    $$= 2x + 2x - 3x$$
    $$= 4x - 3x = x$$

3. But also: $4x + 3x - 5x + 2x - 3x$
    $$= 4x + 3x + (-5x) + 2x + (-3x)$$
    $$= 4x + 3x + 2x + (-5x) + (-3x)$$
    $$= 9x + (-8x) = x$$

Exercise 7.1

Simplify the following:

1. $4x + 3x + 2x$
2. $5x + 2x + 6x$
3. $(4y - 3y) + 2y$
4. $4a + (3a - 2a)$
5. $(5b - 2b) + (6b - 3b)$
6. $10x - 4x + 6x - 7x + 3x$
7. $(6q - 2q) + (8q - 5q) - 6q$
8. $4x - 5x$
9. $6y - 11y$
10. $5a + (2a - 7a) + (12a - a)$

Examples

1. $2(3x) = 2 \times (3 \times x) = (2 \times 3) \times x = 6 \times x = 6x$

2. $a \times (bx) = a \times (b \times x) = (a \times b) \times x = ab \times x = abx$

3. $(-2) \times (3x) = (-2) \times (3 \times x) = [(-2) \times 3] \times x$
    $$= -6 \times x = -6x$$

4. $(2x) \times (-3x) = (2 \times x) \times (-3 \times x) = (2 \times -3) \times (x \times x)$
    $$= -6 \times x^2 = -6x^2$$

5. $(6x)/(3x) = \dfrac{6x}{3x} = \dfrac{^2\cancel{6} \times x^1}{_1\cancel{3} \times x_1} = \dfrac{2}{1} = 2$

6. $(-8x^2)/(4x) = \dfrac{-8 \times x^2}{4 \times x} = -\dfrac{8}{4} \times \dfrac{x^2}{x} = -2x$

Exercise 7.2

Simplify the following:

1. $4 \times (2x)$
2. $3 \times (5x)$
3. $2 \times (px)$
4. $a \times (3x)$
5. $(5a) \times (2x)$
6. $(3a) \times (4b)$
7. $(-5) \times (3t)$
8. $(-2)(-3t)$
9. $(4x) \times (3x)$
10. $(2x^2) \times (3x)$
11. $(2xy) \times (3xy)$
12. $(3pq) \times (4p^2)$
13. $(-7x^2y^3) \times (2x^3y)$
14. $(6x) \div 3$
15. $(8x) \div (4x)$
16. $(-10x) \div (5x)$
17. $(-12a) \div (-3a)$
18. $(4a^2) \div (2a)$
19. $(6ab) \div (3bc)$
20. $(9a^3y^2) \div (3ay)$

Consider the line *PR* (Fig. 7.2) which is divided into two lengths, *PQ* and *QR*, represented by *a* and *b*, and in which we do not know

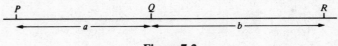

Figure 7.2

the length of *b* in comparison with the length of *a*. Then:

$$PR = PQ + QR = a + b$$

We have no way of abbreviating this: $a + b$ must be either left in that form or written as $b + a$.

Similarly, $a \times b$ cannot be simplified other than by abbreviating it, by convention, to ab or ba.

In the same way, $a - b$ and $a \div b$ (or a/b) cannot be simplified. Note that $-$ and $\div$ do not obey the commutative law, i.e.:

$$a - b \neq b - a \quad \text{and} \quad a/b \neq b/a$$

Examples

1. $2a + 3b + 4a + 5b - 3a = 2a + 4a - 3a + 3b + 5b$
    $$= 3a + 8b$$

2. $(2a) \times (3b) = (2 \times 3) \times (a \times b) = 6 \times ab = 6ab$

3. $(-3a) \times (4b) \times (5c) = (-3 \times 4 \times 5) \times (a \times b \times c)$
    $$= -60 \times abc = -60abc$$

4. $(6a) \times (-7b) \div (3c) = (6 \times -7 \div 3) \times (a \times b \div c)$

    $$= -\frac{{}^2\cancel{6} \times 7}{\cancel{3}_1} \times \frac{a \times b}{c}$$

    $$= -14 \times \frac{ab}{c} = -\frac{14ab}{c} \quad \text{or} \quad -14\frac{ab}{c}$$

Exercise 7.3

Where possible simplify the following:

1. $a + a + b$
2. $2a + 3a + b + 4b$
3. $6a - 5a + 4b - 2b$
4. $7a + 3b - 4a + b$
5. $2a - 5b + 6c - a + 8b + 9c$
6. $11p - 12q - 9r - 5p + 8q + 5r$
7. $(2x) \times (3y)$
8. $(4x) \times (2y) \times (5z)$
9. $(-5p) \times (6q) \times (-2r)$
10. $(4x) \div (2y)$
11. $(-6x) \div (7y)$
12. $(4a^2) \times (3ab^3) \div (2a^2b)$

Suppose square $ABCD$ (Fig. 7.3) has side length a. Then the area of $ABCD$ has a value a^2. So, in this case, a represents a length and a^2 represents an area. And, by constructing a cube side a, a^3 represents a volume.

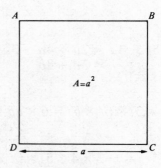

Figure 7.3

Lengths, areas and volumes represent different kinds of quantities, and when they are added together they do not reduce to a common quantity. This means that $x + x^2$, $x + x^3$ and $x^2 + x^3$ cannot be simplified. We say that x, x^2, x^3, and x^4 and so on are *unlike terms*. Thus there is no simpler form for:

$$2x + 5y + 3x^2 + 4xy + 10y^2 + 7x^3$$

Examples

1. $6x(2x + 3y) = (6x) \times (2x) + (6x) \times (3y)$
    $$= (6 \times 2) \times (x \times x) + (6 \times 3) \times (x \times y)$$
    $$= 12 \times x^2 + 18 \times xy$$
    $$= 12x^2 + 18xy$$

2. $5a(3a - 2) = 5a[3a + (-2)] = (5a) \times (3a) + (5a) \times (-2)$
    $$= (5 \times 3) \times (a \times a)$$
    $$+ (5 \times -2) \times a$$
    $$= 15a^2 - 10a$$

3. $(2x + 3y)(5x - 2y) = (2x + 3y)[(5x) + (-2y)]$
    $$= (2x)[(5x) + (-2y)]$$
    $$+ (3y)[(5x) + (-2y)]$$
    $$= (2x)(5x) + (2x)(-2y) + (3y)(5x)$$
    $$+ (3y)(-2y)$$
    $$= 10x^2 - 4xy + 15yx - 6y^2$$
    $$= 10x^2 - 4xy + 15xy - 6y^2$$
    (because $yx = xy$)
    $$= 10x^2 + 11xy - 6y^2$$

4. $4p(6p - 3q + 5r) = 4p[6p + (-3q) + 5r]$
    $$= (4p) \times (6p) + (4p) \times (-3q) + (4p) \times (5r)$$
    $$= 24p^2 - 12pq + 20pr$$

5. $(3x^2 + 4xy)(7xy - 10y^2) = (3x^2)(7xy - 10y^2)$
    $$+ (4xy)(7xy - 10y^2)$$
    $$= (3x^2)(7xy) - (3x^2)(10y^2)$$
    $$+ (4xy)(7xy) - (4xy)(10y^2)$$
    $$= 21(x^2 \times xy) - 30(x^2 \times y^2)$$
    $$+ 28(xy \times xy) - 40(xy \times y^2)$$
    $$= 21x^3y - 30x^2y^2$$
    $$+ 28x^2y^2 - 40xy^3$$
    $$= 21x^3y - 2x^2y^2 - 40xy^3$$

Exercise 7.4

Expand and simplify the following as far as possible:

1. $4(2a + 3b)$
2. $5(2x - 5y)$
3. $7(2a + b - 3c)$
4. $-2(x - 2y)$
5. $3(2x + 3y) - 2(3x + 2y)$
6. $6(5p + 2q) + 2(3p - 4q)$
7. $3x(4x + 2y)$
8. $7p(2p + 5)$
9. $3a(2a + 5) - 2(3a - 2)$
10. $5b(2a + 7b)$
11. $(x + y)(x + y)$
12. $(a - b)(a - b)$
13. $(p + q)(p - q)$
14. $(6a + 5b)(2a + b)$
15. $(4l + 3m)(3l - 4m)$

7.1 Factorization

The distributive law says:

$$a(b + c) = ab + ac$$
$$\text{and} \quad (b + c)a = ab + ac$$

This means that:

$$2(x + y) = 2x + 2y$$

And:

$$2(x - y) = 2(x + (-y)) = 2x + 2 \times -y = 2x - 2y$$

So we can modify the distributive law to give:

$$a(b - c) = ab - ac$$
$$\text{and} \quad (b - c)a = ab - ac$$

In all applications of this we are really exchanging, for a product of a number and a bracket, the sum or the difference of terms. We say we have expanded the original expression. Suppose we now look at the distributive law in reverse:

$$ab + ac = a(b + c)$$
$$\text{or} \quad ab + ac = (b + c)a$$
$$\text{or} \quad ab - ac = a(b - c)$$

Now we are exchanging, for a sum or difference of terms, the product of a number and a bracket. We say we are factorizing the original expression.

Examples

1. $\qquad\qquad 2x + 2y = 2(x + y)$
2. $\qquad\qquad 2x + 6y = 2(x + 3y)$
3. $\qquad\quad 2ax - 6ay = 2a(x - 3y)$
4. $\qquad\qquad 3x^2 - 2x = x(3x - 2)$
5. $\quad 12xyz + 18yzt = 6yz(2x + 3t)$

In each case the number, or factor, which we take outside the bracket on the right-hand side is the HCF of the two terms on the left.

Exercise 7.5

Factorize:

1. $2a + 4b$
2. $3x + 6y$
3. $5p - 10q$
4. $6x - 8y$
5. $2ax + 4bx$
6. $3ax + 6ay$
7. $5px - 10qx$
8. $6ax - 8ay$
9. $2x^2 + 4x$
10. $3xy + 6y^2$
11. $5p^2 - 10p$
12. $6x^2 - 8x$
13. $4x^3 + 3x^2$
14. $2xyz + 4yzt$
15. $2ax^2 + 3ax$

Look again at: $ab + ac = a(b + c)$
This means that: $ba + ca = a(b + c)$
because $ba = ab$ and $ca = ac$
Now, instead of a put $(p + q)$ and we obtain:

$$b(p + q) + c(p + q) = (p + q)(b + c)$$

We have written the left-hand side, which was the sum of two terms, as the product of two brackets. In other words, we have factorized it.

Examples

1. $a(x + 1) + b(x + 1) = (x + 1)(a + b)$
2. $3x(x + 1) + 2(x + 1) = (x + 1)(3x + 2)$
3. $4p(3x + 2) - 3q(3x + 2) = (3x + 2)(4p - 3q)$
4. $2y(5x - 3) - 7(5x - 3) = (2y - 7)(5x - 3)$

In all cases the two large terms on the left have a common factor, the bracket, and the factorization occurs as we see it on the right.

Exercise 7.6

Factorize:

1. $a(y + 1) + b(y + 1)$
2. $y(y + 1) + 3(y + 1)$
3. $2x(x - 1) + 5(x - 1)$
4. $3(a + 2) + 2a(a + 2)$
5. $5(b - 3) - 2b(b - 3)$
6. $a(x + y) + b(x + y)$
7. $a(x + y) - b(x + y)$
8. $a(x - y) + b(x - y)$
9. $a(x - y) - b(x - y)$
10. $3x(2x + 5) + 4(2x + 5)$

So long as the expression is arranged as, for instance:

$$4p(2x + 7) - 3q(2x + 7)$$

we can factorize by the method above. But if it is not, how do we proceed? Look again at:

$$a(x + 1) + b(x + 1) \qquad\qquad \text{(A)}$$

By the distributive law applied twice we obtain:

$$ax + a + bx + b \tag{B}$$

This contains four terms, yet it has factors, $(x + 1)(a + b)$. In order to reach the factors from the four terms (line B) we need to pass through an intermediate stage, line (A). Thus:

$$ax + a + bx + b = a(x + 1) + b(x + 1) = (x + 1)(a + b)$$
$$\text{Step 1} \qquad\qquad\qquad \text{Step 2}$$

In Step 1 we take the two terms $ax + a$ and group them together to give:

$$a(x + 1)$$

and the two terms $bx + b$ and group them together to give:

$$b(x + 1)$$

Step 2 is like the methods we used in Exercise 7.6.

Unless we can see Step 1 we cannot get our material in the proper form to carry out the factorization. Step 1 requires us to group the four terms in pairs. We might have proceeded as follows:

$$
\begin{aligned}
ax + a + bx + b &= ax + bx + a + b \\
&= x(a + b) + (a + b) = x(a + b) + 1(a + b) \\
&= (a + b)(x + 1)
\end{aligned}
$$

These are the same factors as before, but in the reverse order. On this occasion we grouped different pairs together. There is only one other way in which we could have grouped in pairs. Would that way have worked too?

$$ax + a + bx + b = ax + b + a + bx$$

But now neither ax and b nor a and bx have a common factor to effect Step 1. So this method does not work.

Where we have a four-term expression to be factorized by grouping there are usually two methods which are fruitful and one which is not. Therefore we must not abandon our attempts if the first effort is a failure. If factorization is possible the next grouping should be successful.

Examples

1. $$
\begin{aligned}
3x + 4y - 6ax - 8ay &= 3x - 6ax + 4y - 8ay \\
&= 3x(1 - 2a) + 4y(1 - 2a) \\
&= (1 - 2a)(3x + 4y)
\end{aligned}
$$

2. $2x^2 + 3xy + 8px + 12py = x(2x + 3y) + 4p(2x + 3y)$
$$= (2x + 3y)(x + 4p)$$

Exercise 7.7

Factorize the following:

1. $ay + a + by + b$
2. $y^2 + y + 3y + 3$
3. $ax + by - ay - bx$
4. $ax - bx + ay - by$
5. $ax + by + ay + bx$
6. $6al + 8am + 3bl + 4bm$
7. $2x^2 + 3xy + 2xy^2 + 3y^3$
8. $2x^2 - 3xy - 3y^3 + 2xy^2$
9. $18ab + 8b^2 + 27a^3 + 12a^2b$
10. $pqr - qrt + 3pxy - 3txy$

7.2 Standard factors

Figs. 7.4, 7.5 and 7.6 illustrate certain standard factors which it is essential to memorize.

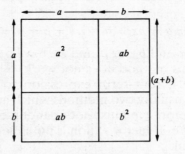

Figure 7.4

From Fig. 7.4 we obtain $(a + b)^2$, which is the area of the large square:

$$a^2 + ab + ab + b^2$$

i.e. the sum of the areas inside is

$$a^2 + 2ab + b^2$$

In reverse this means:

$$a^2 + 2ab + b^2 = (a + b)^2 \qquad 7.1$$

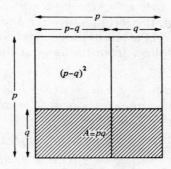

Figure 7.5

From Fig. 7.5 we obtain $(p - q)^2$, the area of the square marked, which is equal to:

$$p^2 - pq - pq + q^2$$

which is the outer square minus two rectangles of area equal to that shaded plus the area of the square side q, which equals:

$$p^2 - 2pq + q^2$$

In reverse this means:

$$p^2 - 2pq + q^2 = (p - q)^2 \qquad 7.2$$

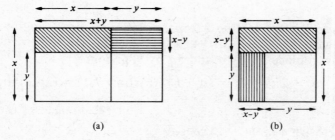

Figure 7.6

Fig. 7.6 represents the area of $(x + y)(x - y)$. The area in (a) is equal to the area in (b), although the horizontal shaded area has been placed in a different position. In (b) the whole shaded area is equal to:

$$x^2 - y^2 \text{ (the difference between the two squares)}$$

Therefore: $$x^2 - y^2 = (x + y)(x - y) \qquad\qquad 7.3$$

The expressions on the left of Laws 7.1 and 7.2 are said to be *perfect squares*. That on the left of Law 7.3 is called the *difference of two squares*. These follow from the laws at the beginning of the chapter:

$$
\begin{aligned}
(a + b)^2 &= (a + b)(a + b) = a(a + b) + b(a + b) \\
&= a^2 + ab + ba + b^2 = a^2 + ab + ab + b^2 \\
&= a^2 + 2ab + b^2
\end{aligned}
$$

$$
\begin{aligned}
(a - b)^2 &= (a - b)(a - b) = a(a - b) - b(a - b) \\
&= a^2 - ab - ba + b^2 = a^2 - ab - ab + b^2 \\
&= a^2 - 2ab + b^2
\end{aligned}
$$

$$
\begin{aligned}
(a + b)(a - b) &= a(a - b) + b(a - b) = a^2 - ab + ba - b^2 \\
&= a^2 - ab + ab - b^2 = a^2 - b^2
\end{aligned}
$$

Examples

1. Factorize $4x^2 + 4xy + y^2$.
   Rewrite as: $(2x)^2 + 2(2x)y + y^2$
   Now replace $2x$ by a, giving:

   $$a^2 + 2ay + y^2 = (a + y)^2 \text{ (by Law 7.1)}$$
   $$= (2x + y)^2 \text{ (putting back } 2x \text{ instead of } a)$$

2. Factorize $9p^2 + 30pq + 25q^2$.
   Rewrite as: $(3p)^2 + 2(3p)(5q) + (5q)^2$
   Now replace $3p$ by a and $5q$ by b, giving:

   $$a^2 + 2ab + b^2 = (a + b)^2 \text{ (by Law 7.1)} = (3p + 5q)^2$$

3. Factorize $49a^2b^2 - 14abc + c^2$.
   Rewrite as: $(7ab)^2 - 2(7ab)(c) + c^2$

Replace $7ab$ by p, giving:
$$p^2 - 2pc + c^2 = (p - c)^2 = (7ab - c)^2$$

4. Factorize $81p^4q^2 - 90p^2qrs^3 + 25r^2s^6$.
   Rewrite as: $(9p^2q)^2 - 2(9p^2q)(5rs^3) + (5rs^3)^2$
   Replace $9p^2q$ by x and $5rs^3$ by y, giving:
   $$x^2 - 2xy + y^2 = (x - y)^2$$
   $$= (9p^2q - 5rs^3)^2$$

5. Factorize $4x^2 - 9y^2$.
   Rewrite as: $(2x)^2 - (3y)^2$
   Replace $2x$ by p and $3y$ by q, giving:
   $$p^2 - q^2 = (p + q)(p - q)$$
   $$= (2x + 3y)(2x - 3y)$$

6. Factorize $(x + 3)^2 - (x - 2)^2$.
   $$[(x + 3) + (x - 2)][(x + 3) - (x - 2)]$$
   $$= (2x + 1)(5) = 5(2x + 1)$$

7. Factorize $x^2 + 4xy + 4y^2 - 9$.
   $$(x + 2y)^2 - 3^2 = [(x + 2y) + 3][(x + 2y) - 3]$$
   $$= (x + 2y + 3)(x + 2y - 3)$$

Exercise 7.8

Factorize:

1. $p^2 + 4pq + 4q^2$
2. $p^2 - 4pq + 4q^2$
3. $4a^2 - b^2$
4. $9a^2 - 4b^2$
5. $9a^2 + 12ab + 4b^2$
6. $9x^2 - 12xy + 4y^2$
7. $9a^4b^2 - 4c^2$

8. $2a^2 + 4ab + 2b^2$ (here first write $2(a^2 + 2ab + b^2)$ and then factorize the bracket as before)
9. $2x^2 - 4xy + 2y^2$
10. $6x^2 - 12xy + 6y^2$
11. $ax^2 + 2axy + ay^2$
12. $3pa^2 - 6pab + 3pb^2$
13. $25a^2 - 49b^2$
14. $64x^4 - 80x^2y + 25y^2$
15. $2a^2 - 2b^2$
16. $3x^2 - 3y^2$
17. $ax^2 - ay^2$
18. $4a^3x - 9ab^2x$
19. $144a^2 + 120ab + 25b^2$
20. $576a^2x^2 - 240axy^2 + 25y^4$
21. $(x + 2)^2 - (x + 1)^2$
22. $(x + 5)^2 - (x - 3)^2$
23. $(2x + 3)^2 - (x + 1)^2$
24. $(3a + 4b)^2 - (2a - 3b)^2$
25. $a^2 + 2ab + b^2 - 1$
26. $a^2 - 2ab + b^2 - 1$
27. $4p^2 + 12pq + 9q^2 - r^2$
28. $4p^2 + 12pq + 9q^2 - q^2$
29. $a^2 + 2ab + b^2 - x^2 - 2xy - y^2$
30. $a^2 - x^2 - y^2 + b^2 + 2ab - 2xy$

8

Solution of Equations

Many students use the following rule for solving equations and manipulating formulae: change the side, change the sign. If the rule is applied accurately it always works. However, a large number of students do not fully understand it, and consequently it is often misapplied. The most common difficulty lies in deciding what is the operative sign, and where such confusion exists the application of the rule is fraught with pitfalls. We will therefore begin with the most elementary ideas and develop the subject in short steps, illustrating with simple examples.

8.1 Expressions

$2x + 3$ is called an expression. Its value depends on the value of x.

When $x = 0$, $2x + 3 = 3$;
when $x = 1$, $2x + 3 = 2 + 3 = 5$;
when $x = 4$, $2x + 3 = 8 + 3 = 11$;
when $x = \frac{1}{2}$, $2x + 3 = 1 + 3 = 4$;
when $x = -2$, $2x + 3 = -4 + 3 = -1$.

Thus the value of $2x + 3$ varies with the value of x. Other expressions are:

$$2x + 3y; \qquad 14x^2 + 5x - 7; \qquad \frac{7x + 3}{5x - 2}$$

179

8.2 Equations

If we write $2x + 3 = 5$ then there is only one value of x which fits the statement; it is $x = 1$, as can be seen from the above.

$2x + 3 = 5$ is an equation: it equates two expressions: $2x + 3$ and 5. So an equation is a statement that two things are equal; the things are expressions which may be simple or complicated. One of the simplest is:

$$x = 2; \quad \text{here, obviously, } x = 2$$

More complicated:

$$5x + 9 = 6; \quad \text{here } x = -3/5$$

Still more complicated:

$$4(3y - 7) = 9; \quad \text{here } y = 3\tfrac{1}{12}$$

And even more complicated:

$$4p^2 + 2p - 3 = 5p + 7; \quad \text{here } p = 2 \text{ or } -1\tfrac{1}{4}$$

An obvious equation is:

$$4 = 2 \times 2$$

From the last chapter, others are:

$$x^2 + 2xy + y^2 = (x + y)^2$$
$$x^2 - 2xy + y^2 = (x - y)^2$$
$$x^2 - y^2 = (x + y)(x - y)$$

The last three are very special equations. No matter what values are substituted for x and y the statements will be true.

8.3 Identities

We call such equations identities; they are true for all values of the letter or letters. In such equations it is common to use three horizontal lines instead of two for an equal sign; for example:

$$(x + 1)(x + 2) \equiv x^2 + 3x + 2$$

8.4 Operations on equations

Adding to, or subtracting from, both sides any number

Starting from an obvious statement, $4 = 2 \times 2$:

$$\text{LHS} = 4 + 7 = 11 \qquad \text{RHS} = 2 \times 2 + 7 = 11$$
$$\text{LHS} = 4 - 9 = -5 \qquad \text{RHS} = 2 \times 2 - 9 = -5$$

The two sides will still be equal.

Multiplying or dividing both sides by the same number

$$\text{LHS} = 4 \times 13 = 52 \qquad \text{RHS} = 2 \times 2 \times 13 = 52$$
$$\text{LHS} = 4/8 = \tfrac{1}{2} \qquad \text{RHS} = \frac{2 \times 2}{8} = \tfrac{1}{2}$$

Again the two sides will be equal.

Carrying out the same sequence of arithmetic operations on the two sides

$$\text{LHS} = \frac{2 \times 4 + 3}{5} = \frac{8 + 3}{5} = \frac{11}{5} = 2\tfrac{1}{5}$$
$$\text{RHS} = \frac{2 \times (2 \times 2) + 3}{5} = \frac{8 + 3}{5} = \frac{11}{5} = 2\tfrac{1}{5}$$

The two sides are still equal.

Basic ideas

Consider the equation $x + 2 = 5$. The solution is easily obtained by guessing, or by trial and error, or by knowing rules for addition. However, let us work out rules of procedure which will help us to solve more difficult problems. We shall use seven basic ideas over and over again:

$$x + 0 = x \qquad\qquad\qquad 8.1$$
$$1 \times x = x \qquad\qquad\qquad 8.2$$

$$a + {}^-a = 0 \qquad\qquad 8.3$$

$$\frac{1}{a} \times a = 1 \qquad\qquad 8.4$$

$$(x + a) + {}^-a = x + (a + {}^-a) = x + 0 = x \qquad\qquad 8.5$$

$$\frac{1}{a} \times (ax) = \left(\frac{1}{a} \times a\right) \times x = 1 \times x = x \qquad\qquad 8.6$$

$$\frac{x}{a} = \frac{b}{c} \rightarrow cx = ab \text{ (called cross-multiplication)} \qquad 8.7$$

Returning to the equation above:

$$x + 2 = 5$$

Step 1: add ${}^-2$ to both sides:

$$(x + 2) + {}^-2 = 5 + {}^-2$$

Step 2: use the associative law (8.5):

$$x + (2 + {}^-2) = 5 - 2$$

Step 3: use Law 8.3 above:

$$x + 0 = 3$$

Step 4: use Law 8.1 above:

$$x = 3$$

Check:

$$3 + 2 = 5$$

Examples

1. $2x - 7 = 11$
    Rewrite:

$$2x + {}^-7 = 11$$

    Add 7:

$$2x + {}^-7 + 7 = 11 + 7$$

By Law 8.5:
$$2x + 0 = 18$$

By Law 8.1:
$$2x = 18$$

Multiply by $\frac{1}{2}$:
$$\tfrac{1}{2} \times 2x = \tfrac{1}{2} \times 18$$

By Law 8.6:
$$x = 9$$

Check:
$$2x - 7 = 18 - 7 = 11$$

2. $\frac{1}{4}x + 2 = 5$

   Add $^-2$:
   $$\tfrac{1}{4}x + 2 + {}^-2 = 5 + {}^-2$$

   By Laws 8.5 and 8.1:
   $$\tfrac{1}{4}x = 3$$

   Multiply by 4:
   $$4 \times \tfrac{1}{4}x = 4 \times 3 \text{ (4 is the multiplicative inverse of } \tfrac{1}{4})$$

   By Law 8.6:
   $$x = 12$$

   Check:
   $$\tfrac{1}{4}x + 2 = \tfrac{1}{4} \times 12 + 2 = 3 + 2 = 5$$

3. $\dfrac{2}{y} - 3 = 1$

   Add 3:
   $$\frac{2}{y} + {}^-3 + 3 = 1 + 3$$

By Law 8.5:

$$\frac{2}{y} = 4, \quad \text{i.e.} \quad 2 \times \frac{1}{y} = 4$$

Multiply by $\frac{1}{2}$:

$$\frac{1}{2} \times 2 \times \frac{1}{y} = \frac{1}{2} \times 4$$

By Law 8.6:

$$\frac{1}{y} = 2 = \frac{2}{1}$$

Invert both sides:

$$\frac{y}{1} = \frac{1}{2}$$

(note: invert only when each side is a single fraction or integer)

(Where $\frac{1}{2} = \frac{1}{3} + \frac{1}{6}$ it is not true that $2 = 3 + 6$.)

$$\text{i.e. } y = \tfrac{1}{2}$$

Check:

$$2/\tfrac{1}{2} - 3 = 2 \times 2 - 3 = 4 - 3 = 1$$

4. $\dfrac{3}{2x + 5} + \dfrac{1}{3} = \dfrac{1}{2}$

Multiply throughout the equation by the LCM of 2, 3, and $2x + 5$:

$$2 \times 3 \times (2x + 5) = 6(2x + 5)$$

$$\frac{3}{(2x+5)} \times 6(2x+5) + \frac{1}{3} \times 6^2(2x + 5) = \frac{1}{2} \times 6^3(2x + 5)$$

$$18 + 2(2x + 5) = 3(2x + 5)$$

$$18 + 4x + 10 = 6x + 15$$

$$4x + 28 = 6x + 15$$

Add ^-4x and $^-15$ to both sides:

$$4x + {}^-4x + 28 + {}^-15 = 6x + {}^-4x + 15 + {}^-15$$
$$0 + 13 = 2x + 0$$
$$13 = 2x$$
$$\tfrac{1}{2} \times 13 = \tfrac{1}{2} \times 2x$$
$$6\tfrac{1}{2} = x$$

Check: LHS $= \dfrac{3}{13 + 5} + \dfrac{1}{3} = \tfrac{3}{18} + \tfrac{1}{3} = \tfrac{1}{6} + \tfrac{1}{3} = \tfrac{1}{6} + \tfrac{2}{6} = \tfrac{3}{6} = \tfrac{1}{2}$

5. $\tfrac{2}{3}(x + 1) - \tfrac{3}{5}(x - 1) = \tfrac{1}{10}$

Multiply both sides by 30:

$$^{10}\cancel{30} \times \frac{2}{\cancel{3}_1} (x + 1) - {}^6\cancel{30} \times \frac{3}{\cancel{5}_1} (x - 1) = {}^3\cancel{30} \times \frac{1}{\cancel{10}_1}$$
$$20(x + 1) - 18(x - 1) = 3$$
$$20x + 20 - 18x + 18 = 3$$
$$2x + 38 = 3$$
$$2x + 38 + {}^-38 = 3 + {}^-38$$
$$2x = -35$$
$$\tfrac{1}{2} \times 2x = \tfrac{1}{2} \times (-35)$$
$$x = -17\tfrac{1}{2}$$

Check: LHS $= \tfrac{2}{3}(-16\tfrac{1}{2}) - \tfrac{3}{5}(-18\tfrac{1}{2}) = -\dfrac{{}^1\cancel{2}}{{}_1\cancel{3}} \times \dfrac{\cancel{33}^{11}}{\cancel{2}_1} + \dfrac{3}{5} \times \dfrac{37}{2}$

$$= -11 + \tfrac{111}{10} = -11 + 11\tfrac{1}{10} = \tfrac{1}{10}$$

6. $ax + b = c$

$$ax + b + {}^-b = c + {}^-b$$
$$ax = (c - b)$$
$$\frac{1}{a} \times ax = \frac{1}{a}(c - b)$$
$$x = \frac{(c - b)}{a}$$

7. $\dfrac{a}{bx + c} = \dfrac{d}{e}$

Multiply both sides by $e(bx + c)$:

$$e(\cancel{bx + c}) \times \frac{a}{(\cancel{bx + c})} = \cancel{e}(bx + c) \times \frac{d}{\cancel{e}}$$

$$ea = (bx + c)d \quad \text{(or cross-multiply (Law 8.7))}$$

$$ae = bdx + cd$$

$$ae + {}^-cd = bdx + cd + {}^-cd$$

$$(ae - cd) = bdx$$

$$\frac{1}{bd}(ae - cd) = \frac{1}{\cancel{bd}} \times \cancel{bd}x$$

$$\frac{(ae - cd)}{bd} = x$$

Check: LHS $= \dfrac{a}{\cancel{b} \times \dfrac{(ae - cd)}{\cancel{b}d} + c} = \dfrac{a}{\dfrac{ae - cd + cd}{d}}$

$$= \frac{a}{ae/d} = \cancel{a} \times \frac{d}{\cancel{a}e} = \frac{d}{e}$$

Exercise 8.1

Solve the following equations:

1. $y + 5 = 9$
2. $y - 6 = 7$
3. $2p + 3 = 8$
4. $3x - 7 = 8$
5. $\frac{1}{2}y + 1 = 3$
6. $\frac{1}{3}p - 2 = 5$
7. $\frac{2}{3}x + 4 = 6$

8. $\dfrac{2}{p} + 4 = 7$

9. $\dfrac{3}{2x} - 1 = 7$

10. $\frac{1}{3}x + \frac{1}{6}x + 5 = 2$
11. $5(2x + 1) + 3(x + 5) = 46$
12. $\frac{1}{2}(2x + 3) - \frac{1}{6}(3x - 4) = \frac{11}{3}$
13. $2(3x + 2) - 5(2 - x) = 4(2x + 3)$

14. $\dfrac{1}{x} + \dfrac{1}{6} = \dfrac{1}{2}$

15. $\dfrac{1}{2x} = \dfrac{1}{6x} + \dfrac{1}{9}$

16. $\dfrac{1}{x + 1} + \dfrac{1}{2} = \dfrac{5}{6}$

17. $2x + a = b$
18. $2ax + b = ax + 2b$
19. $ax + b + ax = 2b$
20. $ax + b + bx = 3b$

21. $\dfrac{x}{a} + c = b$

22. $\dfrac{x}{a} + \dfrac{c}{a} = \dfrac{b}{a}$

23. $\dfrac{1}{x + a} + \dfrac{1}{2b} = \dfrac{1}{b}$

24. $a(x + 2) + b(x - 1) = 5a + 7b$

8.5 Simultaneous linear equations

Consider:

$$x + y = 5$$

in which the values of both x and y are not known. What possible values might x and y have? They could be: $x = 4$, $y = 1$; $x = 5$, $y = 0$; $x = 2$, $y = 3$; $x = -7$, $y = 12$; $x = 3\frac{1}{2}$, $y = 1\frac{1}{2}$; and innumerable other possibilities. This means that, given a single equation involving two unknown values, we can never be certain of discovering either value.

Suppose, however, we know also that:

$$x - y = 1$$

Write these equations one underneath the other:

$$x + y = 5 \qquad \text{(i)}$$
$$x - y = 1 \qquad \text{(ii)}$$

Then (i) + (ii) gives $2x + 0 = 6$, leading to $2x = 6$. (This equation does not involve y; we say we have *eliminated it*.) Therefore $x = 3$. If, in (i), we replace x by the value we have discovered, we obtain:

$$3 + y = 5$$

giving:

$$y = 5 - 3 = 2$$

Check: substitute $x = 3$, $y = 2$ in (ii). (We do not use (i) because we used that equation to calculate y.) LHS is:

$$3 - 2 = 1$$

Method of elimination

Examples

1.
$$2x + 3y = 12 \qquad \text{(i)}$$
$$3x - y = 7 \qquad \text{(ii)}$$

(i) + 3 × (ii) gives:

$$(2x + 9x) + 0 = 12 + 3 \times 7$$
$$11x = 12 + 21 = 33$$
$$x = \frac{33^3}{11_1} = 3$$

Substitute for x in (ii):

$$9 - y = 7$$
$$9 - y - 7 + y = 7 - 7 + y$$
$$2 = y$$

Check in (i):

$$\text{LHS} = 6 + 6 = 12$$

2.
$$\tfrac{1}{4}x + \tfrac{1}{3}y = 8 \qquad \text{(i)}$$
$$\tfrac{1}{8}x - \tfrac{1}{12}y = 1 \qquad \text{(ii)}$$

Multiply (i) by 12:

$$3x + 4y = 96 \text{ (to get rid of fractions)} \qquad \text{(iii)}$$

Multiply (ii) by 24:

$$3x - 2y = 24 \qquad \text{(iv)}$$

(iii) − (iv) gives:

$$0 + 6y = 72$$

$$y = \frac{1}{{}_1\cancel{6}} \times \cancel{72}^{12} = 12$$

Substitute for y in (iii):

$$3x + 48 = 96$$
$$3x = 48$$
$$x = 16$$

Check in (ii):

$$\text{LHS} = \tfrac{1}{8} \times 16 - \tfrac{1}{12} \times 12 = 2 - 1 = 1$$

Note that we must check in one of the original equations, and not in the one leading to (iii) because that was used to derive x. We check in the originals because mistakes might have been made in obtaining (iii) and (iv). An alternative method is often used called the method of substitution.

Method of substitution

In example (1) we might have written equation (ii) as:

$$y = 3x - 7$$

Now substitute this expression for y in (i) to obtain:

$$2x + 3(3x - 7) = 12$$

giving:

$$2x + 9x - 21 = 12$$

Therefore:

$$11x = 12 + 21 = 33$$
$$x = 3$$

Afterwards we substitute for x as before.

Example

$$3x + 4y = 17 \qquad \text{(i)}$$
$$2x - 3y = 11 \qquad \text{(ii)}$$

From (ii):

$$2x = 3y + 11$$
$$x = \tfrac{3}{2}y + \tfrac{11}{2} \qquad \text{(iii)}$$

Substitute for x in (i):

$$3(\tfrac{3}{2}y + \tfrac{11}{2}) + 4y = 17$$
$$\tfrac{9}{2}y + \tfrac{33}{2} + 4y = 17$$

Multiply by 2:

$$9y + 33 + 8y = 34$$
$$17y = 1$$
$$y = \tfrac{1}{17}$$

Substitute for y in (iii):

$$x = \tfrac{3}{2} \times \tfrac{1}{17} + \tfrac{11}{2} = \tfrac{3}{34} + \tfrac{11}{2}$$
$$= \tfrac{3}{34} + 5 + \tfrac{1}{2} = 5 + \frac{3+17}{34} = 5\tfrac{20}{34} = 5\tfrac{10}{17}$$

Check in (i):

$$3(5\tfrac{10}{17}) + 4(\tfrac{1}{17}) = 15\tfrac{30}{17} + \tfrac{4}{17} = 15\tfrac{34}{17} = 15 + 2 = 17$$

Exercise 8.2

Solve the following pairs of equations:

1. $x + y = 5$; $x - y = 3$

2. $p + 2q = 11$; $p + q = 6$
3. $2p + q = 19$; $p + q = 11$
4. $2p - q = 19$; $p + q = 12$
5. $3p - 2q = 10$; $2p + 3q = 24$
6. $5a + 4b = 14$; $3a - 2b = 4$
7. $x + \frac{1}{2}y = 3$; $x - \frac{1}{2}y = 1$
8. $\frac{1}{3}x + \frac{1}{2}y = 2$; $5x - 3y = 2$
9. $11a + 6b = 16$; $7a - 5b = 19$
10. $y = 2x - 5$; $3x + 4y = -6$
11. $10x - 7y = -23$; $x = 17 - 2y$
12. $2x + 3y = -1$; $3x + 7y = 1$
13. $\frac{1}{4}x + \frac{1}{3}y = 0$; $5x - 3y = 96$
14. $0.1x + 0.2y = 0.3$; $0.2x - 0.3y = -0.1$
15. $2.1x - 1.9y = 2.3$; $0.5x + 3.7y = 4.7$
16. $5x + y = 17$; $3x - 7y = -13$
17. $17x - 13y = 219$; $x + 10y = 45$
18. $9x - 8y = 27$; $4x + 3y = -14$

8.6 The use of algebra in solving problems

Certain problems are much more easily solved by using algebra
than by using arithmetic, and some are difficult or even impossible
to solve by purely arithmetic methods.

When using algebraic methods the first task is to represent the
unknown quantity in the problem by a letter: for example, the
length of a rectangle by x metres, the mass of an object by a
kilograms, somebody's age by p years, the time taken to complete
a journey by t minutes, and so on.

We then use this to work out what some other length, or some
other mass, or some other age, or some other time, is. For instance,
the length of a rectangle, a, is extended by 10. The new length,
therefore, is $a + 10$. The mass x kilograms has a lump, y kilograms, cut off it. The new mass, therefore, is $x - y$ kilograms. A
second person is 5 years older than one aged p years. His age,
therefore, is $p + 5$ years. The time to complete a journey of t
minutes is delayed by 11 minutes. The new time, therefore, is
$t + 11$ minutes.

Examples

1. A tray weighing 3 kg contains x plants each weighing 1.2 kg. Total weight of plants is:

$$x \times 1.2 = 1.2x \text{ kg}$$

Total weight of tray and plants is:

$$(1.2x + 3) \text{ kg}$$

2. Each of 10 buckets contains x litres of water and each loses y litres of water due to evaporation. Each bucket, therefore, now contains $(x - y)$ litres, and the total content is $10(x - y)$ litres.

Exercise 8.3

1. A boy is x years old now. How old was he: (a) 1 year ago; (b) 3 years ago; (c) 9 years ago; (d) t years ago? How old will he be (e) 2 years hence; (f) 6 years hence; (g) y years hence? If his father is three times as old as the boy now, how much older than the boy: (h) is he now; (i) will he be in 7 years' time; (j) in w years' time?

2. A car goes 100 km and then a further x kilometres. How far is it then from the starting point? It then travels back towards the starting point for a distance of y kilometres. How far will it then be from the starting point?

3. A stock of sand of estimated size 1000 m³ has x loads each of 3 m³ taken away and y loads each of 3.5 m³ added to it. What is the final size of the stock?

4. The mass of a rivet is decreased from p kilograms to q kilograms. How many more rivets can be produced from 100 kg of metal?

5. The sides of a triangle are a, b and c units. Calculate the perimeter of the triangle. Calculate the total length of the perimeters of x such triangles.

6. The temperature of a specimen of metal is $T°C$. Its temperature is raised steadily by $a°C$ every minute for 20 minutes. What is the temperature of the metal after 20 minutes?

7. In hardening a metal by rapid cooling its temperature falls

from T°C to t°C. What is the fall in temperature? What is the rate of cooling (in degrees per minute) if the fall takes place in: (a) 1 minute; (b) 30 seconds; (c) 20 seconds; (d) 15 seconds?

8. At 5 p.m. on a certain day the temperature in a room is p°C. From then until 6 p.m. the temperature falls by x°C every 10 minutes and then, until 8 p.m., the temperature falls by $(x + y)$°C every 10 minutes. What will the temperature of the room be at: (a) 8 p.m.; (b) 7 p.m.; (c) 7.30 p.m.?

9. The pressure of a fluid at the surface is P units. The pressure in the fluid increases by x units for each 10 m depth below the surface. What is the pressure at: (a) 10 m; (b) 30 m; (c) 45 m; (d) y metres below the surface?

10. A plant requires x employees to operate it for 10 hours per day for five days during the week, y employees to maintain it during the remaining hours of the five days, and z employees to maintain it during the whole of Saturday and Sunday. What is the total number of man-hours necessary to keep the plant operating for the whole of the week?

The use of simple equations to solve problems

Examples

1. A post for a fence has to have one third of its length buried under the ground. If the top of the post is to be 6.2 m above ground what must the length of the post be?

Suppose the length of the post is x metres. Then the length of the post below ground must be $\frac{1}{3}x$, and the length above ground must be $x - \frac{1}{3}x$. Our equation, therefore, is:

$$x - \tfrac{1}{3}x = 6.2$$
$$3x - x = 6.2 \times 3 \quad \text{(multiplying by 3)}$$
$$2x = 18.6$$
$$x = 9.3 \quad \text{(dividing by 2)}$$

The post must be 9.3 m long.
Check:

$$\tfrac{1}{3} \times 9.3 = 3.1$$
$$9.3 - 3.1 = 6.2$$

2. If I think of a number, double it, and then add 11, the result is 37. What number did I think of?
Suppose the number is n. Then double the number is $2n$. Add 11 to that and we have $2n + 11$. Therefore:

$$2n + 11 = 37$$
$$2n = 37 - 11 = 26$$
$$n = 13 \quad \text{(dividing by 2)}$$

The number was 13.
Check:
$$2 \times 13 = 26. \qquad 26 + 11 = 37$$

3. In a circuit two conductors are in series. When an e.m.f. of 50 V is applied to them a current of 0.3 A passes through each. The resistance of one conductor is unknown and that of the other is 100 Ω. Determine the unknown resistance.
First we must construct an equation to determine the unknown resistance, which we shall suppose to be R ohms. Fig. 8.1 represents the circuit.

$$0.3(R + 100) = 50$$
$$\tfrac{3}{10}(R + 100) = 50$$
$$3(R + 100) = 500$$
$$3R + 300 = 500$$
$$3R = 200$$
$$R = 200/3 = 66\tfrac{2}{3}$$

The unknown resistance is $66\tfrac{2}{3}$ Ω.

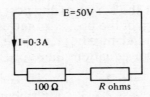

E=50V

I=0·3A

100 Ω   R ohms

Figure 8.1

4. A vehicle is travelling at 10 m/s. It is accelerated uniformly for 10 seconds until its velocity is 30 m/s. During that time the vehicle travels 200 m. Determine the uniform acceleration in m/s².

The relationship between velocity, acceleration and time is:

$$v = u + at$$

where a represents the acceleration. The data are: $u = 10$; $v = 30$; $t = 10$. Then:

$$30 = 10 + a \cdot 10$$
$$a + 1 = 3 \quad \text{(dividing throughout by 10)}$$
$$a = 2$$

The acceleration is 2 m/s^2. We do not need the distance, 200 m, to solve the problem.

5. An unknown volume of gas is under pressure (10^5 N/m^2). When the pressure is decreased by $2 \times 10^4 \text{ N/m}^2$ the volume increases by 2 m^3. Determine the initial volume of the gas assuming that the operative law is Boyle's law.
    The relationship between pressure (p) and volume (v) is:

$$p_1 v_1 = p_2 v_2$$
$$10^5 \cdot v = 8 \times 10^4 (v + 2)$$

where v represents the unknown volume. Dividing by 2×10^4:

$$5v = 4(v + 2)$$
$$5v = 4v + 8$$
$$v = 8$$

The initial volume is 8 m^3.

6. In an experiment to determine the specific heat capacity of a known mass of liquid at room temperature, a given mass of metal of known specific heat capacity at a much higher temperature is immersed in the liquid. The masses of the metal, the liquid and the container of the liquid are: $m_1 = 0.2 \text{ kg}$; $m_2 = 0.15 \text{ kg}$; and $m_3 = 0.05 \text{ kg}$. The specific heat capacities are: $c_1 = 15 \text{ J/(kg. K)}$; and $c_3 = 13 \text{ J/(kg. K)}$. Room temperature $= t_0 = 290 \text{ K}$. Temperature of metal before being added to liquid $= T = 370 \text{ K}$. Common temperature of metal, liquid and container after immersion $= t = 320 \text{ K}$.
    Then:

$$m_1 c_1 (T - t) = (m_2 c_2 + m_3 c_3)(t - t_0)$$

where c_2 is the unknown specific heat capacity of the liquid. From the data:

$$0.2 \times 15(370 - 320) = (0.15c_2 + 0.05 \times 13)(320 - 290)$$
$$0.2 \times 15 \times 50 = (0.15c_2 + 0.65)30$$
$$5 = (0.15c_2 + 0.65)$$
$$4.35 = 0.15c_2$$
$$c_2 = 4.35/0.15 = 29$$

The specific heat capacity of the liquid is 29 J/(kg. K).

Exercise 8.4

1. I think of a number, multiply it by 3, add 7, and the result is 34. What number did I think of?
2. I think of a number, double it, subtract 15, and the result is 67. What number did I think of?
3. I think of a number, halve it, add 16, and the result is 31. What was the number?
4. In a triangle the first side is twice the length of side a and the third is 10 units greater than side a. If the perimeter is 86 what are the lengths of the sides of the triangle?
5. Three numbers, p, q and r, are such that $p = 3q$ and $r = 2q - 5$. If the sum of the numbers is 355 find all the numbers.
6. A father is three times as old as his son. In ten years' time he will be 22 years older than his son. How old are they now?
7. The length of a rectangle is 10 cm longer than the breadth. The total perimeter is 84 cm. What are the dimensions of the rectangle?
8. In an electrical circuit consisting of three lamps in parallel, the total current is 10 A. If two lamps take the same current and the third takes 2 A less, calculate the current through each lamp.
9. The total resistance in a series circuit containing three resistors is 250 Ω. The first resistor has twice the resistance of the second, and the third resistor is 10 Ω more than the second. Calculate the values of all three resistors.
10. When travelling at a uniform speed, v, the distance travelled, s, in time, t, is given by $s = vt$. The distance travelled by a body is made up of three parts during which the three speeds are in the ratio $2v : 3v : (v + 20)$ and the times are in the ratio $30 : 10 : 40$. If the total distance travelled is 5200 calculate the speed of each part of the journey.

Problems involving simultaneous equations

Examples

1. I think of two numbers such that twice the first added to three times the second is 46; and such that three times the first minus twice the second is 17. What are the two numbers?
Suppose the numbers are x and y. Then:

$$2x + 3y = 46 \qquad \text{(i)}$$
$$\text{and} \quad 3x - 2y = 17 \qquad \text{(ii)}$$
$$2 \times \text{(i) gives} \quad 4x + 6y = 92 \qquad \text{(iii)}$$
$$3 \times \text{(ii) gives} \quad 9x - 6y = 51 \qquad \text{(iv)}$$
$$\text{(iii)} + \text{(iv) gives} \quad 13x = 143$$
$$x = 143 \times \tfrac{1}{13} = 11$$

Substituting for x in (i), we obtain:

$$22 + 3y = 46$$
$$3y = 46 - 22 = 24$$
$$y = 24 \times \tfrac{1}{3} = 8$$

The numbers are 11 and 8.
Check these answers in (ii):

$$\text{LHS} = 3 \times 11 - 2 \times 8 = 33 - 16 = 17$$

2. The velocity of a body starting with an initial velocity, u, and moving with uniform acceleration, a, for t seconds is given by the formula:

$$v = u + at$$

When t is 5, $v = 45$ m/s, and when t is 8, $v = 69$ m/s. Determine the values of u and a.
By the formula, when $t = 5$:

$$45 = u + a \times 5$$

That is

$$u + 5a = 45 \qquad \text{(i)}$$

Again, when $t = 8$:

$$69 = u + a \times 8$$

That is

$$u + 8a = 69 \qquad \text{(ii)}$$

(ii) − (i) gives
$$3a = 24$$
Then
$$a = 24 \times \tfrac{1}{3} = 8$$

Substitute for a in (i):
$$u + 40 = 45$$

Then $u = 5$.
Check in (ii):
$$5 + 8 \times 8 = 5 + 64 = 69$$

The initial speed is 5 m/s and the acceleration is 8 m/s^2.

Exercise 8.5

1. I think of two numbers such that twice the first added to the second is 23 and such that 3 times the first minus the second equals 17. Determine the two numbers.
2. Two brothers have ages differing by 7 years. Twice the age of the first added to the age of the second equals 38 years. What are the ages of the brothers?
3. Two quantities are connected by the formula $y = mx + c$. When $x = 2$, $y = 17$ and when $x = 7$, $y = 42$. Determine the values of m and c.
4. For many machines the relationship between P, the effort, and L, the load, can be taken to be of the form $P = aL + b$. For such a machine, when L is 25, P is 12.1, and when L is 46, P is 29.6. Calculate the values of a and b.
5. Two moulds are used for making models of a frog and a gnome. 28 kg of metal are required to produce 10 gnomes and 16 frogs, while 22 kg of metal are required to produce 8 gnomes and 12 frogs. How much metal is required to make each gnome and each frog?
6. A small patio is to be made with large flagstones and small moulded imitation bricks. The cost of a patio using 20 flagstones and 60 bricks is £49, while the cost using 30 flagstones and 120 bricks is £78. Determine the costs of one flagstone and one brick.
7. A lever, order 1, balanced on a fulcrum, has weights 12 kg and 20 kg at the two ends. When 6 kg is added to the 12 kg and an

extra 12 kg is placed on the side of the 20 kg, 1 m nearer to the fulcrum, the lever is still balanced. Determine the lengths of the two arms of the lever.

8. Two different types of coping stones are to be used in making a short wall: 5 of type A and 4 of type B. The total mass of all the stones is 790 kg. Type B is heavier than type A by 40 kg. Determine the masses of the two types of coping stones.

9

Manipulation of Formulae

To simplify the calculation of lengths, areas, volumes, velocities, time, forces, voltages and so on in certain standard problems we use formulae. For instance, the perimeter, P, of a rectangle is:

$$2x + 2y = 2(x + y) \quad \text{(by the distributive law)}$$

where x and y are length and breadth. If A is the area of the rectangle then:

$$A = x \cdot y$$

The area of a circle is:

$$A = \pi r^2$$

We have already had practice in such problems as finding the value of the required measure when the values of all the other quantities are given. These formulae are expressed in such a form that when we substitute in them the values of the measures given we are able to extract the value of the required measure or quantity. For example, where:

$$y = mx + c$$

by substituting for m, x and c we are able to calculate y. In fact the formula is a machine for extracting y after putting in the values of m, x and c. We say that the formula is arranged with y as the subject.

However, the formula relates four different things to one another, namely y, x, m and c, so it ought to be possible to extract the value of any one of these given the values of the other three. Suppose now we are given y, m and x and we wish to determine c. To facilitate this we rearrange the formula to make c the subject.

Examples

1.
$$y = mx + c$$
$$y + {}^-mx = mx + c + {}^-mx = c + mx + {}^-mx = c$$
Then $\quad y - mx = c \quad$ or $\quad c = y - mx$

Now calculate c when $x = 2.35$, $m = 1.42$ and $y = 6.75$.

$$c = 6.75 - 1.42 \times 2.35 = 3.413 \quad \text{(by calculator)}$$

2. Now make x the subject.
$$y = mx + c$$
$$y + {}^-c = mx + c + {}^-c$$
$$(y - c) = mx$$

$$\frac{1}{m}(y - c) = \frac{1}{m} \times mx$$

$$\frac{(y - c)}{m} = x \quad \text{or} \quad x = \frac{(y - c)}{m}$$

Calculate x when $y = 6.75$, $m = 1.42$ and $c = 3.413$.

$$x = \frac{6.75 - 3.413}{1.42} = 2.35 \quad \text{(by calculator)}$$

Check with the answer above.

3. $V = \frac{1}{3}\pi r^2 h$. Make r the subject.
$$V = \frac{1}{3}\pi h \cdot r^2$$

$$\frac{3}{1} \times \frac{1}{\pi h} \times V = \frac{3}{1} \times \frac{1}{\pi h} \times \frac{1}{3} \pi h \cdot r^2$$

$$\frac{3V}{\pi h} = r^2$$

$$\text{But} \quad r = \sqrt{r^2} = \sqrt{\frac{3V}{\pi h}}$$

Evaluate r when $V = 87.53$ and $h = 3.08$.

$$r = \sqrt{\frac{3 \times 87.53}{\pi \times 3.08}} = 5.209 \quad \text{(by calculator)}$$

Check by substitution for r and h in the original formula to find V:

$$V = \frac{1}{3} \times \pi \times 5.209^2 \times 3.08 = 87.516119 \approx 87.52$$

4. $T = 2\pi\sqrt{\dfrac{L}{g}}$. Make g the subject.

$$\frac{1}{2\pi} \times T = \frac{1}{2\pi} \times 2\pi\sqrt{\frac{L}{g}}$$

$$\frac{T}{2\pi} = \sqrt{\frac{L}{g}} \quad \text{or} \quad \left(\frac{T}{2\pi}\right)^2 = \frac{L}{g}$$

Invert: $\quad \dfrac{g}{L} = \left(\dfrac{2\pi}{T}\right)^2 = \dfrac{4\pi^2}{T^2}$

$$L \times \frac{g}{L} = L \times \frac{4\pi^2}{T^2} \quad \text{or} \quad g = \frac{4\pi^2 L}{T^2}$$

Evaluate g when $L = 1.095$ and $T = 2.1$.

$$g = \frac{4 \times \pi^2 \times 1.095}{2.1^2} = 9.8024642$$

$$\approx 9.80 \text{ (to two decimal places)}$$

5. Calculate A from the formula:

$$A = \frac{35.75x^{1.24}y^{-3.07}}{z^{4.32}}$$

when $x = 6.3$, $y = 4.9$ and $z = 3.4$. Then:

$$A = \frac{35.75(6.3)^{1.24}(4.9)^{-3.07}}{(3.4)^{4.32}}$$

For this calculation the key y^x is needed on the calculator.

To determine $6.3^{1.24}$ key in (1) 6.3 (2) y^x (3) 1.24 (4) =.
Display 9.7990.
To determine $4.9^{-3.07}$ key in (1) 4.9 (2) y^x (3) 3.07 (4) +/−
(5) =. Display 0.0076.
Similarly $3.4^{4.32} = 197.6919$.
Then:

$$A = \frac{35.75 \times 9.7990 \times 0.0076}{197.6919} \approx 0.01347 \text{ (by calculator)}$$

$$\approx 0.013 \text{ (to three decimal places)}$$

Exercise 9.1

Rearrange the following formulae:

1. $y = x + b$. Make x the subject. Evaluate x when $y = 3.8$ and $b = 2.7$.
2. $p = q - r$. Make q the subject. Evaluate q when $p = 27.5$ and $r = 74.1$.
3. $y = ax + b$. Make x the subject. Evaluate x when $y = 2.65$, $a = 1.7$ and $b = 2.4$.
4. $v = u + at$. Make u the subject. Evaluate u when $v = 375$, $a = 9.8$ and $t = 10$.
5. $V = IR$. Make I the subject. Evaluate I when $V = 240.1$ and $R = 168.2$.
6. $T = k \cdot \dfrac{x}{L}$. Make x the subject. Evaluate x when $T = 74.32$, $k = 2.5$ and $L = 17.61$.
7. $F = Ma$. Make a the subject. Evaluate a when $F = 37.8$ and $M = 12.9$.
8. $E = Mgh$. Make h the subject. Evaluate h when $E = 3420.7$, $M = 50.28$ and $g = 9.8$.
9. $E = \frac{1}{2}Mv^2$. Make v the subject. Evaluate v when $E = 3420.7$ and $M = 50.28$.
10. $s = ut + \frac{1}{2}at^2$. Make u the subject. Evaluate u when $s = 584.6$, $a = 9.8$ and $t = 23.5$.
11. $s = ut + \frac{1}{2}at^2$. Make a the subject. Evaluate a when $s = 308.5$, $u = 26.4$ and $t = 20.7$.
12. $A = \pi r^2$. Make r the subject. Evaluate r when $A = 73.09$.
13. $V = \pi r^2 h$. Make h the subject. Evaluate h when $V = 908.7$ and $r = 12.8$.

14. $V = \pi r^2 h$. Make r the subject. Evaluate r when $V = 3294$ and $h = 25.8$.

15. $F = G \cdot (M_1 \cdot M_2)/d^2$. Make M_1 the subject. Evaluate M_1 when $G = 6.7 \times 10^{-11}$, $F = 7.2 \times 10^3$, $d = 3.8 \times 10^6$ and $M_2 = 5.9 \times 10^8$.

16. $F = G \cdot (M_1 \cdot M_2)/d^2$. Make d the subject. Evaluate d when $G = 6.7 \times 10^{-11}$, $M_1 = 9.4 \times 10^9$, $M_2 = 5.9 \times 10^8$ and $F = 7.2 \times 10^3$.___

17. $T = 2\pi\sqrt{L/g}$. Make L the subject. Evaluate L when $g = 9.8$ and $T = 2.78$.

18. $L = L_0(1 + at)$. Make L_0 the subject. Evaluate L_0 when $L = 66.7$, $t = 82.3$ and $a = 3.1 \times 10^{-4}$.

19. $L = L_0(1 + at)$. Make t the subject. Evaluate t when $L = 71.2$, $L_0 = 70.5$ and $a = 2.6 \times 10^{-3}$.

20. $L = L_0(1 + at)$. Make a the subject. Evaluate a when $L = 120.3$, $L_0 = 118.9$ and $t = 95.6$.

21. Evaluate P from $P = aW^n$
    (a) when $a = 3.2 \times 10^{-3}$, $W = 6.7 \times 10^3$ and $n = 1.45$;
    (b) when $a = 7.6 \times 10^{-1}$, $W = 1.05 \times 10^2$ and $n = 3.05$;
    (c) when $a = 5.4 \times 10^{-2}$, $W = 9.25 \times 10^3$ and $n = -1.6$.

22. Evaluate z from $z = Ax^m y^n$
    (a) when $A = 4.6 \times 10^2$, $x = 5.2 \times 10^3$, $m = 2.52$, $y = 7.8 \times 10^{-2}$ and $n = 3.40$;
    (b) when $A = 6.5 \times 10^{-1}$, $x = 4.1 \times 10^{-2}$, $m = -1.61$, $y = 3.9 \times 10^2$ and $n = 2.42$;
    (c) when $A = 3.2 \times 10^{-2}$, $x = 1.7 \times 10^3$, $m = -3.56$, $y = 7.4 \times 10^2$ and $n = -4.36$.

23. Evaluate W from $W = ax^p + by^q$
    (a) when $a = 2.7$, $x = 5.4$, $p = 3.6$, $b = 9.5$, $y = 1.8$ and $q = 4.5$;
    (b) when $a = 5.8$, $x = 2.3$, $p = -1.9$, $b = -3.8$, $y = 4.6$ and $q = -2.5$.

24. Evaluate P from $P = ax^p/(bx^q + cy^r)$
    (a) when $a = b = 1.7 \times 10^2$, $c = -3.6 \times 10$, $x = 5.6 \times 10^2$, $y = 3.7 \times 10^3$, $p = 2.3$, $q = 4.5$ and $r = 1.6$;
    (b) when $a = 9.2 \times 10$, $b = 8.5 \times 10^2$, $c = 3.1 \times 10^2$, $x = 4.3 \times 10^{-2}$, $y = 6.5 \times 10^{-1}$, $p = -2.6$, $q = -1.9$ and $r = -3.4$.

10

One-to-one Relationships

Sooner or later we shall all have to get used to using the Celsius (sometimes called centigrade) scale for measuring temperature instead of the Fahrenheit which has been commonly used in the past. 32°F is equivalent to 0°C and 212°F is equivalent to 100°C. This means that, for a rise in temperature of 212° − 32° = 180°F we have a rise of 100°C. Or, since the rises in temperature on both scales are assumed to be uniform, for every rise of 18°F there will be a rise of 10°C.

Examples

1. The relationship between F and C is:

$$F = \tfrac{9}{5}C + 32 \quad \text{(to determine } F\text{)}$$
$$\text{or} \quad C = \tfrac{5}{9}(F - 32) \quad \text{(to determine } C\text{)}$$

When $F = 86$, $C = 30$; when $C = 40$, $F = 104$. The following table of values is partly completed. Using the above relationships fill in the blank spaces.

F in degrees:

32	50	68	86		140		176	194	212

C in degrees:

0	10	20		40	50		70	80		100

Answers (in sequence): $C = 30, 60, 90$; $F = 104, 122, 158$.

2. A car accelerates from 30 km/h to 80 km/h in 10 seconds uniformly. V increases by 5 km/h every second.

    $$V - 30 = 5t \quad \text{or} \quad V = 5t + 30 \quad \text{and} \quad t = (V - 30)/5$$

    The table, partly completed, is shown below. Fill in the blank spaces.

t:	0	1	2		4		7		9	10
V:	30	35		45		55		70		80

    Answers: $t = 3, 5, 8$; $V = 40, 50, 65, 75$.

3. Interest with a building society is 8.5 per cent of the money deposited. That is, in a year, the interest on £100 is £8.50. Fill in the following table relating deposits to interest.

Deposit (£):							
100	200	300	400	600	800	1000
Interest (£):							
8.5	17		42.5	59.5	76.5	

    The relationship is interest (I) increases by £8.50 for every £100 increase in deposit (D).

    $$\text{To obtain } I: \quad I = \frac{8.5}{100} \times D$$

    $$\text{To obtain } D: \quad D = \frac{100}{8.5} \times I$$

    Answers: $D = 500, 700, 900$; $I = 25.5, 34, 51, 68, 85$.

Exercise 10.1

1. For many goods VAT is 15 per cent of the retail price. Make out a table of related values of retail prices with VAT for prices ranging from £10 to £110 in steps of £10.
2. 1 inch is approximately equivalent to 2.54 cm. Make out a table of related values for measures ranging from 1 inch to 21 inches in steps of 1 inch.
3. 1 lb is approximately equivalent to 454 g or 0.454 kg. Make out a table relating pounds to kilograms for measures ranging from 1 lb to 56 lb in steps of 5 lb.

4. 1 km is approximately 0.621 miles. Make out a table relating speeds in m.p.h. and km/h ranging from 10 km/h to 160 km/h in steps of 10 km/h.

5. At the moment standard income tax on taxable income is 30 per cent, i.e. for every £100 of taxable income earned the income tax on it is £30. Make out a table of related values between tax and taxable income ranging from £1000 to £2000 in steps of £50 of taxable income.

6. At the moment national insurance contributions for employed persons is at the rate of 5.75 per cent for the employee for incomes ranging up to a certain level. Make out a table of contributions in pounds for incomes ranging from £2000 to £3000 in steps of £100.

7. Use the table in Example 1 to estimate the temperatures in Celsius equivalent to 40°F, 60°F, 75°F, 80°F and 90°F. Also use the table to estimate, in degrees Fahrenheit, temperatures equivalent to 5°C, 15°C, 24°C and 32°C.

8. Use the table in Example 2 to estimate the speed when $t = 1$, 3, 5, 6.5 and 9.5 seconds and to estimate the time in seconds, when $V = 37.5$, 42.5, 58 and 73 km/h.

9. Use the table in Example 3 to estimate the interest in pounds when the deposits are £150, £250, £340, £560 and £820. Also estimate the deposits in pounds when the interest is £12, £31.50, £58.25, £74.50 and £83.50.

10.1 Relationships in diagrammatic form

In the previous section we related two sets of values in table form. Now let us look at the problem when we represent the values diagrammatically on two scales, side by side.

Examples

1. In Fig. 10.1 the lines and arrows illustrate certain values on scale *A* related to values on scale *B*. The marked intervals on each scale are two units. The lines and arrows show that 2, 1, 0, −1, −2 and −3 on scale *A* are related respectively to 5, 3, 1, −1, −3 and −5 on scale *B*. The points on scale *A* mentioned

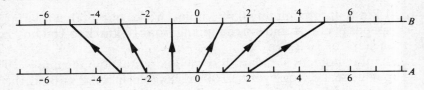

Figure 10.1

are at intervals of 1 unit, while the corresponding points on scale *B* are at intervals of 2 units; i.e., the relationship magnifies the interval on scale *A* by 2.

Filling in further values of the relationship, we obtain the following results. For 3, 5, 8, 9, −4, −6 and −7 on scale *A* we get 7, 11, 17, 19, −7, −11 and −13 on scale *B*, and for the values 9, 7, 5, −7 and −9 on scale *B* we get 4, 3, 2, −4 and −5 on scale *A*. If *x* represents a point on scale *A* and *y* the corresponding point on scale *B*, the relationship is represented by the formula:

$$y = 2x + 1$$

2. Fig. 10.2 represents a different relationship. This time the lines and arrows show that 0, 1, 2, 3 and 4 on scale *C* are related respectively to −5, −2, 1, 4 and 7 on scale *D*.

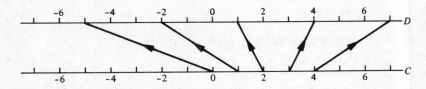

Figure 10.2

The intervals between the points mentioned on scale *C* are all 1 unit, while the corresponding intervals on scale *D* are all 3 units. Check that the values on scale *D* corresponding to −1, −2, −3 and 5 on scale *C* are −8, −11, −14 and 10, and that the values on scale *C* corresponding to 10, −8, −11 and 13 on scale *D* are 5, −1, −2 and 6. If a point on scale *C* is represented by *y* and that corresponding to it on scale *D* is represented by *z*, the relationship would be:

$$z = 3y - 5$$

Note that the magnification of a unit interval on scale C is 3.

3. Fig. 10.3 represents yet another relationship. The lines and arrows show that -2, 0, 2, 4 and 6 on scale E are related to 0, 1, 2, 3 and 4 on scale F. The intervals between the specified

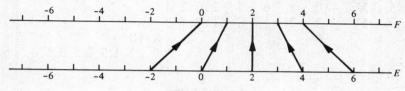

Figure 10.3

points are 2 units on scale E and 1 unit on scale F, so this time the magnification is $\frac{1}{2}$. In other words, the relationship diminishes the intervals. Check that the values on scale F corresponding to 8, 10, -4, -6, -8 and -10 on scale E are 5, 6, -1, -2, -3 and -4, and that the values on scale E corresponding to 7, 8, 9, 10, -4, -5, -6, -7, -8, -9 and -10 on scale F are 12, 14, 16, 18, -10, -12, -14, -16, -18, -20 and -22. If a point on scale E is represented by z and the corresponding one on scale F is represented by w, the relationship between z and w is:

$$w = \tfrac{1}{2}z + 1$$

Exercise 10.2

Represent the following pairs of sets of values on parallel lines as in the examples. Find the relationship between the intervals on the two scales. Fill in the missing values. Discover the formula connecting Y and X.

1. | X | -2 | -1 | 0 | 1 | 2 | 3 | 4 | 5 | 6 | 7 | ? | ? | ? | ? | ? | ? |
    |---|---|---|---|---|---|---|---|---|---|---|---|---|---|---|---|---|
    | Y | -1 | 0 | 1 | 2 | 3 | ? | ? | ? | ? | ? | 0 | -1 | -2 | -3 | -4 | -5 |

2. | X | -4 | -5 | -6 | -7 | -8 | ? | ? | ? | ? | ? | ? | 3 | 4 | 5 | 6 | 7 |
    |---|---|---|---|---|---|---|---|---|---|---|---|---|---|---|---|---|
    | Y | -6 | -7 | -8 | -9 | -10 | -5 | -4 | -3 | -2 | -1 | 0 | ? | ? | ? | ? | ? |

3. | X | 1 | 2 | 3 | 4 | 5 | 0 | −1 | −2 | −3 | −4 | −5 | ? | ? | ? | ? | ? |
|---|---|---|---|---|---|---|----|----|----|----|----|---|---|---|---|---|
| Y | 1 | 3 | 5 | 7 | 9 | ? | ? | ? | ? | ? | ? | 0 | 2 | 4 | 6 | 8 |

4. | X | 0 | 1 | 2 | 3 | −1 | −2 | −3 | −4 | −5 | ? | ? | ? | ? | ? |
|---|---|---|---|---|----|----|----|----|----|---|---|---|----|---|
| Y | 5 | 7 | 9 | 11 | 3 | ? | ? | ? | ? | 6 | 8 | 10 | 4 | 2 |

5. | X | −10 | −8 | −6 | −4 | −2 | 0 | 2 | 4 |
|---|-----|----|----|----|----|---|---|---|
| Y | −3 | −2 | −1 | 0 | 1 | ? | ? | ? |

				6	8	10	?	?	?	?	?
				?	?	?	1.5	2.5	3.5	4.5	6.5

6. | X | 0 | 1 | 2 | 3 | 4 | 5 | 6 | 7 | 8 | 9 | 10 | ? | ? | ? | ? | ? |
|---|---|---|---|---|---|---|---|---|---|---|----|---|---|---|---|---|
| Y | −3 | −2$\frac{1}{2}$ | −2 | −1$\frac{1}{2}$ | −1 | −$\frac{1}{2}$ | ? | ? | ? | ? | ? | 3 | 3$\frac{1}{2}$ | 4 | 4$\frac{1}{2}$ | −3$\frac{1}{2}$ |

7. | X | −1 | −2 | −3 | −4 | −5 | −6 | −7 |
|---|----|----|----|----|----|----|----|
| Y | 2 | 3 | 4 | 5 | 6 | ? | ? |

	−8	−9	?	?	?	?	?
	?	?	−1	−2	−3	−4	−5

8. | X | 2 | 1 | 0 | −1 | −2 | −3 | −4 | −5 | −6 | −7 | ? | ? | ? | ? | ? |
|---|---|---|---|----|----|----|----|----|----|----|---|---|----|----|----|
| Y | 1 | 2 | 3 | 4 | 5 | ? | ? | ? | ? | ? | 0 | −1 | −2 | −3 | −4 |

9. | X | −5 | −4 | −3 | −2 | −1 | 0 | 1 | 2 | 3 | 4 | 5 | ? | ? | ? | ? | ? |
|---|----|----|----|----|----|---|---|---|---|---|---|---|---|---|---|---|
| Y | 11 | 9 | 7 | 5 | 3 | 1 | −1 | ? | ? | ? | ? | ? | 2 | 4 | 6 | 8 | 10 |

10. | X | −4 | −3 | −2 | −1 | 0 | 1 | 2 | 3 | 4 | 5 | 6 | 7 | ? | ? | ? | ? | ? |
|---|----|----|----|----|---|---|---|---|---|---|---|---|---|---|---|---|---|
| Y | −10 | −7 | −4 | −1 | 2 | 5 | ? | ? | ? | ? | ? | ? | ? | 0 | 3 | 6 | −2 | −5 |

Examples

1. Now draw the scales at right angles to each other instead of
    parallel (Fig. 10.4). The *x* scale is horizontal, and the *y* scale
    vertical. Draw a line, *AB*, to bisect the angle between the
    scales, or axes. From each of the points 3, 1, −2 and −4 on the

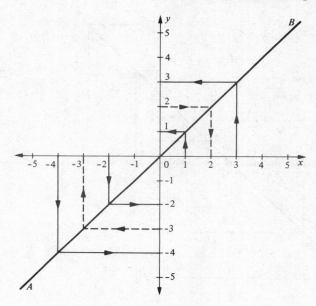

Figure 10.4

x axis draw a line vertically to meet AB. From the point where that line meets AB draw another line horizontally to meet the y axis, thus obtaining on the y axis the points 3, 1, −2 and −4. We can also use the diagram to discover, for example, the points on the x axis corresponding to 2 and −3 on the y axis. These points are 2 and −3. Notice that the value of the point on the y axis is always the same as the corresponding value on the x axis. The formula connecting the two scales is, then, $y = x$. We also say this is the equation of the line AB.

2. Draw a similar diagram to that in Example 1 (Fig. 10.5). Using the diagram the same way as before work out corresponding values of points on the y axis for the following points on the x axis: −5, −7, −3 and −2. Work out the points on the x axis which correspond to the following points on the y axis: 1, 5, 7, −1, −2 and −4. Work out the formula connecting y and x. That is the equation of the line CD.

Answers: $y = -2, -4, 0, 1$; $x = -2, 2, 4, -4, -5, -7$. The equation of the line CD is $y = x + 3$.

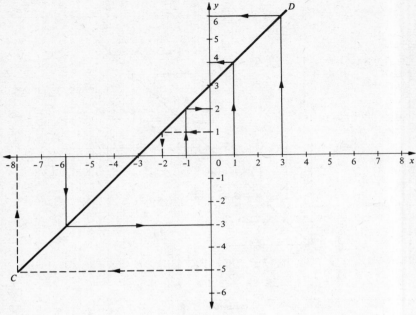

Figure 10.5

3. In the two previous examples we took a line drawn in some fashion to provide a link between two sets of points on the x and the y axes. Suppose now we know the formula connecting the sets of points on the two axes and we use the formula to calculate pairs of corresponding points on the axes and from those pairs of points discover the line which connects them. Suppose the formula is:

$$y = \tfrac{1}{2}x + 10$$

Make out a table of pairs of values of y and x. We shall specify the values along the x axis and work out, from the formula, the y values.

x	−10	−6	−2	2	6	10
y	5	7	9	11	13	15

In Fig. 10.6 the points L, M, N, P, Q and R all lie on a straight line. Its equation is:

$$y = \tfrac{1}{2}x + 10$$

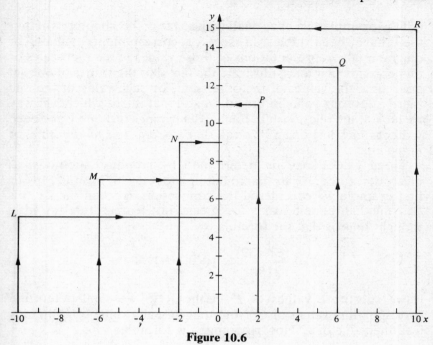

Figure 10.6

In these examples both x and y represent variable quantities. We call x the independent variable, and y the dependent variable.

Exercise 10.3

Use a technique similar to that used in Example 3 to draw the lines whose equations are:

1. $y = x + 1$
2. $y = x - 2$
3. $y = 2x - 1$
4. $y = 2x + 5$
5. $y = \frac{1}{2}x + 2$
6. $y = \frac{1}{2}x - 3$
7. $y = 1 - x$
8. $y = 3 - x$
9. $y = 1 - 2x$
10. $y = 3x + 2$

All the examples we have dealt with so far in this chapter, whether they have been tables of sets of corresponding values, or diagrammatic representations of those values in parallel scales or on perpendicular axes, illustrate the fact that the values of one set determine the values of the other set. For each value of the one there is just one value of the other, and that is true whichever way we look at the relationship. Each x determines just one y and each y determines just one x. We call that a *one-to-one relationship*, or *mapping*.

These values may be determined by graphical methods, as illustrated earlier, or by manipulating the relevant formula. In our first example we considered the connection between the Celsius and the Fahrenheit scales for measuring temperature. A little thought tells us that the formula is:

$$C = \frac{(F - 32)}{180_9} \times 100^5 = \tfrac{5}{9}(F - 32)$$

If we substitute values of F in the RHS we shall determine corresponding values of C. Note that for each value of F there is just one value of C. Now rearrange the formula:

$$\tfrac{9}{5} \times C = \frac{9}{5} \times \frac{5}{9} (F - 32) = \tfrac{9}{5}C = F - 32$$

$$\tfrac{9}{5}C + 32 = F - 32 + 32 = F$$

Substitute values of C and calculate the corresponding values of F. Again, for each value of C there is just one value of F.

The equations in Exercise 10.3 are really formulae for determining y when we are given x. For each value of x there is only one value of y. If we rearrange the equations to make x the subject, they are then formulae for determining x when we are given y. In fact, each question in Exercise 10.3 is the same question, in another form, as the corresponding number in Exercise 10.2.

Exercise 10.4

Rearrange each of the equations in Exercise 10.3. In the rearranged form use it to determine values of x for certain selected values of y taken from the corresponding question in Exercise 10.2.

Some of the simplest examples of one-to-one mappings are between quantities which are directly proportional, e.g. $y = 2x$, $y = 7x$, $y = \frac{1}{2}x$ and so on. All these are covered by $y = kx$, where k is a constant. There are many such physical relationships: Hooke's law, $T = kx$, where x is the extension of an elastic wire and T is the tension required to produce that extension; $F = Ma$ for a given mass, M (i.e. constant), where F is the force acting on the mass and a is the acceleration produced in it; $V = R \cdot I$ (Ohm's law), where R is a constant resistance, V is the voltage applied to it and I is the current flowing through it.

Example

At a fixed rate of interest the interest (I) is proportional to the deposit (D). That is:

$$I = k \times D = \frac{5.5}{100} \times D \quad \text{if the rate is 5.5 per cent}$$

i.e. $\quad I = \dfrac{\overset{11}{\cancel{55}}}{\underset{200}{\cancel{1000}}} \times D = \dfrac{11}{200} \times D$

Substitute the following values of D – 100, 200, 400, 600, 900 – to obtain the corresponding values of I. They are: 5.5, 11, 22, 33 and 49.5. Rearrange the formula:

$$\frac{200}{11} \times I = \frac{\overset{1}{\cancel{200}}}{\underset{1}{\cancel{11}}} \times \frac{\overset{1}{\cancel{11}}}{\underset{1}{\cancel{200}}} \times D$$

$$\text{i.e.} \quad D = \frac{200}{11} \times I$$

Substitute the following values of I – 22, 33, 77, 143, 13.2 – to obtain corresponding values of D. They are: 400, 600, 1400, 2600 and 240.

Exercise 10.5

1. Hooke's law, for a specimen wire, says $T = 2500x$. Calculate T for the following values of x: 2, 3, 5, 1.2, 0.75. Calculate values of x when $T = 25\,000$, 1250, 500, 62.5, 750 000.
2. Ohm's law for a particular conductor says $V = 80I$. Calculate values of V when $I = 2$, 3.5, 4.2, 0.4, 0.025. Calculate values of I when $V = 100$, 250, 320, 45, 27.5.

3. Newton's law for a particular mass says $F = 35 \times a$. Calculate values of F when $a = 1.2, 1.7, 3.8, 8.5$. Calculate values of a when $F = 65, 72, 98, 112, 17.5$.

Right-handed axes

To fix the position of a point in space we usually use three axes all passing through the same point, Ox, Oy and Oz. Each axis is perpendicular to the other two. In a rectangular room we could take the three edges, one vertical, the other two horizontal, which meet at a corner of the floor. Suppose Fig. 10.7 represents such a

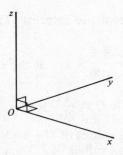

Figure 10.7

system. We call it a right-handed system because a clockwise rotation about the axis Oz would turn Ox into position Oy after a right-angle rotation. Similarly, it would rotate Oz into Ox after a similar rotation about Oy, and Oy into Oz after another similar rotation about Ox.

Place the letters x, y and z on the circumference of a circle as in Fig. 10.8, with arrows 1, 2 and 3. Arrow 1 tells us that Ox rotates

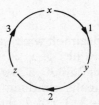

Figure 10.8

into position Oy about the other axis, Oz. Arrow 2 tells us that Oy rotates into position Oz about the other axis, Ox. Arrow 3 tells us that Oz rotates into position Ox about the other axis, Oy. We often call this a cyclic order.

When all our points lie in a plane we take that plane to be the one including Ox and Oy, and we imagine Oz to be emerging out of that plane towards us. So we represent the plane as in Fig. 10.9.

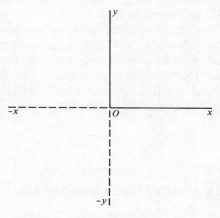

Figure 10.9

This is a right-handed system. Rotating Ox into Oy by a clockwise rotation about Oz means rotating it by an anti-clockwise rotation about O as we look at it. In the plane, then, our axes Ox and Oy are extended in the opposite directions by the dotted lines to deal with negative values along those axes.

If we are representing an equation such as $y = 5x - 2$ graphically on the plane we would measure the y values along the axis marked in the diagram and the x values along Ox. What do we do when we wish to represent, say, $T = 2500x$, as in question 1 in Exercise 10.5? T is the subject of that formula, and normally we measure the subject along the direction of Oy and the other values along Ox. For example, in $V = 80I$ we would measure V along Oy and I along Ox. In $F = 35a$ we would measure a along Ox and F along Oy.

Let us return to the question $T = 2500x$. For the range of values of x from 0 to 10 the range of values for T turns out to be from 0 to 25 000. Obviously we could not use the same scale for both measurements, since if for x we used 1 cm for each unit we would require 25 000 cm to represent each *T* unit, and that is beyond reason. So we would have to choose a much smaller scale for the *T* values. If, for instance, we had 10 cm available on the paper to represent all the values of *T* we would have to choose a scale 2500 units for 1 cm.

In question 2 of the same exercise, if the range of values for *I* went from 0 to 100 we might choose a scale of 10 units for 1 cm. The range for *V* would be from 0 to 8000, and that would require a scale of, say, 800 units per 1 cm.

To some extent the choice of scale is a matter of individual preference, but we should never choose such a small scale that our graph is too small to read values from accurately. The rule here is to choose a scale that makes maximum use of the size of graph paper we are working with, and one that will make calculation of values and distances as easy as possible.

Example

Our first problem, relating Fahrenheit and Celsius temperatures, was:

$$F = \tfrac{9}{5}C + 32$$

Step 1.   Select *C* to be measured along *Ox* and *F* along *Oy*.

Step 2.   Suppose the range of temperature for *C* is from −10 to 110. Then the range for *F* is from 14 to 230, but call it from 0 to 230. That is a total of 120 for *C* and 230 for *F*.

Step 3.   Suppose our graph paper measures 20 cm by 28 cm. We represent *C* along the shorter side. (Even if *C* had had a greater range than *F* we would have represented the subject along the longer side.) We can easily afford to use a scale of 1 cm per 10 degrees *C*. What do we do about the scale for *F*? We have 28 cm to represent 230°F, and we could use, say, 1.2 cm to represent 10°F. We would utilize the paper to the full by that method, but we would give ourselves some awkward calculations of lengths and values when we came to use the graph to extract additional values as well as to fix the position of points on the graph. So instead we opt for a simple scale which makes as much use of the paper as possible. The scale we choose is 1 cm per 10°F.

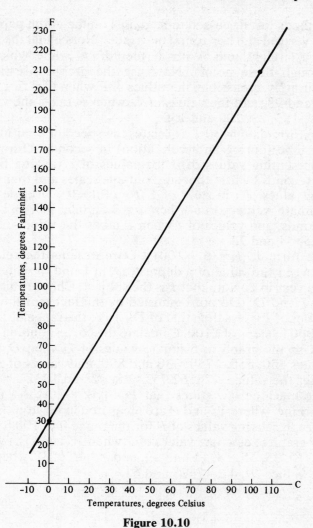

Figure 10.10

Step 4. We mark the scales along the axes carefully and label the axes appropriately. Our graph will then look something like the one shown in Fig. 10.10.

Exercise 10.6

1. Use the formula $F = \frac{9}{5}C + 32$ to calculate the values of F when C takes the values -10, 0, 10, 20, etc., to 110. Use the

methods just discussed to fix points on the graph paper where the vertical and horizontal lines meet. Notice that the points lie on a straight line. With a ruler draw a line which passes through these points. Now use the graph to estimate, as accurately as possible, the values of F when $C = 5, 15, 65, 34,$ 42 and 98, and the values of C when F takes the values 95, 149, 185, 23, 200 and 150.

2. The formula $v = 30 + 5t$ relates the speed of a car in km/h to the time (during an acceleration) in seconds. Draw a graph representing values of v for values of t ranging from 0 to 10 seconds by first choosing suitable scales and then substituting values of t in steps of 1 from 0 to 10. Use the graph to estimate values of v when $t = 2.5, 6.5, 9.5, 3.2$ and 4.7 seconds, and values of t when v takes the values 32.5, 47.5, 62.5, 54 and 73.

3. The formula $I = (5.5/100) \times D$ represents the relationship between the value of a deposit, D, in £ and the interest, I, in one year in £. Note that I is the subject. Choose suitable axes for I and D. (Do not be misled by the fact that the range of values of I is less than that of D.) Take the range of D as £0 to £2000 in steps of £100. Calculate the corresponding values of I. Use the graph to estimate values of I when D takes the values 150, 650, 1750, 330 and 890, and values of D when I takes the values 7.75, 62.75, 43.8, 97 and 103.

4. The machine law states that $P = \frac{3}{10}W + 20$ for a particular machine, where W and P are measured in newtons (N). Draw a graph relating values of P for the range 0 to 100 for W. Use the graph to estimate values of P when W takes the values 10, 30, 70, 35, 55, 68, 71 and 99, and values of W when P takes the values 29, 41, 47, 25 and 61.

10.2 The gradient of a straight line graph

Example

Draw a graph from the following data:

x	0	1	2	3	4	5
y	5	7	9	11	13	15

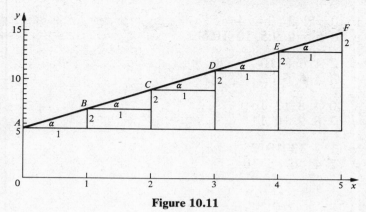

Figure 10.11

In Fig. 10.11 we notice that the graph is a straight line. How can we measure its slope, or gradient? As we progress from A to F through B, C, D and E, for each stage we move a horizontal distance 1 and a vertical distance 2. The ratio:

$$\frac{\text{change in vertical distance}}{\text{change in horizontal distance}}$$

is called the gradient.

We usually refer to it as m. The line AF makes a constant angle α with Ox at every point in its path. In this case the gradient $m = 2$. Notice that:

$$m = 2 = \tan \alpha$$

Exercise 10.7

Calculate the gradients of the following straight line graphs:

1. x 0   1   2   3   4   5
   y 4   7   10   13   16   19

2. x 1   2   3   4   5
   y 2   6   10   14   18

3. x 1   3   5   7   9
   y 2   8   14   20   26

4. x 0   4   7   9   15
   y 5   13   19   23   35

5. | x | 0 | 1 | 2 | 3 | 4 | 5 |
    | --- | --- | --- | --- | --- | --- | --- |
    | y | 8 | 8.5 | 9 | 9.5 | 10 | 10.5 |

6. | x | 2 | 4 | 6 | 8 | 10 |
    | --- | --- | --- | --- | --- | --- |
    | y | 3 | 4 | 5 | 6 | 7 |

7. | x | 0 | 4 | 8 | 12 | 16 |
    | --- | --- | --- | --- | --- | --- |
    | y | 7 | 8 | 9 | 10 | 11 |

8. | x | 1 | 7 | 13 | 19 | 25 |
    | --- | --- | --- | --- | --- | --- |
    | y | 2 | 4 | 6 | 8 | 10 |

Example

Refer back to the previous example:

x	0	1	2	3	4	5
y	5	7	9	11	13	15
$2x$	0	2	4	6	8	10

We have added an extra row of values obtained by multiplying the x row by 2. Now compare row y with row $2x$. What is the relationship between them? Every value in the y row is the corresponding value in the $2x$ row + 5. This means:

$$y = 2x + 5$$

In other words, the equation of the line. We calculated the gradient of the line to be 2. The multiple (or coefficient) of x in the equation is also 2. Is this a coincidence?

Examples

1. Consider $y = 3x + 5$.
    Take:

x	0	1	2	3	4	5

    Using the equation obtain:

y	5	8	11	14	17	20

$$\text{Gradient} = \frac{\text{Change in } y}{\text{Change in } x} = \frac{8-5}{1-0} = \frac{3}{1}$$

$$\text{Also} = \frac{11-8}{2-1} = \frac{14-11}{3-2} = \frac{17-14}{4-3}$$

$$= \frac{20-17}{5-4} = \frac{20-5}{5-0} = 3$$

Draw the graph and show from it that the gradient is 3. The multiple of x in the equation is 3.

2. Now consider $y = mx + c$, where m and c are unspecified values.

x	0	1	2	3	4	5
y	c	$m+c$	$2m+c$	$3m+c$	$4m+c$	$5m+c$

Substitute for x in the equation to find y.
As Fig. 10.12 shows, the gradient is:

$$BL/AL = m/1 = m = \tan \theta$$
$$\text{Also} = CM/AM = 2m/2 = m$$
$$\text{Again} = DN/AN = EP/AP = FQ/AQ = m$$

Gradient $= \tan \theta = m$, which is the coefficient of x in the equation of the line when it is written in the form:

$$y = mx + c \qquad\qquad 10.1$$

When we do not know the equation but we do know that the line passes through two points, which are sufficient to determine the line, we use the co-ordinates of the two points. If the points are $P_1(x_1, y_1)$; $P_2(x_2, y_2)$ then the formula for the gradient is:

$$m = (y_2 - y_1)/(x_2 - x_1) \qquad\qquad 10.2$$

From Fig. 10.12 we see that c represents the intercept on the y axis. Where the equation is written in the form $y = mx + c$ it is an easy matter to write down the values of the gradient and of the intercept. However, more often than not, the equation is not written in that form, and in that event we must adjust the form to the standard one.

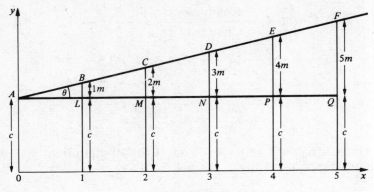

Figure 10.12

Examples

1. $y - 2x = 7$: $y - 2x + 2x = 2x + 7$; $y = 2x + 7$.

2. $3y = x + 6$: $\frac{1}{3} \cdot 3y = \frac{1}{3}x + \frac{1}{3} \cdot 6$; $y = \frac{1}{3}x + 2$.

3. $4y - 5x = 7$: $4y - 5x + 5x = 5x + 7$; $4y = 5x + 7$;
    $$y = \frac{5}{4}x + \frac{7}{4}.$$

Exercise 10.8

Rearrange the following equations into the required form, $y = mx + c$, and then give their gradients and intercepts.

1. $y - 3x = 6$
2. $y - 5x = 8$
3. $y = \frac{2}{3}x - 5$
4. $y - \frac{1}{2}x = 10$
5. $y - \frac{1}{3}x - 5 = 0$
6. $2y = x + 4$
7. $2y = 3x + 6$
8. $2y = 3x - 5$
9. $2y - x = 4$
10. $2y - x - 3 = 0$
11. $2y - 3x = 8$
12. $2y - 3x - 7 = 0$
13. $5y - 6x + 3 = 0$
14. $10y - 13x - 16 = 0$

Negative gradients

Consider the equation: $y + x = -2$
Rearranged this gives: $y = -x - 2$
The tables of values is:

x	-3	-2	-1	0	1	2	3	4
y	1	0	-1	-2	-3	-4	-5	-6

Notice that, as x increases, y decreases. The gradient (by Law 10.2) is:

$$\frac{-6 - 0}{4 - (-2)} = \frac{-6}{4 + 2} = -6/6 = -1$$

Draw the graph. What do you notice about its slope?
    If the gradient is negative this means that y decreases as x increases.

Exercise 10.9

Calculate the gradients of the following straight lines. Draw the graphs of the first three. Determine all the intercepts.

1. $y = -2x + 3$
2. $y = -\frac{1}{2}x + 4$
3. $2y + x = 5$
4. $3y + x = 7$
5. $3y + 2x = 6$
6. $4y + 3x + 8 = 0$
7. $7x - 4y = 3$
8. $3x = 4y - 1$
9. $5 + 2x = -3y$
10. $11 - 2x - 3y = 0$
11. $6x + 4y - 3 = 2y + 7$
12. $2(y + 3x - 6) - 5(2y + 5x - 2) = 11$

Zero gradient

When a graph is a horizontal line, $\theta = 0$. Fig. 10.13 represents such a line.
Then: $\tan \theta = 0$; i.e. $m = 0$
Its equation becomes: $y = c$
That is, y retains the same value for all values of x.

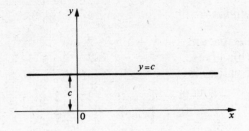

Figure 10.13

10.3 The equation of a line with gradient (m) passing through (x_1, y_1)

From Fig. 10.14 suppose $P(x, y)$ represents a variable point on the line which passes through the fixed point $P_1(x_1, y_1)$. Draw P_1L and

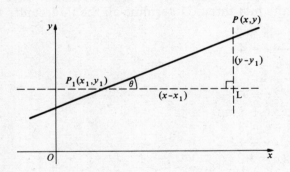

Figure 10.14

LP parallel to Ox and Oy to meet at L. Then:

$$PL = (y - y_1); \quad P_1L = (x - x_1)$$

and $m = \tan\theta = PL/P_1L = \dfrac{y - y_1}{x - x_1}$

giving $y - y_1 = m(x - x_1)$ *10.3*

10.4 The equation of a line joining two points $P_1(x_1, y_1)$ and $P_2(x_2, y_2)$

In Fig. 10.15 suppose $P(x, y)$ represents a variable point on the line which passes through the fixed points $P_1(x_1, y_1)$ and $P_2(x_2, y_2)$.

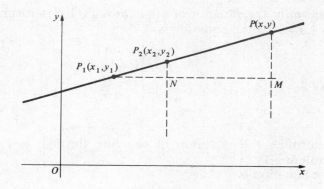

Figure 10.15

Draw MP and NP_2 parallel to Oy to meet P_1NM (parallel to Ox) in M and N respectively. Then triangles P_1P_2N and P_1PM are similar because they are equiangular (see Chapter 13). Therefore:

$$PM/P_1M = P_2N/P_1N$$

i.e.

$$\frac{y - y_1}{x - x_1} = \frac{y_2 - y_1}{x_2 - x_1} \qquad 10.4$$

By rearranging Law 10.4 we obtain:

$$\frac{y - y_1}{y_2 - y_1} = \frac{x - x_1}{x_2 - x_1} \qquad 10.5$$

Law 10.5 is the more usual form in which we remember and use the equation. Another alternative is:

$$y - y_1 = \frac{y_2 - y_1}{x_2 - x_1}(x - x_1) \qquad 10.6$$

By using Law 10.2 we see that Law 10.6 is really:

$$y - y_1 = m(x - x_1)$$

And that is the same as Law 10.3.

Examples

1. Determine the equation of a line through $(1, 5)$ with gradient $\frac{1}{4}$.
    By Law 10.3 the equation is:

    $$y - 5 = \tfrac{1}{4}(x - 1)$$

    i.e. $y - 5 = \tfrac{1}{4}x - \tfrac{1}{4}$

    giving: $y = \tfrac{1}{4}x + 4\tfrac{3}{4}$

    or: $4y = x + 19$

2. Determine the equation of the line through $(-4, 3)$ with gradient $-1\tfrac{1}{2}$.
    The equation is:

    $$y - 3 = -\tfrac{3}{2}(x + 4)$$
    $$y - 3 = -\tfrac{3}{2}x - 6$$
    $$y = -\tfrac{3}{2}x - 3$$
    $$\text{or} \quad 2y + 3x + 6 = 0$$

3. Prove that the line $3y + 4x + 7 = 0$ passes through $(-7, 7)$.
    At $(-7, 7)$ $x = -7$. Substitute that value for x in the equation above to obtain:

    $$3y - 28 + 7 = 0$$
    $$3y - 21 = 0$$
    $$3y = 21$$
    $$y = 7$$

    In other words, when $x = -7$ then $y = 7$: the line passes through the point $(-7, 7)$. Alternatively, we say that the line will pass through $(-7, 7)$ when the equation is satisfied by these values of x and y. With that approach we substitute $(-7, 7)$ in the LHS of the equation. We obtain $21 - 28 + 7$ which is 0, and that is the value of the RHS. If the value of the LHS had not been equal to that of the RHS then the line would not pass through $(-7, 7)$.

4. Determine the equation of the line through $(2, 3)$ and $(5, 8)$.

    By Law 10.5 the line is:

    $$\frac{y - 3}{8 - 3} = \frac{x - 2}{5 - 2}$$

    i.e.
    $$\frac{(y - 3)}{5} = \frac{(x - 2)}{3}$$

    Cross-multiply:
    $$3(y - 3) = 5(x - 2)$$
    $$3y - 9 = 5x - 10$$
    $$3y = 5x - 1$$

    or:
    $$y = \tfrac{5}{3}x - \tfrac{1}{3}$$

    The gradient is $5/3$ and the intercept is $-\tfrac{1}{3}$.

Exercise 10.10

Determine the equations of the lines subject to the following conditions. Calculate the gradients and intercepts in each case.

1. Through $(1, 2)$; gradient 2.
2. Through $(4, 5)$; gradient $\tfrac{1}{4}$.
3. Through $(3, 0)$; gradient 5.
4. Through $(2\tfrac{1}{2}, 3\tfrac{1}{3})$; gradient $1\tfrac{1}{2}$.
5. Through $(2, -1)$; gradient $1\tfrac{1}{4}$.
6. Through $(-4, -1\tfrac{1}{3})$; gradient $4\tfrac{1}{4}$.
7. Through $(3, 2)$; gradient -2.
8. Through $(2\tfrac{1}{3}, 3\tfrac{1}{2})$; gradient $-\tfrac{1}{2}$.
9. Through $(-2, 1)$; gradient -3.
10. Through $(-2, -3\tfrac{1}{2})$; gradient $-2\tfrac{1}{4}$.
11. Through $(1, 2)$ and $(2, 3)$.
12. Through $(2, 5)$ and $(6, 9)$.
13. Through $(1\tfrac{1}{2}, \tfrac{1}{2})$ and $(2\tfrac{1}{2}, 1\tfrac{1}{2})$.
14. Through $(5\tfrac{1}{4}, 3\tfrac{1}{3})$ and $(2, 7)$.
15. Through $(0, 3)$ and $(5, 0)$.
16. Through $(0, 2)$ and $(-2, 7)$.
17. Through $(-2, -3)$ and $(5, 8)$.
18. Through $(-4, -5)$ and $(12, 17)$.
19. Through $(-4, -5)$ and $(-2, -7)$.
20. Through $(6, 2)$ and $(-5, -8)$.
21. Show that the line through $(1, 2)$ with gradient 7 passes through $(0, -5)$.

22. Show that the line $3x + 5y = 4$ passes through $(-2, 2)$.
23. Show that the line through the points $(2, 0)$ and $(0, 3)$ passes through $(-1, 4\frac{1}{2})$.
24. Show that the line through $(-1\frac{1}{2}, 2\frac{1}{4})$ and $(0, 5\frac{1}{2})$ passes through $(-1, 3\frac{1}{3})$.
25. If a line through $(-4, 2)$ also passes through $(-2, 4)$ what is its gradient?
26. A line parallel to the x axis passes through $(-3\frac{1}{4}, 4\frac{1}{3})$. What will the y co-ordinate of a point on the line be when its x co-ordinate is $-14\frac{1}{11}$?

10.5 Non-linear relationships

It is possible to have a one-to-one relationship even when a graph is non-linear.

Examples

1. Draw the graph from the following data, choosing suitable scales for x and y. From the graph determine y when $x = 3, 5, 7$ and 9.

x	2	4	6	8	10
y	0.30	0.60	0.78	0.90	1.00

From the graph (Fig. 10.16) the related values of y are 0.48, 0.70, 0.84 and 0.95.

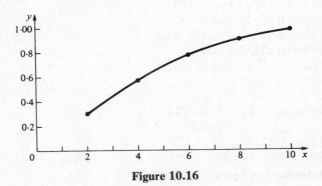

Figure 10.16

2. Draw the graph from the following data. From the graph determine the values of y when x takes the values 2, 4, 6 and 8.

x	1	3	5	7	9
y	0.17	0.5	0.77	0.94	1.00

The related values of y (from Fig. 10.17) are 0.34, 0.64, 0.87 and 0.98.

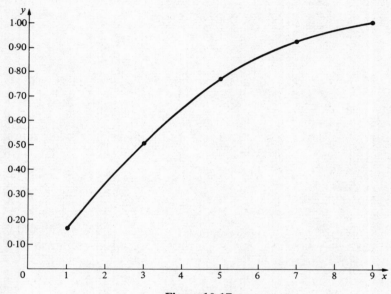

Figure 10.17

Exercise 10.11

Draw graphs from the following data, choosing suitable scales and plotting y against x. Determine from the graphs the values of y for the given values of x.

1.
x	45	46	47	48	49	50
y	1	1.04	1.07	1.11	1.15	1.19

Determine y when x = 45.5, 46.5, 47.5 and 48.5.

2.
x	6.0	6.2	6.4	6.6	6.8	7.0
y	1.73	1.88	2.05	2.24	2.48	2.75

Determine y when x = 6.1, 6.3, 6.5, 6.7 and 6.9.

3.

x	0	2	4	6	8
y	1	0.94	0.77	0.5	0.17

Determine y when $x = 1, 3, 5$ and 7.

4.

x	3	5	7	9	11
y	1.10	1.61	1.94	2.20	2.40

Determine y when $x = 4, 6.5, 8$ and 10.5.

11

Simple Statistics

One function of statistics is the collection of data (facts, usually in a numerical sense), the recording of those data and the attempts to discover what conclusions can be made about those data.

Data may be obtained from textbooks, from official statistics of one sort or another, or from facts which we have collected ourselves. Let us proceed to collect data for ourselves in the following ways:

1. By tossing a coin a large number of times, letting it fall in the same way each time (as far as this is possible) and recording the number of times it comes down heads and the number of times it comes down tails.
2. By throwing a die with six faces, again the same way each time, and recording the number of times each number appears uppermost.
3. By throwing two dice together and repeating what we did in (2).
4. By recording the dates of birth of as many people as possible in the school or college and tabulating them according to the month of birth.
5. By recording the dates of birthdays in the present year and tabulating them according to the day of the week on which they fall, irrespective of the month.
6. By asking members of a group or section to measure a given distance, length or angle, and recording their measurements.
7. By asking members of the section or group to measure a given mass.

8. By drawing a random irregular area on a sheet of graph paper, estimating the area by counting whole squares and estimating fractions of them, and recording the results obtained within the group or section.

9. By counting the number of people in your school or college who are left-handed and the number who are right-handed.

10. By finding out the amount of money each person in a large group has at a given time, to the nearest £1 or 50p.

11. By finding out the number of bricks which the members of a given group can lay in a particular test hour.

Having collected the data we must next tabulate them in a suitable form. Suppose that in our investigations for (5) we discovered that of 500 people questioned 69 have birthdays on a Sunday, 72 have birthdays on a Monday, 68 on a Tuesday, 66 on a Wednesday, 74 on a Thursday, 73 on a Friday and 78 on a Saturday. We would tabulate our information as shown in Table 11.1.

Table 11.1 *Days on which birthdays fall*

Sun.	Mon.	Tues.	Wed.	Thurs.	Fri.	Sat.
69	72	68	66	74	73	78

The toss of a coin would have only two intervals: head and tail. The throw of a die would have six intervals, for the six different numbers which could be thrown. The throw of two dice would require 11 intervals.

The number of intervals required for (10) would depend upon the answers obtained. If the amounts varied between zero and £2 we might decide to divide the range into equal intervals of 20p. But if the money varied between 12p and £23·17 we would have to choose much larger intervals.

In such problems as (6) the measurements might vary between, say, 16.30 m and 17.50 m, and, in that event, it might be advisable to select intervals of 0.20 m. We try to select an interval which does not conceal wide variation in the data, yet which does not spread the data out too sparsely among the intervals. For instance, if we had 50 measurements we would not divide them into as many as 20 intervals.

Exercise 11.1

In each of the questions (1) to (11) group your data into an appropriate number of equal intervals.

Suppose the measurement of a certain angle by a group of 30 students came out as follows (measurements in degrees to the nearest tenth of a degree):

38.0, 38.1, 38.7, 38.6, 38.5, 38.9, 38.2, 38.4, 38.5, 38.3,
38.6, 38.8, 38.4, 38.5, 38.2, 38.7, 38.6, 38.5, 38.9, 38.4,
38.3, 38.5, 38.7, 38.1, 38.9, 38.7, 38.2, 38.5, 38.7, 38.3

The measurement of the angle is called the variate.

The data are grouped into the equal intervals given in the left-hand column in Table 11.2, which represents a *tally chart*. Run carefully through the list of values obtained by the class and place a bar (*tally mark*) in the appropriate column for each value. The bars are usually grouped in fours and crossed through to denote a group of five.

Table 11.2 *A tally chart*

Interval From	To	Central point and value credited to group	Number with this measurement	Frequency
37.95	38.15	38.05	‖‖	3
38.15	38.35	38.25	‖‖‖ ‖	6
38.35	38.55	38.45	‖‖‖ ‖‖‖	9
38.55	38.75	38.65	‖‖‖ ‖‖	8
38.75	38.95	38.85	‖‖‖	4

The results are: interval 1, 3; interval 2, 6; interval 3, 9; interval 4, 8; interval 5, 4. The final column gives the total tally for each interval. The total frequency is

$$3 + 6 + 9 + 8 + 4 = 30$$

The relative frequency for an interval is the frequency for that interval divided by the total frequency. The relative frequencies, therefore, are 3/30, 6/30, 9/30, 8/30 and 4/30, or, cancelling down, 1/10, 1/5, 3/10, 4/15 and 2/15.

The relative frequency percentages are found by converting the relative frequencies to percentages. Thus the relative frequency percentages here are: 10 per cent, 20 per cent, 30 per cent, 26.7 per cent and 13.3 per cent.

11.1 Representation of data

Diagrammatic or pictorial representation of data is done in a variety of ways.

100 per cent bar chart

Figure 11.1 represents the data above in the form of a 100 per cent bar chart. Take the total length of the chart to be 100 mm. The individual sections are:

1. 10 per cent × 100 mm = 10 mm
2. 20 per cent × 100 mm = 20 mm
3. 30 per cent × 100 mm = 30 mm
4. 26.7 per cent × 100 mm = 26.7 mm
5. 13.3 per cent × 100 mm = 13.3 mm

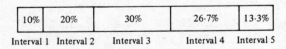

10%	20%	30%	26·7%	13·3%
Interval 1	Interval 2	Interval 3	Interval 4	Interval 5

Figure 11.1

Pie chart

In a pie chart the areas of the sectors are proportional to the percentages, as Fig. 11.2 shows.

The areas of the sectors are proportional to the angles subtended at the centre. The individual angles are:

1. 10 per cent × 360° = 36°
2. 20 per cent × 360° = 72°
3. 30 per cent × 360° = 108°

4. 26.7 per cent × 360° = 96.12°
5. 13.3 per cent × 360° = 47.88°

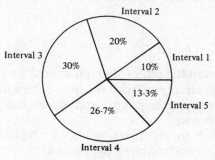

Figure 11.2

Pictogram

Sometimes data lend themselves to pictorial representation, called
a pictogram. Here we use some easily recognizable symbol to
represent a unit. In Fig. 11.3, each complete car represents 20 000

Figure 11.3

cars. Table 11.3 gives fictional car sales for five different makes of
car.

Table 11.3   *Car sales*

Make of car	A	B	C	D	E
Car sales over given period	60 000	80 000	115 000	93 000	47 000

Although this method is interesting and has visual appeal it does not give an accurate diagrammatic representation of the relative frequencies because it is impossible to represent, say, 0.72 of a car.

Exercise 11.2

Tabulate and group the data collected in numbers (1) to (11) at the beginning of this chapter. From those grouped data calculate the relative frequency percentages and draw bar charts and pie diagrams in each case.

If we refer back to the question about which days of the week people's birthdays occur during the present year, of 500 people we would say that 69 represented the frequency with which the event (birthday) occurred on Sundays, 72 the frequency with which the event occurred on Mondays, and so on. The frequency of an event in a particular group, or of a measurement being in a particular interval, is the number of times it happens out of the total number of events examined. So we might retabulate that information as shown in Table 11.4.

Table 11.4   *Frequency of day of birthday this year*

Interval	Frequency	Relative Frequency Percentage
Sunday	69	$\frac{69}{500} \times 100 = \frac{69}{5} = 13.8$
Monday	72	$\frac{72}{500} \times 100 = \frac{72}{5} = 14.4$
Tuesday	68	$\frac{68}{500} \times 100 = \frac{68}{5} = 13.6$
Wednesday	66	$\frac{66}{500} \times 100 = \frac{66}{5} = 13.2$
Thursday	74	$\frac{74}{500} \times 100 = \frac{74}{5} = 14.8$
Friday	73	$\frac{73}{500} \times 100 = \frac{73}{5} = 14.6$
Saturday	78	$\frac{78}{500} \times 100 = \frac{78}{5} = 15.6$

The relative frequency of an event is:

$$\frac{\text{frequency of the event}}{\text{total number of events}}$$

The relative frequency percentage is:

$$\text{relative frequency} \times 100$$

We might represent the above information by means of a horizontal bar chart as shown in Fig. 11.4.

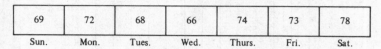

69	72	68	66	74	73	78
Sun.	Mon.	Tues.	Wed.	Thurs.	Fri.	Sat.

Figure 11.4

The difficulty with this arrangement is that it requires the insertion of the actual frequencies in number form to make the result intelligible, and that means that the diagram is really unnecessary. The actual frequencies are so close together that the eye cannot easily distinguish between their magnitudes.

We could arrange frequencies in either of two forms (Figs 11.5 and 11.6) to make comparison much easier.

Fig. 11.5 is called a *horizontal bar chart*, and Fig. 11.6 is a *vertical bar chart*. They have a better visual effect because it is possible to

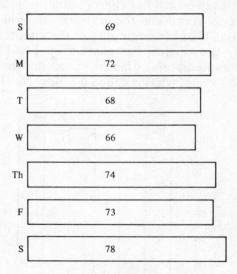

Figure 11.5

use a bigger scale to represent the different lengths, and also, by having the frequencies side by side, it is easier to compare their relative lengths, which are proportional to the frequencies.

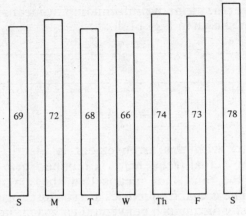

Figure 11.6

Exercise 11.3

Use horizontal and vertical bar charts (either one or the other for each question) to represent the data which you collected for questions (1) to (11) at the beginning of the chapter.

If we modify the vertical bar chart (Fig. 11.6) and place the vertical blocks immediately adjacent to one another, without any spaces between, we get what is called a *histogram* (Fig. 11.7). It is

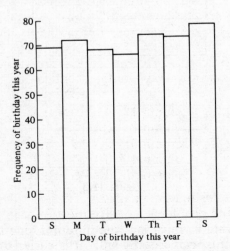

Figure 11.7

now even easier to compare the frequencies, since, where the class intervals are equal, the heights of the columns of the histogram are proportional to the associated frequencies.

Strictly speaking, however, in a histogram the frequencies are represented by the *areas of the rectangular columns*. This is a very important fact, which will be required in later work on statistics. Where the class intervals are unequal we must take that fact into account.

Example

Suppose the examination marks of 100 students are classified as shown in Table 11.5. (Here the variate is the mark obtained.)

Table 11.5   *Examination marks of 100 students*

		Marks		
	1–30 inclusive	31–45 inclusive	46–54 inclusive	55–69 inclusive	70–99 inclusive
Credited mark of group	15	38	50	62	85
No. of students	11	24	34	19	12

If we assume that it is possible to give a mark of any value, e.g. a decimal, and not just an integer, then the ranges for the above intervals are: 0.5 to 30.5 (range of 30); 30.5 to 45.5 (range of 15); 45.5 to 54.5 (range of 9); 54.5 to 69.5 (range of 15); 69.5 to 99.5 (range of 30). Since 11, 24, 34, 19 and 12 represent the areas of the columns of the histogram we obtain the heights of the columns as follows:

$$\text{Column 1:} \quad 11/30 = 0.37$$
$$\text{Column 2:} \quad 24/15 = 1.60$$
$$\text{Column 3:} \quad 34/9 = 3.78$$
$$\text{Column 4:} \quad 19/15 = 1.27$$
$$\text{Column 5:} \quad 12/30 = 0.40$$

Fig. 11.8 is the histogram we obtain.

In most of the problems we have met so far in this chapter the variate takes values which increase in jumps, or stages, of measurable amounts, e.g. by increases of 0.1, 10 or 1.0. However, if we are considering, for example, the weights of a very large population it seems reasonable to suppose that the weights will vary gradually from the lowest to the highest in the smallest possible steps: so small that they cannot readily be measured. In such a problem we say the variate is *continuous*.

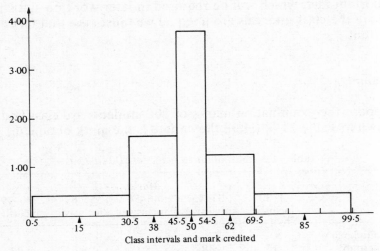

Figure 11.8

Where the steps or stages are measurable the variate is said to be *discrete*. In problem (1) at the beginning of the chapter the variate is discrete, since it can only be head or tail. In problem (2) it is also discrete, since there are just six different values it can take, i.e. 1, 2, 3, 4, 5 or 6. It is also discrete in problems (3), (4) and (5). If, in problems (6) and (7), the group is large enough, ideally many thousands, the measurement may be assumed to be continuous.

Exercise 11.4

1. Represent the data collected for problems (1) to (11) in histogram form. Label your diagrams carefully to show what they are supposed to portray. For instance, in Fig. 11.7, although there is variation of frequency from one day to another, they are all at a fairly uniform level. Is that to be expected? In other examples, for instance, the angle measurements in Table 11.2, the frequencies were certainly

not uniform throughout. Is that what we would expect? In each case try to interpret the information which your histogram seems to be pointing out.

2. The sizes of shoes (measured in half sizes) worn by a group of 130 students were grouped as follows:

Size of shoe:	6	$6\frac{1}{2}$	7	$7\frac{1}{2}$	8	$8\frac{1}{2}$	9	$9\frac{1}{2}$	10	$10\frac{1}{2}$	11
Frequency:	2	6	11	13	19	22	19	16	12	7	3

    Represent this information in histogram form. Try to explain why there is a wide variation in frequency of sizes. Calculate the relative frequency of each group. (Here the variate is discrete, since sizes increase in steps of $\frac{1}{2}$.)

3. The heights of 300 people were measured to the nearest centimetre and recorded. The heights and frequencies were as follows:

Height:	182	183	184	185	186	187	188	189	190
Frequency:	6	3	42	90	72	36	30	12	9

    Represent this information in histogram form. Calculate the group relative frequencies.

4. The numbers of words in 50 successive pages of a book were counted. The numbers were then corrected to the nearest five. The condensed information is as follows:

No. of words to nearest five:	385	390	395	400	405	410	415
Frequency:	2	6	14	12	8	5	3

    Draw a histogram conveying this information. Calculate the relative frequency of pages carrying 395 or 400 words.

12

Further Statistics

In Chapter 11 we discussed the collection and presentation of data about some event or issue. One graphical method which we developed was the histogram. Along the horizontal axis of the histogram we measure the number of different outcomes for that event, and along the vertical axis we measure the frequency of each outcome. In Fig. 12.1 (a), (b) and (c) represent three sets of data. In (a) and (b) 50 represents the measure about which the data are grouped more or less evenly, whereas in (c) 52 represents that measure. However, although (a) and (b) have this measure in common they differ in the amount of spread of the data about 50.

Once we have put forward the histogram as a representation of information, immediately we are presented with the problem of measuring any histogram, and distinguishing it from another. In other words, we have invented a new kind of quantity and now we want to know how to measure it, just as we needed to know how to measure squares, rectangles, triangles and so on.

In the first place we choose to calculate the value about which the data are evenly grouped. We call that the *average* or the *mean*. In the second place we need to calculate the spread of the data around the mean. We call this the *dispersion*.

The explanation above is very loosely worded, but it should give us an idea of our aim. Later we shall need to be much more precise. We will begin by restating the definitions of Chapter 11.

The *frequency* of a particular outcome of an event is the number of times it takes place in the total number of different outcomes of the event. For example, in a normal pack of 52 playing cards

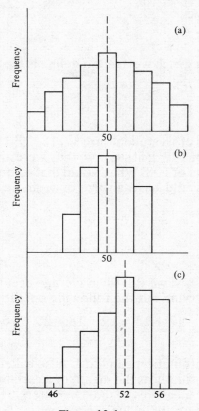

Figure 12.1

suppose that, out of 200 selections of a card from the pack, on 48 occasions a club was drawn. Then the frequency with which a club is drawn is 48.

The *relative frequency* of a particular outcome is the number of times it takes place (as above) divided by the total number of different outcomes. For example, the relative frequency of choosing a club is then, in this case, $\frac{48}{200}$.

The *relative frequency percentage* is the relative frequency converted to a percentage. For example, the relative frequency percentage of choosing a club is:

$$\frac{48^{\,24}}{200_{2}{}_{1}} \times 100^{1} = 24 \text{ per cent}$$

246 — *Mathematics level 1*

12.1   The mean

Another concept which we need to define is the *mean*, or *average*.

Example

Suppose the ages of six students are 17, 18, 19, 18, 20 and 16. They have a total age of 108. But suppose they were all the same age and still had a total age of 108. What would that common age be? Call it y. Six of them would have an age of y, and a total age of 108. Therefore:

$$6y = 108$$

$$y = \frac{108}{6} = 18$$

This common age, y, we call their average age, or their mean age. We find it by carrying out the following operation:

$$\text{Mean age} = \frac{17 + 18 + 19 + 18 + 20 + 16}{6} = \frac{108}{6} = 18$$

We define the arithmetic mean (AM) (also called the average, and often referred to simply as the mean) of a certain characteristic (x) as the sum of the measures of that characteristic or events divided by the number of individuals or events. This sounds rather complicated, so let us use symbols to try to make it simpler. Suppose there are n different outcomes of an event, and suppose that $x_1, x_2, x_3, \ldots, x_n$ represent the measures of the n different outcomes. Further, suppose $\bar{x}$ denotes the mean. Then:

$$\bar{x} = \frac{x_1 + x_2 + x_3 + \cdots + x_n}{n} = \frac{\sum\limits_{r=1}^{n} x_r}{n}$$

Exercise 12.1

Calculate the means of the following:

1. Eight students measured the height of a building, in metres, as 12.05, 12.10, 11.95, 11.90, 11.95, 12.00, 12.05 and 12.00.

2. One worker was timed on ten different occasions in the execution of one particular operation. The times, in minutes, were 16.5, 16.7, 17.1, 16.7, 16.8, 16.7, 16.4, 16.6, 16.9 and 16.6.

3. The ages of twelve students, in years and months, are 17.7, 18.10, 17.11, 18.3, 17.11, 18.4, 18.5, 18.1, 17.9, 18.4, 17.10 and 17.10.

4. The life, in hours, of ten 100-watt electric light bulbs proved to be 985, 1005, 1025, 990, 1030, 965, 995, 1015, 1000 and 995.

With some sets of data the number of different measures is strictly limited, and certain of these measures occur more than once. For example, in throwing a die the possible scores (outcomes) are 1, 2, 3, 4, 5 and 6.

Example

Suppose that out of 60 different throws of a die score 1 occurred 6 times, score 2 occurred 5 times, score 3 occurred 12 times, score 4 occurred 10 times, score 5 occurred 14 times and score 6 occurred 13 times. What is the total score?

$$
\begin{aligned}
\text{The totals of score } 1 &= 1 \times 6 &&= & 6 \\
\text{The totals of score } 2 &= 2 \times 5 &&= & 10 \\
\text{The totals of score } 3 &= 3 \times 12 &&= & 36 \\
\text{The totals of score } 4 &= 4 \times 10 &&= & 40 \\
\text{The totals of score } 5 &= 5 \times 14 &&= & 70 \\
\text{The totals of score } 6 &= 6 \times 13 &&= & \underline{78} \\
\text{Gross score} & && = & \overline{240}
\end{aligned}
$$

$$\text{Mean score} = \frac{240}{60} = 4$$

In the above analysis we would say that:

The outcome (score 1) occurred 6 times, or had a frequency of 6.
The outcome (score 2) occurred 5 times, or had a frequency of 5.
The outcome (score 3) occurred 12 times, or had a frequency of 12.
The outcome (score 4) occurred 10 times, or had a frequency of 10.
The outcome (score 5) occurred 14 times, or had a frequency of 14.
The outcome (score 6) occurred 13 times, or had a frequency of 13.
The mean was

$$\frac{1 \times 6 + 2 \times 5 + 3 \times 12 + 4 \times 10 + 5 \times 14 + 6 \times 13}{60}$$

In other words, we multiplied each outcome (measured by its score in this case) by the frequency with which it occurred, added all those results together and then divided by the total number of throws (60). So the formula will appear as follows:

The outcome, measured by x_1, occurs with frequency $f(x_1)$.
The outcome, measured by x_2, occurs with frequency $f(x_2)$.
The outcome, measured by x_3, occurs with frequency $f(x_3)$.
The outcome, measured by x_r, occurs with frequency $f(x_r)$.
The outcome, measured by x_n, occurs with frequency $f(x_n)$.

Suppose that the total of the frequencies, i.e. $f(x_1) + f(x_2) + f(x_3) + \cdots + f(x_r) + \cdots + f(x_n) = N$, the total number of outcomes. Then:

$$\bar{x} = \frac{x_1 \times f(x_1) + x_2 \times f(x_2) + \cdots + x_n \times f(x_n)}{f(x_1) + f(x_2) + \cdots + f(x_n)}$$

$$= \frac{\sum_{1}^{n} x_r \cdot f(x_r)}{\sum_{1}^{n} f(x_r)} = \frac{\sum_{1}^{n} x_r \cdot f(x_r)}{N}$$

In all four questions in Exercise 12.1 we could have saved ourselves much calculation if we had modified our procedure. In question (1) all eight measurements were 11+ or 12+. We might have argued that they were all either just less than 12 or just greater than 12, so the mean would be either 12+ or 12−. All we need to know is by how much it differs from 12 and whether it is above or below it. We take 12, then, to be what we call a *working zero*, and we represent each of the eight measurements by its difference from 12.

Example

Real measurement:

12.05, 12.10, 11.95, 11.90, 11.95, 12.00, 12.05, 12.00

Measure from 12:

+0.05, +0.10, −0.05, −0.10, −0.05, 0.00, +0.05, 0.00

To find the mean with reference to the working zero we add all the values in the second row together. That gives:

$$+0.20 - 0.20 = 0.00 = \text{total new measure}$$

$$\frac{\text{total new measure}}{8} = \frac{0.00}{8} = 0.00$$

Therefore the mean $= 12.00 + 0.00 = 12.00$

In question (2) we would take 16.00 as our working zero, in question (3) we would take 18.00 as our working zero, and in question (4) we would take 1000 as our working zero.

Exercise 12.2

Repeat the questions in Exercise 12.1, taking the working zeros as indicated above.

Exercise 12.3

1. The number of delphinium seeds in 50 packets of the same size, from one firm, were found to be as follows:

Number of seeds:	87	88	89	90	91	92	93
Number of packets:	10	6	20	6	5	2	1

    Calculate the mean number of seeds per packet.

2. Battery produced eggs from a poultry farm arrive at a depot in batches of 1000. In the sorting of 100 sample batches the number of defective eggs per batch was found to be as follows:

No. of defective eggs:	10	11	12	13	14	15	16	17	18
No. of batches:	2	5	6	21	35	20	8	2	1

    Calculate the mean number of defective eggs per batch.

3. The following table represents information obtained when testing a sample of 100 of a new type of building block:

Compressive strength
(kg/cm²):   200–210   210–220   220–230
Number of blocks: 2   6   25

Compressive strength (kg/cm²):	200–210	210–220	220–230
Number of blocks:	2	6	25

Compressive strength (kg/cm²):	230–240	240–250	250–260
Number of blocks:	39	21	7

Attribute to blocks with compressive strength 200–210 a standard compressive strength of 205 (i.e., the mid-interval). Similarly, attribute to the 220–230 interval a value of 225, and so on. Then calculate the mean compressive strength of the blocks.

4.   In a random sample of 48 pages of a novel the number of words per page was counted. The results were:

Number of words per page:	380–389	390–399	400–409	410–419
Number of pages:	2	6	15	17

Number of words per page:	420–429	430–439
Number of pages:	5	3

What word value will you attach to each interval? Calculate the average number of words per page.

In the example concerning the throwing of the die the measures of the outcomes were limited and clearly distinct from each other. It is not possible to throw any score other than 1, 2, 3, 4, 5 or 6: we cannot have any score between any two of these values.

In the problem about ages we took each age to be the age at the last birthday, i.e. an integer. But real ages are in years, months, days, and even hours, and if we were being strictly accurate we would take that fact into account. Similarly, with heights we should not stop short at the nearest inch, centimetre or millimetre, and with weights we should not stop short at the nearest pound, kilogram or gram, but take into account the fine gradations between close values.

In practice that would mean we would have to make the measurements delicate and precise, and the resulting calculations would be more tedious and complicated. Therefore we sort out measurements into a manageable number of groups, preferably between equal intervals. This is what we did in the last two examples in Exercise 12.3. For instance, with ages, we would classify all those with ages from 16 and up to, but not including, 17 as of a certain age. As a matter of fact we might argue here in two different ways.

In Fig. 12.2 we are classifying each person by his age at his last birthday, and each interval is one year.

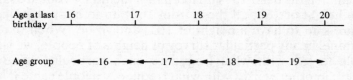

Figure 12.2

However, a more realistic measure of each interval is not the whole number below but the age at the mid-interval (Fig. 12.3). Yet, having said that, we realize that we are reluctant to credit the group with a value which is not a whole number. As a matter of fact, since every group in this approach is credited with a value

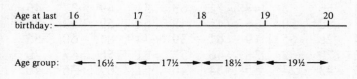

Figure 12.3

which is a half greater than in the first approach, we could, if we wished, evaluate the mean by the first method and simply add a half to our answer to meet the requirements of the second method.

However, many other problems require us to look at the matter in yet another way. Suppose we are measuring the heights of people, and suppose we claim we can give the height of a person correct to the nearest centimetre. Fig. 12.4 represents what we mean by that.

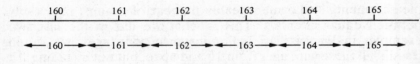

Figure 12.4

The top line represents the heights in steps of 1 cm from just below 160 to just above 165. The bottom line shows which real measures are credited with the heights of 160, 161 etc. All those with real heights from $159\frac{1}{2}$ up to but not including $160\frac{1}{2}$ are said to have a height of 160; all those from $160\frac{1}{2}$ up to but not including $161\frac{1}{2}$ are said to have a height of 161; and so on. When that has been done, in any particular survey of heights of people, we would be able to say with what frequency each particular value was credited; in other words, with what frequency people came in each group.

We will now consider a case where our first task is to rearrange the data into a number of manageable groups of equal interval.

Example

Suppose the examination marks of 101 students are as follows:

22	56	83	48	71	63	51	49	37	45	
73	82	50	36	41	48	64	69	53	26	
54	28	65	19	61	39	44	81	60	55	
51	70	62	38	46	52	31	56	47	70	
42	43	24	55	34	46	51	67	36	40	
34	39	77	48	45	57	27	41	59	56	
41	65	54	79	58	46	68	86	49	40	
23	59	35	29	51	43	55	67	76	32	
74	48	54	61	63	45	78	46	52	62	
56	44	71	50	41	32	59	48	25	37	44
470	534	575	463	511	471	528	610	494	463	44

The numbers in the row under the line represent the totals of the columns above. If we were to represent these marks, as they stand, by a histogram, each frequency would be small and the histogram would be extended sideways to an unmanageable size. Therefore we rearrange the data into classes of equal intervals of, say, 5. This means we rewrite each mark correct to the nearest 5.

All marks in the interval $17\frac{1}{2}$ up to but not including $22\frac{1}{2}$ are credited with the mark 20 (the value at the mid-interval); marks from $22\frac{1}{2}$ up to but not including $27\frac{1}{2}$ are credited with the value 25; and so on. So our data become:

Credited value:	20	25	30	35	40	45	50
Frequency:	2	5	5	7	10	13	15
Credited value × frequency:	40	125	150	245	400	585	750

Credited value:	55	60	65	70	75	80	85
Frequency:	12	9	7	6	4	4	2
Credited value × frequency:	660	540	455	420	300	320	170

A third row of figures has been added. This has been obtained by multiplying the two rows above together.

To calculate the mean mark obtained by the 101 students we use the formula given in the example about 60 throws of a die.

Mean mark:

$$= \frac{40 + 125 + 150 + 245 + 400 + 585 + 750 + 660 + 540 + 455 + 420 + 300 + 320 + 170}{101}$$

$$= \frac{5160}{101} \approx 51.1$$

If, instead of grouping the data, we had used the original set of marks, we would have found that the sum was 5163 instead of 5160, so our modified data give an answer which is in extremely close agreement with the original. Fig. 12.5 is a histogram representing the modified data.

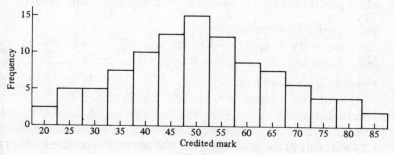

Figure 12.5

Exercise 12.4

1. The following results were obtained in a certain examination:

Mark:	0–9	10–19	20–29	30–39	40–49
No. of candidates:	11	31	70	85	150

Mark:	50–59	60–69	70–79	80–89	90–99
No. of candidates:	123	74	32	19	6

    Draw a histogram representing the data. Calculate the mean.

2. Eighty samples of castings from a particular machine were classified by weight as follows:

Weight in kilograms:	9.00–9.02	9.02–9.04	9.04–9.06
No. of castings:	3	4	19

Weight in kilograms:	9.06–9.08	9.08–9.10
No. of castings:	25	20

Weight in kilograms:	9.10–9.12	9.12–9.14
No. of castings:	7	2

    Draw a histogram to represent the data. Calculate the mean mass of the castings.

3. A random sample of bricks (101) is tested for percentage absorption of water by weight, with the following results:

Percentage absorption of water by weight:	43–45	45–47	47–49	49–51
No. of bricks:	6	9	20	33

Percentage absorption of water by weight:	51–53	53–55	55–57
No. of bricks:	18	10	5

    Draw a histogram and calculate the mean percentage absorption.

4. The following table shows the distribution of ages at marriage for a certain group of people:

Age at marriage:	13–17	18–22	23–27	28–32	33–37	38–42
Husbands:	22	403	695	265	93	40
Wives:	108	751	470	119	36	15

Age at marriage:	43–47	48–52	53–57	58–62	63–67	68–72
Husbands:	16	10	4	6	2	1
Wives:	8	2	1	1	0	0

Draw a histogram for each distribution. Calculate the mean age for marrying for both men and women.

12.2 The mode, or modal class

A manufacturer of shoes is not so much interested in the mean size of shoe for the population as a whole. In fact, a calculation of the mean size might turn out to be, say, 8.56, although shoes are manufactured in sizes rising in steps of $\frac{1}{2}$.

He is interested in what is the most common size of shoe worn, in other words, what size is bought with the greatest frequency. This is called the *mode* or the *modal class*.

Example

Consider the following data about the purchase of men's shoes:

Size bought:	6	$6\frac{1}{2}$	7	$7\frac{1}{2}$	8	$8\frac{1}{2}$	9	$9\frac{1}{2}$	10	$10\frac{1}{2}$	11
Frequency:	5	8	15	32	66	63	40	25	14	9	6

The mode, or modal class, is size 8, because it is sold with the greatest frequency.

If we refer back to Exercise 12.1, question (1), we note that there were three modal classes, or modes. Two students measured the height of the building to be 12.05, two measured it to be 11.95, and two measured it to be 12.00. So *there can be more than one mode or modal class*.

Exercise 12.5

1. Calculate the modes, or modal classes, in questions (1), (2), (3) and (4) in Exercise 12.1.
2. Calculate the modal classes in all the questions in Exercise 12.3. In questions (3) and (4) in that exercise what values would you attach to the modal classes? In other words, what would you say was the mode?
3. Calculate the modal classes in Exercise 12.4. What is the mode in each case?

12.3 The median

There is another kind of average in which we are frequently interested. It is called the median.

Example

Suppose the marks obtained by seven students are:

$$48 \quad 32 \quad 56 \quad 39 \quad 78 \quad 43 \quad 35$$

To calculate the median we rank the marks in order, either from the lowest to highest or from highest to lowest. Usually we choose the former method. The ranked marks are, then:

$$32 \quad 35 \quad 39 \quad 43 \quad 48 \quad 56 \quad 78$$

The mark of the student in the middle, 43, is the median.

In this case, because the number of students is an odd number, there is an actual middle student. However, suppose we brought in an extra student, who has a mark of 52. Then our ranked order would be:

$$32 \quad 35 \quad 39 \quad 43 \quad 48 \quad 52 \quad 56 \quad 78$$

Now there is no middle student. But there are two students in the middle, with marks of 43 and 48. It is customary to take the average of these as the median, and in that event the median would be $45\frac{1}{2}$. If, however, we were unhappy about this because the median then involved a $\frac{1}{2}$ mark and we took it for granted that we could not mark correct to $\frac{1}{2}$ mark, then we would get around the problem by saying that one half of the students had a mark of 43 or less and the other half had 48 or more.

Exercise 12.6

Calculate the median values of the following data:

1. 3, 7, 10, 5, 4, 8, 16.
2. 5.6, 3.2, 4.9, 7.2, 5.6, 6.3, 4.7.
3. 6.5, 2.3, 9.4, 5.3, 6.7, 6.9, 4.7.
4. 8.6, 5.4, 3.9, 4.5, 7.2, 5.6, 6.3, 4.7.
5. 11, 53, 47, 92, 48, 39, 18, 21, 84, 76, 23, 91, 66.
6. 131, 142, 156, 144, 129, 103, 178, 158, 163, 145, 127, 133, 128, 115.
7. Calculate the median values of the data in questions (1), (2), (3) and (4) of Exercise 12.1.

12.4 The range

The mean, median and mode are all methods of measuring the central tendency of data. Another important factor to be taken into account in data is the way it is spread or dispersed about that central tendency. An extremely rough guide to the measure of this is the range. This is defined to be the difference between the largest and the smallest sample observations.

Examples

1. In Exercise 12.1, question (1), the range is $12.10 - 11.90 = 0.20$.
2. In Exercise 12.1, question (4), the range is $1030 - 965 = 65$.
3. In Exercise 12.3, question (1), the range is $93 - 87 = 6$.
4. In Exercise 12.3, question (2), the range is $18 - 10 = 8$.

Exercise 12.7

Determine the range for questions (1)–(6) in Exercise 12.6.

12.5   The frequency polygon

Often we replace the histogram by the frequency polygon, which is obtained by joining together the mid-points of the tops of the rectangles, as in Fig. 12.6.

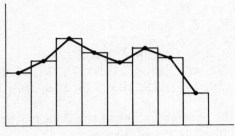

Figure 12.6

12.6   The frequency curve

As the width of the class intervals decreases and the number of intervals increases the polygon approaches nearer and nearer to a smooth curve. Examples of such curves are shown in Fig. 12.7(a), (b) and (c). All these curves are unimodal, i.e. they have only one mode.

In Fig. 12.7(a) we have a frequency curve which is symmetrical. The axis of symmetry coincides with the values of the mean, the mode and the median.

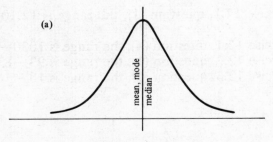

Figure 12.7

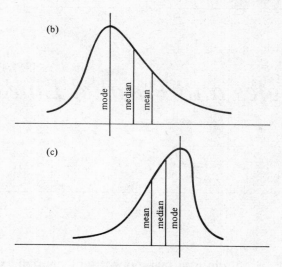

Figure 12.7 *Continued*

Fig. 12.7(b) is a frequency curve which is not symmetrical. It is said to be *skew*. Notice that the mean, the median and the mode no longer coincide.

Fig. 12.7(c) is another frequency curve exhibiting this characteristic of skewness.

The greater the skewness of a curve the more the three 'averages' are separated from one another.

13

Angles and Parallel Lines

In Chapter 10, in relation to standard right-handed axes Ox and Oy, we talked about an anti-clockwise rotation from Ox to Oy. A rotation of four times that amount, by reference to such a diagram, would return the axis Ox to its original position. That corresponds to a complete revolution about O. The rotation from Ox to Oy we call a right angle. So:

$$4 \text{ right angles} = 1 \text{ revolution}$$

But the revolution and the right angle represent large units of angle. To obtain a smaller unit we subdivide the revolution into 360 equal divisions, called degrees. We abbreviate 4 degrees to $4°$. So:

$$1 \text{ revolution} = 360°$$
$$4 \text{ right angles} = 360°$$
$$\text{Therefore} \quad 1 \text{ right angle} = 90°$$

To measure accurately to $1°$ in the drawings which we will have to do is a reasonable exercise of dexterity and skill. Yet in angle measurements in relation to the earth and the position of the stars we require even greater accuracy.

We divide the degree into 60 equal divisions called minutes (3 minutes is expressed as $3'$), and:

$$1° = 60'$$

In Fig. 13.1 consider OA to be the initial position of a line OP which rotates about O. The lines OA, OB, OC and OD divide the

260

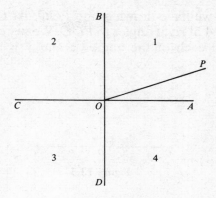

Figure 13.1

complete revolution about *O* into 4 quarters (right angles), which we also call quadrants. If *OP* stops in quadrant 1 the rotation (or angle) is said to be *acute*. If *OP* stops in quadrant 2 the rotation is said to be *obtuse*. If the rotation stops in quadrants 3 or 4 the rotation is said to be *reflex*.

This means that 65° (<90°) is acute; 124° (>90° and <180°) is obtuse; 225° (<270° and >180°) is reflex; and 300° (>270° and <360°) is also reflex.

Exercise 13.1

Place the following angles in the categories 'acute', 'obtuse' or 'reflex': 25°, 89°, 100°, 190°, 299°, 91°, 179°, 269°, 271°, 359°.

In Fig. 13.2 we indicate the marked angle in two different ways: as angle $A\hat{O}B$; as *x*.

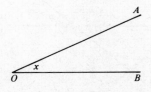

Figure 13.2

In Fig. 13.3 we have drawn a line *POQ*. At *O* we have drawn another line *OA* at right angles to *POQ*. We say it is perpendicular to *POQ*. Then each of the angles x and y is a right angle. So $x + y = 180°$.

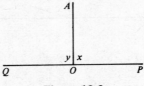

Figure 13.3

In Fig. 13.4 *XOY* is a straight line. So:

$$40° + t = 180°$$
$$t = 180° - 40° = 140°$$

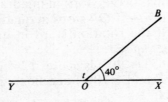

Figure 13.4

In Fig. 13.5 we have continued *BO* (from Fig. 13.4) to *C* so that *BOC* is a straight line. Then:

$$s + 140° = 180°$$
$$s = 180° - 140° = 40°$$
$$\text{So} \quad B\hat{O}X = C\hat{O}Y.$$

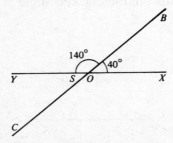

Figure 13.5

Exercise 13.2

Redraw Fig. 13.5 several times, each time marking $B\hat{O}X$ values different from 40°. In each case calculate $B\hat{O}Y$ and $C\hat{O}Y$. What conclusion do you come to about the pair of angles $B\hat{O}X$ and $C\hat{O}Y$ in all cases?

They are always equal. We call them *vertically opposite* angles.

Exercise 13.3

In Figs 13.6 and 13.7 write down the pairs of angles which are vertically opposite angles.

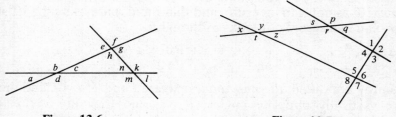

| **Figure 13.6** | **Figure 13.7** |

In arriving at the result we also notice that angles such as x and y in Fig. 13.8 are related so that $x + y = 180°$. When POQ is a straight line we call x and y *adjacent* angles, and, because their sum is 180°, we also refer to them as *supplementary* angles.

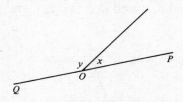

Figure 13.8

Suppose in Fig. 13.9 AB and CD are parallel. They have the same direction. Line $LMNP$, which crosses them, is said to be a *transversal*. Suppose $L\hat{M}B = 70°$. Then $A\hat{M}L = 110°$, because the two angles are adjacent. Then $y = 70°$ (vertically opposite) and $x = 110°$ (vertically opposite).

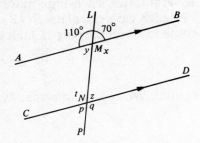

Figure 13.9

Draw such a diagram using a ruler and a protractor. Now measure the angles z, t, p and q. You will find that z and p are as near $70°$ as you can measure, and that t and q are as near $110°$ as you can measure. So it looks as though:

$$z = y = 70°$$
$$\text{and} \quad t = x = 110°$$

z and y are called *alternate angles*. So are t and x. $q = t$, and they are vertically opposite angles; $p = z$, and they are vertically opposite angles.

Draw similar diagrams but where *LMB* is an angle other than $70°$. Do you still find that $z = y$ and $t = x$?

It appears from our diagrams and our measurements that, within the accuracy of our drawing and measurement, we can reach certain conclusions. For instance, in Fig. 13.10 a and c, b and d, e and g, and f and h are pairs of vertically opposite angles and are equal; a and b, c and d, a and d, b and c, e and f, f and g, g and h,

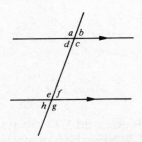

Figure 13.10

and *h* and *e* are pairs of adjacent angles and therefore supplementary angles; *d* and *f*, and *c* and *e* are pairs of alternate angles. Also, $a = e$, $b = f$, $d = h$, and $c = g$. These pairs of equal angles we call *corresponding angles*. We also notice that:

$$d + e = 180°$$
$$c + f = 180°$$

d and *e* are called *interior angles*. They are *supplementary*. So are *c* and *f*.

Exercise 13.4

1.   In Fig. 13.11 *XY* is parallel to *ZT* (indicated by single arrows in the same direction). Calculate all the angles in the figure.

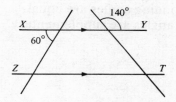

Figure 13.11

2.   In Fig. 13.12 *AB*, *CD* and *EF* are all parallel (single arrows) and *LM* and *NP* are parallel (double arrows). Calculate all the angles in the figure.

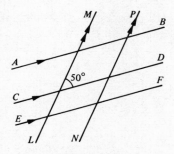

Figure 13.12

In Fig. 13.13, where *AB* and *XY* are not parallel and *RSTU* is a transversal, note that corresponding angles are not equal, alternate

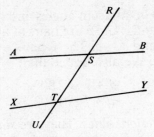

Figure 13.13

angles are not equal and interior angles are not supplementary.

The following, then, provide methods of establishing that lines are parallel:

1. When alternate angles are equal.
2. When corresponding angles are equal.
3. When interior angles are supplementary.

14
Triangles

In Fig. 14.1 consider a triangle ABC in which angle $C = 40°$ and angle $B = 80°$. If we produce CB to D and draw BE parallel to

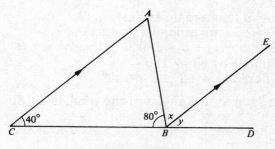

Figure 14.1

CA, then $80°$ and $D\hat{B}A$ are adjacent, so supplementary.

$D\hat{B}A = x + y$
So $80° + x + y = 180°$
Therefore $x + y = 100°$
But y and $40°$ are corresponding
So $y = 40°$
Therefore $x + 40° = 100°$
$x = 60°$
And angle $A = x$ (alternate angles) $= 60°$
The sum of the angles of the triangle is $40° + 60° + 80° = 180°$

Draw other triangles *ABC* with different values for angles *B* and *C*. Is it always true that the sum of the angles of a triangle is 180°? Let us see if we can prove that it is true. Take Fig. 14.2, where

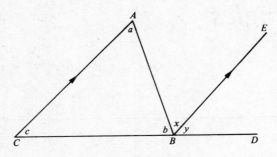

Figure 14.2

angles *B* and *C* can have any values that will be consistent with *ABC* representing a triangle. In the figure:

$$x = a \quad \text{(alternate angles)}$$
$$y = c \quad \text{(corresponding angles)}$$
$$\text{But } (x + y) + b = 180° \quad \text{(adjacent angles)}$$
$$\text{So } (a + c) + b = 180°$$
$$\text{Therefore } a + b + c = 180°$$

Therefore the sum of the angles of the triangle is 180°.

Exercise 14.1

Calculate the angles in Figs 14.3 to 14.8.

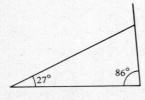

Figure 14.3

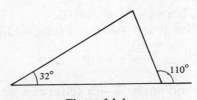

Figure 14.4

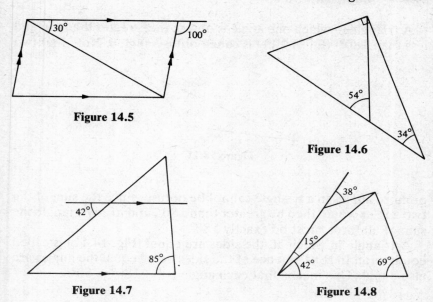

Figure 14.5

Figure 14.6

Figure 14.7

Figure 14.8

A triangle such as the one in Fig. 14.9 is called acute angled. All its angles are acute.

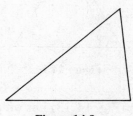

Figure 14.9

A triangle in which one angle is a right angle, as in Fig. 14.10, is called right angled.

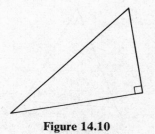

Figure 14.10

A triangle in which one angle is obtuse (i.e. greater than 90° and less than 180°) (Fig. 14.11) is called obtuse angled. Note that two

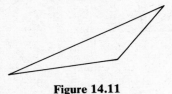

Figure 14.11

or more angles in a triangle cannot be obtuse, since the sum of the two angles would then be greater than 180°, and in any triangle the sum of all three must be exactly 180°.

A triangle in which all the sides are equal (Fig. 14.12) is called equilateral. In consequence of the sides being equal the angles are also equal. This means that each angle is $\frac{1}{3} \times 180° = 60°$.

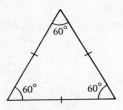

Figure 14.12

An isosceles triangle (Fig. 14.13) has only two sides equal. The angles opposite those sides, often called the *base angles* (x), are also equal. The remaining angle (y) is often called the *vertical angle* of the triangle.

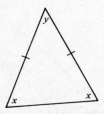

Figure 14.13

In the right-angled triangle ABC, in Fig. 14.14, $A\hat{C}B$ is a right angle and $A\hat{B}C = 30°$. Suppose $B\hat{A}C = a$. Then:

$$a + 30° + 90° = 180°$$

Therefore $\quad a = 180° - 90° - 30° = 60°$

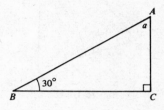

Figure 14.14

a and $30°$ are said to be complementary angles because their sum is $90°$.

Any right-angled triangle contains, besides the right angle, two other angles, each of which is acute. In triangle PQR (Fig. 14.15):

$$p + q = 90°$$
$$\text{or} \quad q = 90° - p$$

p and q are complementary.

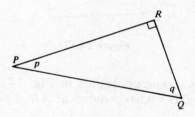

Figure 14.15

Exercise 14.2

1. Calculate the unknown angles in Fig. 14.16. ($AB = AC$. AD is perpendicular to BC.)

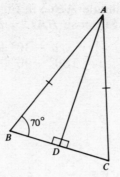

Figure 14.16

2. Calculate the unknown angles in Fig. 14.17. ($A\hat{C}B$ is a right angle. $AD = AC$.)

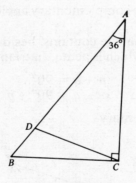

Figure 14.17

3. Calculate the unknown angles in Fig. 14.18. ($AB = BC = CA = CD = DB$.) Also prove that AB is parallel to CD.

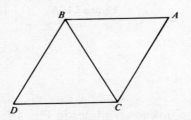

Figure 14.18

4. Calculate the unknown angles in Fig. 14.19. (Angle $B\hat{A}C$ is a right angle. AD is perpendicular to BC.)

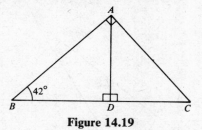

Figure 14.19

5. Calculate the unknown angles in Fig. 14.20. Also calculate $A\hat{B}D$.

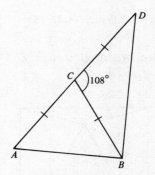

Figure 14.20

6. Calculate the unknown angles in Fig. 14.21. ($AB = BC = CD = DE = EA$. $OA = OB = OC = OD = OE$.)

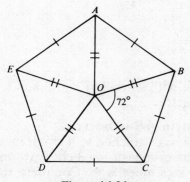

Figure 14.21

7. Calculate the unknown angles in Fig. 14.22. (*AB = BC. CA = CD.*)

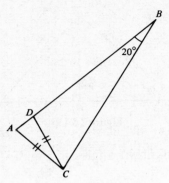

Figure 14.22

8. Calculate the unknown angles in Fig. 14.23. (*AB = BC = CD = DA = EA = EC.*)

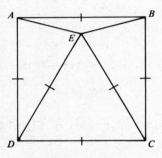

Figure 14.23

Example

Construct a triangle with sides 3, 4 and 5 and measure the three angles with a protractor.

Step 1. Measure length *AB* to be 5 cm.
Step 2. With compasses stretched to 4 cm draw an arc, centre *A*.
Step 3. With compasses measuring 3 cm draw an arc, centre *B*.
Step 4. Where the arcs meet is *C*. Complete the triangle *ACB*, Fig. 14.24.

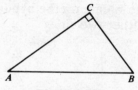

Figure 14.24

Now measure angle $A\hat{C}B$. If the construction has been done well it should have a value close to 90°. Theoretically it should be exactly 90°. The other measurements should be approximately $A\hat{B}C$ = 53° and $B\hat{A}C$ = 37°, although in fact they are slightly different from those values.

Exercise 14.3

Construct the following triangles:

1. With sides 5, 12 and 13. Measure the angle opposite 13.
2. With sides 7, 24 and 25. Measure the angle opposite 25.
3. With sides 8, 15 and 17. Measure the angle opposite 17.
4. With sides 9, 40 and 41. Measure the angle opposite 41.

In each case the angle should measure approximately 90°, because in all the triangles above there is a special relationship between the sides. For example:

$$3^2 + 4^2 = 9 + 16 = 25; \text{ and } 25 = 5^2; \text{ so } 3^2 + 4^2 = 5^2$$
$$5^2 + 12^2 = 25 + 144 = 169; \text{ and } 169 = 13^2; \text{ so } 5^2 + 12^2 = 13^2$$
$$7^2 + 24^2 = 49 + 576 = 625; \text{ and } 625 = 25^2; \text{ so } 7^2 + 24^2 = 25^2$$
$$8^2 + 15^2 = 64 + 225 = 289; \text{ and } 289 = 17^2; \text{ so } 8^2 + 15^2 = 17^2$$
$$9^2 + 40^2 = 81 + 1600 = 1681; \text{ and } 1681 = 41^2; \text{ so } 9^2 + 40^2 = 41^2$$

They illustrate that, for a triangle sides a, b and c, and where $a^2 + b^2 = c^2$, the triangle is right-angled, with the right angle opposite side c, which is called the *hypotenuse*. That result is not the Pythagoras theorem but the converse of Pythagoras. It tells us that when the sides of a triangle fulfil a certain condition, namely $a^2 + b^2 = c^2$, then a certain angle is a right angle.

However, sometimes we know that a triangle has a right angle in it. When that is the case there is another theorem which tells us that there is a certain relationship between the sides of the triangle, and that theorem is Pythagoras. It says that when a triangle is known to be right angled then the square on the hypotenuse equals the sum of the squares on the other two sides.

Examples

1. Given that in a right-angled triangle the hypotenuse is 2 and one other side is 1, determine the third side.
   In Fig. 14.25 suppose the third side is represented by x. Then, by Pythagoras:

   $$x^2 + 1^2 = 2^2$$
   $$\text{i.e.} \quad x^2 + 1 = 4$$
   $$x^2 = 3$$
   $$x = \sqrt{3}$$

   The third side is $\sqrt{3}$.

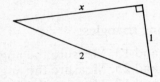

Figure 14.25

2. Given that in a right-angled triangle the two sides containing the right angle are 4 and 5, determine the hypotenuse.
   In Fig. 14.26 suppose the hypotenuse is represented by y. Then, by Pythagoras:

   $$y^2 = 4^2 + 5^2 = 16 + 25$$
   $$y^2 = 41$$
   $$y = \sqrt{41}$$

   The hypotenuse is $\sqrt{41}$.

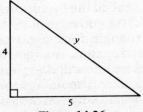

Figure 14.26

Exercise 14.4

Consider a right-angled triangle XYZ where the right angle is $Y\hat{Z}X$ and the sides opposite the vertices are labelled with corresponding small letters, i.e. x is opposite X and so on. Calculate the third side in each of the following triangles:

1. $x = 6$, $y = 8$, $z = ?$
2. $x = 9$, $y = 12$, $z = ?$
3. $x = 15$, $y = 20$, $z = ?$
4. $x = 21$, $y = 28$, $z = ?$
5. $x = 10$, $y = 24$, $z = ?$
6. $x = 15$, $y = 36$, $z = ?$
7. $x = 20$, $y = ?$, $z = 52$
8. $x = 2.5$, $y = ?$, $z = 6.5$

In each of questions (1) to (4) look at the ratios of the sides to one another. What do you notice about them? They are all in the ratio $3:4:5$. In (1) the sides are all twice the sides of a 3, 4, 5 triangle. In (2) they are three times. In (3) they are five times. And in (4) they are seven times. In other words, if the sides of a triangle are multiples of 3, 4 and 5 the triangle will be right angled.

Have you noticed anything common to the triangles in questions (5) to (8)? Take any common multiples of the numbers 7, 24 and 25 and verify that the result is a triangle which is right angled. Repeat that procedure with 8, 15 and 17.

If we draw triangles with sides equal to the values given in questions (1), (2), (3) and (4) what do we notice about them other than that they are all right angled? They are of the same shape. *Figures which are of the same shape are said to be similar.*

In Fig. 14.27 $ABCDE$ is a five-sided figure (pentagon). O is any point outside $ABCDE$. A_1 is the point mid-way along OA. Draw $A_1B_1C_1D_1E_1$ so that A_1B_1, B_1C_1, C_1D_1 and D_1E_1 are parallel to AB, BC, CD and DE respectively. Join E_1 and A_1. In a similar way construct $A_2B_2C_2D_2E_2$ so that $OA_2 = \frac{3}{2}OA$.

Measure the angles of the three pentagons. Notice that the figures are approximately equiangular. If we could construct the figures accurately and measure the angles accurately we would find that the figures were equiangular. Measure and compare the sides of the figures $A_1B_1C_1D_1E_1$ and $A_2B_2C_2D_2E_2$ with those of $ABCDE$. What are your conclusions? The sides of the first are all $\frac{1}{2}$ those of $ABCDE$ and the sides of the second are $\frac{3}{2}$ those of $ABCDE$.

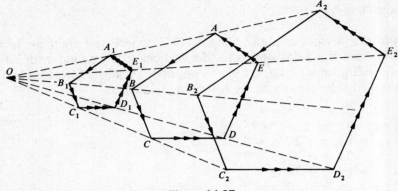

Figure 14.27

The figures have the same shape but are not the same size. They are said to be similar, and they possess the property that they are equiangular and have their corresponding sides in the same ratio, i.e. corresponding sides are proportional.

We might have constructed similar figures on the principle of Fig. 14.28, where O is taken inside the quadrilateral.

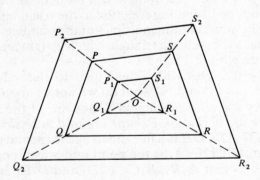

Figure 14.28

In Fig. 14.29 the figures do not have the same shape even though $LPNM$ and LP_1N_1M are equiangular. They are equiangular but do not have corresponding sides in the same ratio. For example, LM remains the same in both figures, and so the ratio is $1:1$, but $LP_1/LP < 1$. This means that figures are similar only if they are equiangular and have corresponding sides in the same ratio.

Now let us have a closer look at similar triangles.

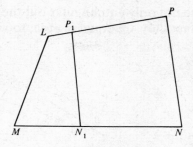

Figure 14.29

In Fig. 14.30 draw triangle OAB and produce both OA and OB. Then draw A_1B_1, A_2B_2, A_3B_3, A_4B_4 etc. parallel to AB. All the triangles OAB, OA_1B_1, etc. are similar, and we drew them equiangular. This tells us that triangles which are drawn equiangular are automatically similar.

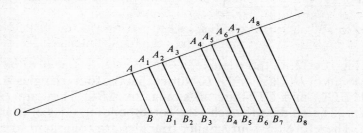

Figure 14.30

Now construct triangles with sides 6, 8 and 9 and 12, 16 and 18. What do you notice about them? They are of the same shape and therefore similar. But we drew them so that there was a special relationship between their sides. Compare the sides 6/12, 8/16, 9/18. In each case the answer is 1/2, i.e., they are in the same ratio. So when we draw triangles with their sides in the same ratio they are automatically similar.

Check this conclusion by drawing a pair of triangles with sides 6, 9 and 12 and 4, 6 and 8. Note that their corresponding sides are in the ratio 4/6, 6/9, 8/12, i.e. 2/3.

In Fig. 14.31 draw any pentagon $ABCDE$ and then draw AA_0, BB_0, CC_0, DD_0, EE_0 all parallel to one another. Take A_1 any point in AA_0. Draw A_1B_1, B_1C_1, C_1D_1 and D_1E_1 parallel to AB, BC, CD and DE. Join E_1A_1. Measure the angles and sides of the two pentagons. They are not only equiangular but their corresponding sides are equal. In fact they are equal in area, too. They are said to be congruent.

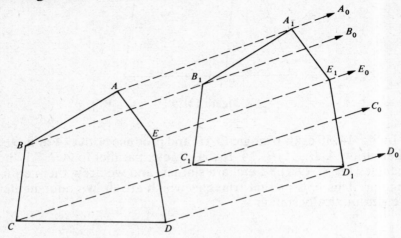

Figure 14.31

In Fig. 14.32, in the triangle *ABC* take *D*, *E* and *F* to be the mid-points of *BC*, *CA* and *AB*. Notice that the four triangles *AFE*, *FBD*, *EDC*, and *DEF* are all similar to *ABC*. They are equiangular. Their sides are each $\frac{1}{2}$ the corresponding sides of triangle *ABC*. Therefore the four smaller triangles are congruent to each other.

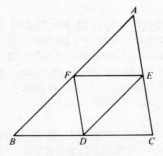

Figure 14.32

Congruent triangles are triangles which are similar and in which the ratio of corresponding sides is 1 : 1, i.e. they are equal to one another.

So far we have discovered two different ways of proving that triangles are similar. The first is if they are equiangular, and the second is if corresponding sides are in the same ratio. Are there any more ways of establishing similarity?

In Fig. 14.33 draw triangle *ABC* with sides 6, 9 and 12. Mark points *P* and *Q* on *AB* and *AC* so that *AQ* = 2 and *AP* = 3. Join

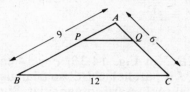

Figure 14.33

PQ. We now have two triangles, *ABC* and *APQ*. They are such that *AQ/AC* = 2/6 = 1/3 and *PAQ* = *BAC*. By measurement of the angles *APQ*, *ABC*, *AQP* and *ACB* we find that the two triangles are equiangular, so they are similar. So two triangles which have two pairs of sides in the same ratio and which enclose the same angles or equal angles must be similar.

To determine sides and angles in similar triangles

Examples

1. In Fig. 14.34(a) and (b) triangles *ABC* and *XYZ* are similar because *XY/AB* = 4/6 = 2/3 = 6/9 = *ZY/CB*. The angles between the proportional sides are equal (= β), so the triangles are equiangular. Therefore if we know that angle $B\hat{A}C$ is α then angle $Y\hat{X}Z$ is also α. If we know that angle $X\hat{Z}Y$ is γ then

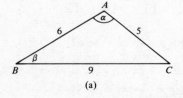

(a)   (b)

Figure 14.34

angle $A\hat{C}B$ is also γ. Further, the sides are proportional, so:

$$XZ/AC = XY/AB = YZ/BC$$

i.e. $\dfrac{XZ}{5} = \tfrac{4}{6} = \tfrac{2}{3}$

$$XZ = \tfrac{2}{3} \times 5$$

Therefore $XZ = 3\tfrac{1}{3}$.

2. In triangle ABC in Fig. 14.35, $c = 14$ cm, $b = 11$ cm and $a = 12$ cm. LM is parallel to BC, so triangles ALM and ABC are similar because they are equiangular. Suppose $AL = 6$ cm. Calculate AM and LM.

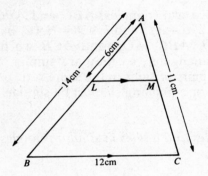

Figure 14.35

Corresponding sides are proportional, so:

$$\frac{AM}{AC} = \frac{AL}{AB} = \frac{LM}{BC}$$

i.e. $\dfrac{AM}{11} = \dfrac{6}{14} = \dfrac{LM}{12}$

giving $AM = 11 \times \dfrac{\cancel{6}^{\,3}}{\cancel{14}_{7}} = \tfrac{33}{7} = 4\tfrac{5}{7}$

and $LM = 12 \times \dfrac{\cancel{6}^{\,3}}{\cancel{14}_{7}} = \tfrac{36}{7} = 5\tfrac{1}{7}$

3. In Fig. 14.36, with the dimensions given, show that triangles *XYZ* and *VWZ* are equiangular and therefore similar. Calculate *VW* and *ZW*.

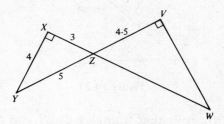

Figure 14.36

Angles *VZW* and *XZY* are equal (vertically opposite). The angles at *X* and *V* are right angles. So by the angle sum property of the triangle the remaining angles must be equal. The triangles are equiangular, therefore corresponding sides are proportional.

$$VW/4 = ZW/5 = 4.5/3$$

$$\text{i.e.} \quad VW = 4 \times \frac{4.5}{3} = 6$$

$$ZW = 5 \times \frac{4.5}{3} = 7.5$$

To summarize similarity: there are three different ways of proving triangles similar other than by definition. They are:

1. If they are equiangular.
2. If corresponding sides are in the same ratio.
3. If two pairs of sides are in the same ratio and they enclose equal angles.

Exercise 14.5

1. In Fig. 14.37 prove that triangles *ABC* and *DBE* are equiangular. If *AB* = 5, *BC* = 6, *AC* = 4 and *DB* = 3, calculate the lengths *ED* and *EB*.

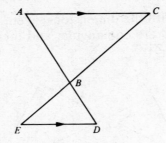

Figure 14.37

2. In Fig. 14.38 prove that triangles OAB and OCD are equi-angular. Calculate OD and OC.

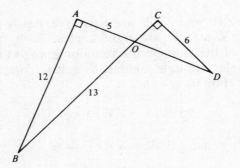

Figure 14.38

3. In Fig. 14.39 calculate p.

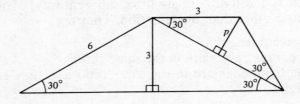

Figure 14.39

4. In Fig. 14.40 $A\hat{B}C$ is a right angle. BD is perpendicular to AC. Calculate AC. Show that triangles BDC, ADB and ABC are equiangular. Calculate BD, DC and AD.

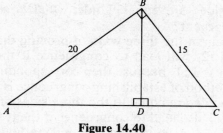

Figure 14.40

5. In Fig. 14.41 $PR = 17$, $PQ = 8$ and $PS = 3$. Calculate QR, PT and ST.

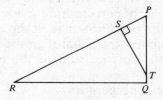

Figure 14.41

6. In Fig. 14.42 $L\hat{M}N$ is a right angle. $LN = 25$, $LM = 24$, $LP = 12$ and $LQ = 12.5$. Calculate MN. Prove that $L\hat{P}Q$ is a right angle. Prove $L\hat{Q}P = L\hat{N}M$. Calculate PQ.

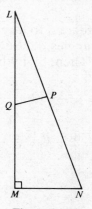

Figure 14.42

Triangles which are congruent are very special cases of triangles which are similar. The ratio of corresponding sides is $1:1$, i.e., corresponding sides are equal. Under what circumstances will triangles be congruent?

If we look again at the three ways of proving that triangles are similar, method (2) will lead to congruence if the ratio of corresponding sides is $1:1$, because then corresponding sides will be equal. So one method of establishing congruence is when the three sides of one triangle are equal to the three sides of the other.

Method (3) will also lead to congruence if the two pairs of sides are in the ratio $1:1$ (i.e. equal). So a second method of establishing congruence is when two sides of one triangle are equal to two sides of the other, and enclose equal angles.

Method (1) will lead to congruence only if, in addition to the equiangularity, one pair of corresponding sides are equal. And, in fact, we can discard the condition that all three pairs of angles are equal because if two pairs are equal then the third pair of angles must be equal, because of the sum of the angles of a triangle property.

So triangles will be congruent if:

1. The three sides of one are equal to the three sides of the other (SSS).
2. Two pairs of sides are equal and the angles included between them are equal (SAS).
3. Two pairs of angles are equal and one pair of corresponding sides are equal (AAS).

There is a fourth method related to a very special case. Consider the two right-angled triangles, *ABC* and *PQR*, which are represented in Fig. 14.43. Then, by Pythagoras:

$$p^2 = 9^2 - 4^2 \qquad\qquad x^2 = 9^2 - 4^2$$
$$= 81 - 16 = 65 \qquad\qquad = 81 - 16 = 65$$
$$p = \sqrt{65} \qquad\qquad x = \sqrt{65}$$
$$\text{So} \quad p = x$$

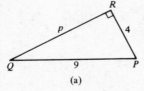

(a)

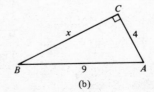

(b)

Figure 14.43

In other words, all three pairs of sides are equal, so the triangles are congruent.

Look at the right-angled triangles, *ABC* and *DEF*, in Fig. 14.44. $A\hat{B}C$ and $D\hat{E}F$ are right angles. Each hypotenuse is *l* and each

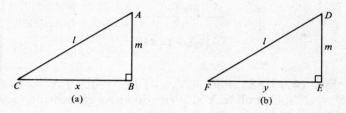

Figure 14.44

triangle has one other side = *m*. Suppose the remaining sides are *x* in *ABC* and *y* in *DEF*. By Pythagoras:

$$x^2 + m^2 = l^2 \qquad\qquad y^2 + m^2 = l^2$$
$$x^2 = l^2 - m^2 \qquad\qquad y^2 = l^2 - m^2$$
$$\text{Therefore} \quad x = y$$

This means that the remaining sides of the triangles are equal, so the triangles are congruent (SSS). We could also mention the case of two right-angled triangles in which the two pairs of sides surrounding the right angle are equal. However, this case has really been covered in method (2), i.e. SAS, so we do not need to state it again in relation to right-angled triangles. The one item in addition to the three we have already quoted is the one we have just discussed:

4. Two triangles have right angles, hypotenuses equal, and one other pair of sides equal (RHS).

Exercise 14.6

1. In Fig. 14.45 *AB* = 8, *AC* = 6 and *BC* = 7. *P*, *Q* and *R* are the mid-points of *BC*, *CA* and *AB*. Calculate the lengths of *RQ*, *RP* and *PQ*.

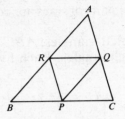

Figure 14.45

2. In Fig. 14.46 $LM = 9$, $MN = 7$, $LN = 15$, $LX = \frac{2}{3}LM$ and $LY = \frac{2}{3}LN$. Calculate XY. Write down an expression for angle $L\hat{Y}X$.

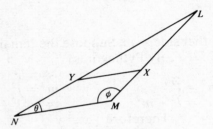

Figure 14.46

3. In Fig. 14.47 $OA_1 = 2OA$, $OB_1 = 2OB$ and $OC_1 = 2OC$. $AC = 3$, $BC = 5$ and $AB = 6$. Calculate A_1C_1, B_1C_1 and A_1B_1.

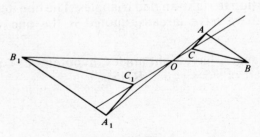

Figure 14.47

4. In Fig. 14.48 $ABCD$ is a parallelogram. $AB = 8$, $BC = 5$ and $AC = 9$. Calculate DC and AD. Then prove that triangles ABC and CDA are congruent.

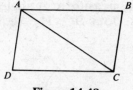

Figure 14.48

5.   In Fig. 14.49 $AC = 12$, $LC = 9$ and $AB = 7$. Calculate LM.

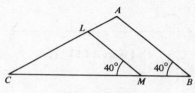

Figure 14.49

6.   In Fig. 14.50 triangle XVW is similar to triangle XZY. Calculate angle $V\hat{W}Y$.

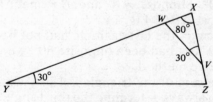

Figure 14.50

Construction of triangles

In the first example in this chapter the method of construction of a triangle when three sides are known was illustrated for the case when the triangle happened to be right angled. The principle is the same for triangles of any shape.

Example

Construct a triangle with sides 6 cm and 7 cm which include an angle of 50° (two sides and included angle). Measure $AB = 7$ cm.

Then, with a protractor, measure at A angle $X\hat{A}B = 50°$. Measure $AC = 6$ cm along AX. Join BC. The required triangle is ABC (Fig. 14.51).

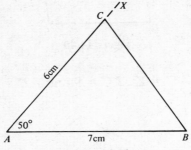

Figure 14.51

Example

Construct a triangle in which two angles are 50° and 60° and the side between them is 7.5 cm (two angles and one side). Measure $AB = 7.5$ cm. At A measure angle $X\hat{A}B = 50°$, and at B measure angle $Y\hat{B}A = 60°$. Suppose AX and BY meet at C. Then the required triangle is ABC (Fig. 14.52).

If the side 7.5 cm in the last example had not been between the angles 50° and 60° but had been opposite 60°, we would have had to modify the above method.

Since the angle sum of the triangle is 180°, where we are given two angles we can always determine the third angle. In this case it is 70°. In this case the side 7.5 cm lies between the angles 50° and 70°. In Fig. 14.52 we would replace the angle 60° by one of 70°.

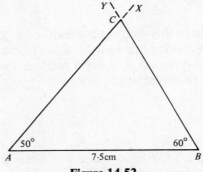

Figure 14.52

Example

Construct a right-angled triangle with hypotenuse 8.4 cm and one other side 5.5 cm (right angle, hypotenuse and one side). Measure $AB = 5.5$ cm. At B construct angle $A\hat{B}N = 90°$, either with a set square or a protractor. With compasses stretched to 8.4 cm draw an arc, centre A, to cut BN at C. Join AC. The required triangle is ABC (Fig. 14.53). If it is argued that one should not use a

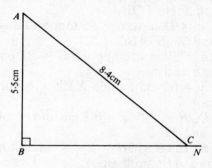

Figure 14.53

protractor or set square for the right angle, then measure $AB = 5.5$ cm. With centre B, radius BA, draw a large arc of a circle. With compasses mark AL, $LM = AB$. With centres L and M draw arcs of equal radius to intersect at N. Join BN. Then angle $A\hat{B}N$ is a right angle (Fig. 14.54).

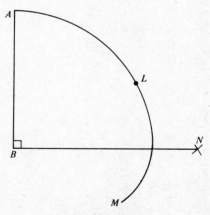

Figure 14.54

Exercise 14.7

Construct triangles given the following data:

1. *ABC* where $a = 8$ cm, $b = 7$ cm and $c = 6$ cm. Measure angle $A\hat{C}B$.
2. *XYZ* where $x = 6.5$ cm, $y = 7.5$ cm and $z = 4.5$ cm. Measure angle $X\hat{Y}Z$.
3. *PQR* where $p = 8$ cm, $q = 7$ cm and angle $Q\hat{R}P = 45°$. Measure r and angle $P\hat{Q}R$.
4. *ABC* where $c = 95$ mm, $b = 35$ mm and angle $B\hat{A}C = 20°$. Measure a and angle $A\hat{B}C$.
5. *ABC* where $a = 80$ mm, angle $A\hat{B}C = 30°$ and angle $A\hat{C}B = 70°$. Measure b and c.
6. *XYZ* where $y = 65$ mm, angle $X\hat{Y}Z = 65°$ and $Z\hat{X}Y = 55°$. Measure x and z.
7. *PQR* where $P\hat{Q}R = 90°$, $q = 6.8$ cm and $r = 4.6$ cm. Measure angles $R\hat{P}Q$ and $P\hat{R}Q$.
8. *ABC* where $C\hat{A}B = 90°$, $b = 47$ mm and $a = 93$ mm. Measure angles $A\hat{B}C$ and $B\hat{C}A$.

15

The Circle

A circle is a curve such that every point on it is the same distance from a fixed point which we call its centre. That is, in Fig. 15.1, OP = constant, called the radius.

Figure 15.1

In Fig. 15.2 $OX = OL = OT = OM = OY$ = radius of circle (r). XY is a diameter (a line passing through the centre).

$$XY = XO + OY = 2r \quad (d, \text{ diameter, } = 2r)$$

The ratio of the circumference of a circle to its diameter is always constant. The constant is denoted by the letter π, the value of which is approximately 3.1416.

Circumference = C = distance around the circle = $2\pi r = \pi d$

15.1

If AB meets the circle at L and M then LM is called a *chord*. $ALMB$ is called a *secant*. It divides the area of the circle into two parts, LTM and $LXZYM$. Each of these areas is called a *segment*. LTM is the *minor segment*, and the other area is the *major segment*.

RS meets the circle at only one point, *T*. *RS* is said to touch the circle and is called a *tangent*. The point of contact of the tangent is *T*.

The area *OLTM* is called a *sector* of a circle. So is the area *OMYZXL*.

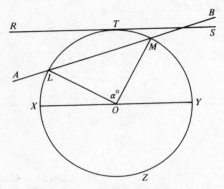

Figure 15.2

The area of the segment *LTM* equals the area of sector *OLTM* minus the area of triangle *OLM*.

The length of the curve *LTM* is called an *arc* of the circle. *MYZ* and *ZXL* are also arcs. Arc *LTM* is said to subtend angle α at the centre of the circle. The circumference subtends an angle at the centre of the circle = 360°.

Arcs of circles are proportional to the angles which they subtend at the centre. Consequently:

$$\frac{\text{arc } LTM}{\text{circumference}} = \frac{\alpha}{360}$$

$$\text{arc } LTM = \frac{\alpha}{360} \times \text{circumference} = \frac{\alpha}{360} \times \pi d \quad 15.2$$

$$\text{or} \quad = \frac{\alpha}{360} \times 2\pi r \quad 15.3$$

Examples

In all the following calculations π has been taken to be 3.142, which is a reasonable value when using four-figure tables. When a calculator which has a π key is used instead, the answers to the examples below will be slightly different.

1. Calculate the circumference of a circle: (a) with radius 4.5; and (b) with diameter 8.36.
   (a) $C = 2\pi \times r = 2 \times 3.142 \times 4.5 = 28.278$
      (by calculator) ≈ 28.28
   (b) $C = \pi \times 8.36 = 3.142 \times 8.36 = 26.26712 \approx 26.27$

2. Calculate the diameter of a circle whose circumference is 53.47.

$$d = C/\pi = 53.47/3.142 = 17.017823 \approx 17.02$$

3. Determine the radius of a circle whose circumference is 104.52 mm.

$$r = C/2\pi = 104.52/(2 \times 3.142) = 16.632718 \approx 16.63 \text{ mm}$$

4. Calculate the arc of a circle, radius 15 cm, which subtends at the centre an angle of 43°.
   By Law 15.3:

$$\text{arc} = \frac{43}{360} \times 3.142 \times 2 \times 15 = 11.258829 \approx 11.26 \text{ cm}$$

5. Calculate the angle which an arc of 27.59 mm subtends at the centre of a circle, radius 15.25 mm.
   By manipulation of Law 15.3:

$$\text{angle} = (\text{arc} \times 360)/2\pi r$$
$$= (27.59 \times 360)/(2 \times 3.142 \times 15.25) = 103.64495$$
$$\approx 103.64°$$

6. Determine the diameter of a circle in which an arc measuring 452.7 mm subtends at the centre an angle of 234.5°.

By manipulation of Law 15.2:

$$d = (\text{arc} \times 360)/(\text{angle} \times \pi)$$
$$= (452.7 \times 360)/(234.5 \times 3.142) = 221.18922$$
$$\approx 221.19 \text{ mm}$$

7. Determine the radius of a circle in which an arc measuring 345.7 cm subtends at the centre an angle of 317.8°.
   By manipulation of Law 15.3:

   $$r = (\text{arc} \times 360)/(\text{angle} \times 2 \times \pi)$$
   $$= (345.7 \times 360)/(317.8 \times 2 \times 3.142) = 62.317756$$
   $$\approx 62.32 \text{ cm}$$

Exercise 15.1

In all questions take $\pi = 3.142$.

1. Calculate the circumference of a circle: (a) with diameter 10; (b) with radius 30; (c) with diameter 6.78; (d) with radius 13.45.
2. Calculate the diameter of a circle whose circumference is: (a) 6.284; (b) 9.426; (c) 15.71; (d) 23.75.
3. Calculate the radius of a circle whose circumference is: (a) 31.42; (b) 62.84; (c) 35.05; (d) 106.6.
4. Calculate the arc of a circle, radius 10, which subtends at the centre an angle of: (a) 36°; (b) 144°; (c) 216°; (d) 100°; (e) 56.5°.
5. Calculate the angles which the following arcs subtend at the centre of a circle, radius 20: (a) 15.71; (b) 31.42; (c) 47.13; (d) 83.06; (e) 123.4.

15.1 Angle properties of the circle

Draw any circle and two radii, OA and OB, so that $A\hat{O}B = 100°$. Mark Q on the major arc. Join QA, QB and OQ and produce QO to P (Fig. 15.3). Arc APB subtends $A\hat{O}B = 100°$ at the centre.

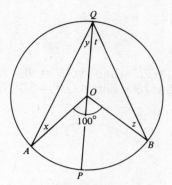

Figure 15.3

Arc APB subtends $A\hat{Q}B$ at the circumference. Suppose we calculate $A\hat{Q}B$. Let us suppose we have drawn Q so that $A\hat{O}P = 40°$. Then:

$\qquad Q\hat{O}A = 140°$ (supplementary to $A\hat{O}P$)
$\qquad$ Then $x + y = 180° - 140° = 40°$
$\qquad$ But $OA = OQ = r$, so triangle AOQ is isosceles.
$\qquad$ Therefore $x = y$
$\qquad$ So $2x = 40°$
$\qquad x = 20°$
$\qquad$ Now $B\hat{O}P = 100° - 40° = 60°$
$\qquad$ Therefore $B\hat{O}Q = 180° - 60° = 120°$
$\qquad$ Then $z + t = 180° - 120° = 60°$
$\qquad$ But $z = t$
$\qquad$ So $2z = 60°$
$\qquad z = 30°$
$\qquad y + t = 20° + 30° = 50° = \frac{1}{2} \times 100° = \frac{1}{2}A\hat{O}B$
$\qquad$ This means that $A\hat{Q}B = \frac{1}{2}A\hat{O}B$

In other words, the angle which the arc APB subtends at the circumference is half the angle which it subtends at the centre. Is this relationship always true?

Repeat the above construction with angles $A\hat{O}B$ and $A\hat{O}P$ taking different values. Both by measurement and calculation find the values of $A\hat{O}B$ and $A\hat{Q}B$ in each case. We discover that the relationship is true in all cases.

> The angle at the centre is twice
> the angle at the circumference

15.4

Remember that both angles must be subtended by the same arc.

Exercise 15.2

1. Using Fig. 15.4:

    (a) Calculate $A\hat{Q}B$ when $A\hat{O}B = 90°, 45°, 135°, 180°$
    (b) Calculate $A\hat{O}B$ when $A\hat{Q}B = 30°, 60°, 90°, 75°$

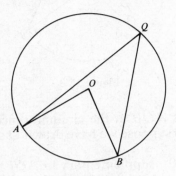

Figure 15.4

2. Using Fig. 15.5:

    (a) Calculate $A\hat{P}B$ and $A\hat{Q}B$ when $A\hat{O}B = 80°, 60°, 120°, 140°$
    (b) Calculate $A\hat{O}B$ when $A\hat{P}B = 35°, 25°, 75°, 47°$
    (c) Calculate $A\hat{O}B$ when $A\hat{Q}B = 35°, 25°, 75°, 47°$
    (d) Calculate $A\hat{Q}B$ when $A\hat{P}B = 45°, 52°, 63°, 87°$

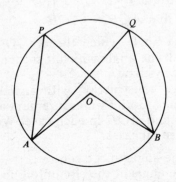

Figure 15.5

3. Using Fig. 15.6, calculate $A\hat{P}B$ when $A\hat{O}B$ is:

    (a)   100°
    (b)   64°
    (c)   90°
    (d)   120°
    (e)   140°
    (f)   160°

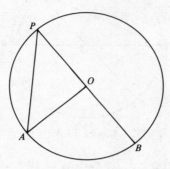

Figure 15.6

4. Using Fig. 15.7, calculate $A\hat{Q}O$, $B\hat{Q}O$ and $A\hat{Q}B$ when:

    (a) $A\hat{O}P = 80°$ and $B\hat{O}P = 120°$
    (b) $A\hat{O}P = 90°$ and $B\hat{O}P = 110°$
    (c) $A\hat{O}P = 130°$ and $B\hat{O}P = 130°$
    (d) $A\hat{O}P = 140°$ and $B\hat{O}P = 160°$

In each case compare reflex angle $A\hat{O}B$ with $A\hat{Q}B$.

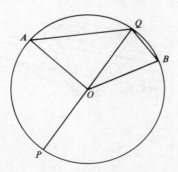

Figure 15.7

5. In Fig. 15.8 *AOB* is a diameter of the circle.

    (a) What, therefore, is $A\hat{O}B$?

    (b) Calculate $A\hat{Q}O$, $B\hat{Q}O$ and $A\hat{Q}B$ when $A\hat{O}P$ is equal to 40°, 60°, 80°, 20°.

    (c) What do you notice about the angle $A\hat{Q}B$ in every case?

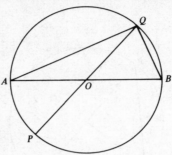

Figure 15.8

6. In Fig. 15.4, suppose the radius of the circle is 10. Calculate the arc of the circle, *AB* (minor arc), when $A\hat{Q}B = 90°$, 45°, 135°, 57°, 28.5°.

Draw *AB* meeting a circle at *L* and *M*. Suppose *O* is the centre of the circle. *OL* and *OM* make equal angles, *x*, with *AB* (Fig. 15.9). By the sum of the angles of a triangle:

$$2x + L\hat{O}M = 180°$$

$$\text{Therefore} \quad 2x = 180° - L\hat{O}M$$

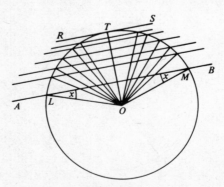

Figure 15.9

Now draw more chords parallel to AB but farther away from the centre. $L\hat{O}M$ becomes smaller. Therefore x becomes larger. When RTS touches the circle (at T), this means that RTS is a tangent, and $L\hat{O}M = 0$, and $2x = 180°$. So $x = 90°$. This means that OT is perpendicular to RS. In other words:

A radius to the point of contact of a
tangent is perpendicular to the tangent.   *15.5*

In Fig. 15.10 OT is perpendicular to XTY, i.e.

$$O\hat{T}X = O\hat{T}Y = \text{a right angle}$$

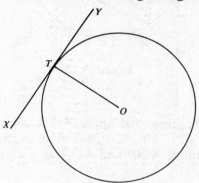

Figure 15.10

Exercise 15.3

1. In Fig. 15.11 calculate angles $O\hat{P}T$, $T\hat{O}P$, $P\hat{O}S$, $O\hat{P}S$, $O\hat{S}P$, $T\hat{P}S$ when angle $P\hat{T}X = 60°$, $50°$, $40°$, $30°$, $28°$, $88°$.

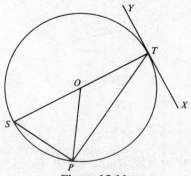

Figure 15.11

2. In Fig. 15.12 calculate angles $O\hat{T}P$, $O\hat{P}T$, $P\hat{O}T$, $P\hat{Q}T$ when angle $P\hat{T}X = 24°, 38°, 49°, 83°, 57°$.

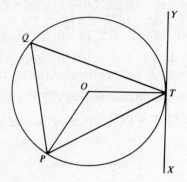

Figure 15.12

3. In Fig. 15.13, given that angle $A\hat{O}B$ takes the values $120°$, $110°, 100°, 140°, 160°, 170°$, calculate in each case the angles $A\hat{C}B$, reflex angle $A\hat{O}B$ and $A\hat{D}B$. In each case find the value of $A\hat{C}B + A\hat{D}B$.

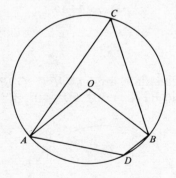

Figure 15.13

4. In Fig. 15.14, given that angle $T\hat{A}B$ takes the values $50°, 60°$, $70°, 80°, 55°, 61°, 37°$, calculate in each case the angles $D\hat{A}B$, reflex angle $D\hat{O}B$, $D\hat{O}B$ and $D\hat{C}B$. In each case compare the values of $T\hat{A}B$ and $D\hat{C}B$.

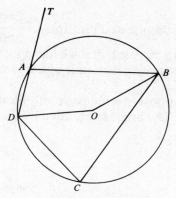

Figure 15.14

15.2 Radian measure of an' angle

Most sets of four-figure tables have pages devoted to the conversion from degree measure of angle to radian measure of angle and vice versa. It is quite a simple matter to use such tables, and so the method will not be explained here.

In the first place it is necessary to understand the reason for the adoption of another unit of angle. In the second place, we must understand the principles on which the conversion is based.

Look once again at the arc of a circle, Fig. 15.15, which subtends angle $\alpha°$ at the centre of the circle. Arc length is:

$$\frac{\alpha}{360} \times 2\pi r = \frac{\alpha \times 2\pi}{360} \times r$$

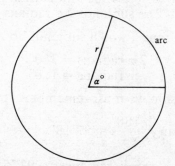

Figure 15.15

The arc length is a complicated multiple $\left(\dfrac{\alpha \times 2\pi}{360}\right)$ of the radius. It would be much more convenient if we had a simpler multiple of the radius. We shall discover a new unit of angle which will bring this about.

In Fig. 15.16, suppose we measure off, along the circle, an arc equal to the radius. The angle subtended by that arc at the centre is

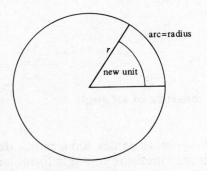

Figure 15.16

our new unit. We call it a *radian*. How is the radian related to the degree? First of all:

An arc length r subtends 1 radian at the centre.
An arc length $2r$ subtends 2 radians at the centre.
An arc length $3r$ subtends 3 radians at the centre.
An arc length $2\pi r$ subtends 2π radians at the centre.

But $2\pi r$ = circumference, which subtends 360° at the centre. So:

$$2\pi \text{ radians} = 360°$$
$$\pi \text{ radians} = 180° \qquad\qquad 15.6$$

This is the relationship we must remember. It means that:

$$1 \text{ radian} = \frac{180°}{\pi} \approx 57°18'$$

and $\quad 1° = \dfrac{\pi}{180} \text{ radians} \approx 0.0175 \text{ radians}$

Examples

1. Convert 1.35 radians to degrees and minutes.

$$1.35 \text{ radians} = 1.35 \times \frac{180}{\pi} \approx 77° + 0.34 \times 60'$$
$$\approx 77° + 20.4'$$
$$\approx 77°20'$$

Number	Logarithm
1.35	0.1303
180	2.2553
	2.3856
π	0.4972
77.34	1.8884

2. Convert 108°37′ to radians.

$$108°37' \approx 108.62° = \frac{108.62 \times \pi}{180} \text{ radians}$$
$$\approx 1.895 \approx 1.90 \text{ radians}$$

Number	Logarithm
108.6	2.0359
π	0.4972
	2.5331
180	2.2553
	0.2778

Exercise 15.4

1. Convert to degrees and minutes the following angles measured in radians: 2, 0.5, 1.5, 3.142, 6.284, 2.7, 1.05, 0.128.

2. Convert the following angles to radians: 32.5°, 47.8°, 158.2°, 270.1°, 35°30′, 73°45′, 194°51′.

  1 revolution or
  1 complete rotation = 2π radians.

  3 revs = $3 \times 2\pi$ radians = 6π radians.
  7 revs = $7 \times 2\pi$ radians = 14π radians.
  n revs = $n \times 2\pi$ radians = $2n\pi$ radians.

Put another way:

$$2\pi \text{ radians} = 1 \text{ rev}$$

$$1 \text{ radian} = \frac{1}{2\pi} \text{ revs}$$

$$x \text{ radians} = \frac{1}{2\pi} \times x \text{ revs} \qquad\qquad 15.7$$

Exercise 15.5

1. Express in radians the following: 2 revs, 6 revs, 100 revs, 1500 revs, 86 revs.
2. Express in revs the following angles: 73 rads, 148 rads, 55.6 rads, 19.7 rads.

Now look at the following relationships:

For circle radius r and angle at centre 1 radian, the arc is $r = 1r$.
For circle radius r and angle at centre 2 radians, the arc is $2r$.
For circle radius r and angle at centre 3 radians, the arc is $3r$.
For circle radius r and angle at centre θ radians, the arc is θr.

The formula relating arc (s), angle at centre in radians (θ) and the radius (r) is:

$$s = r\theta \qquad\qquad 15.8$$

This means $\quad s \times \dfrac{1}{\theta} = r\theta \times \dfrac{1}{\theta} = r$

i.e. $\quad r = \dfrac{s}{\theta} \qquad\qquad 15.9$

Similarly:

$$s \times \frac{1}{r} = \not{r}\theta \times \frac{1}{\not{r}} = \theta$$

i.e. $\quad \theta = \dfrac{s}{r}$ *15.10*

In the above formulae s and r are measured in the same units (millimetres, centimetres, metres, kilometres, etc.) and θ is measured in radians.

Exercise 15.6

1. Calculate the arc lengths of circles where the radius and angle subtended at the centre take the following pairs of values: 5 m, 2 rad; 5 m, 2.6 rad; 10 cm, 5.7 rad; 2 km, 0.32 rad; 11.3 m, 1.75 rad; 62.5 cm, 58.4°.
2. Calculate the radii of the circles in which the following arc lengths subtend the angles paired with them: 10 m, 2 rad; 14 cm, 7 rad; 8.2 km, 0.0023 rad; 885 mm, 23.2°; 1000 m, 250 rev.
3. Calculate the angles, in radians, at the centres of circles which are subtended by arcs of given lengths, paired in each case with the radius: 57.2 m arc, 14.9 m radius; 109.5 cm arc, 33.5 cm radius; 59.4 mm arc, 3.69 cm radius; 0.894 cm arc, 11.25 mm radius.

16

Areas and Volumes

16.1 Rectangular areas

If we wish to calculate areas and volumes of various surfaces and solids we must first begin by calculating those of certain simple figures and solids. First we shall concentrate on areas.

What facts do we know about rectangles? (See Fig. 16.1.)

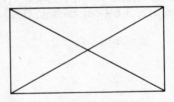

Figure 16.1

1. A rectangle has its opposite sides equal and parallel.
2. Any one angle of it is a right angle, so all the angles are right angles.
3. The diagonals are equal and bisect each other.
4. Each diagonal divides the area into two equal parts.

What facts do we know about squares? (See Fig. 16.2.)

A square is a special kind of rectangle. It is a rectangle with any two adjacent sides equal. That means, of course, that all the sides are equal.

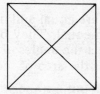

Figure 16.2

What facts do we know about parallelograms? (See Fig. 16.3.)

1. The opposite sides are equal and parallel.
2. No angle is a right angle.
3. Opposite angles are equal.
4. The diagonals are not equal, but they do bisect each other.
5. Each diagonal bisects the area of the parallelogram.

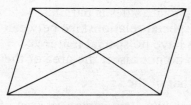

Figure 16.3

What facts do we know about a rhombus? (A rhombus is a diamond shape, Fig. 16.4.)

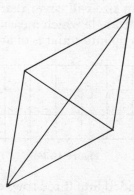

Figure 16.4

1. Its opposite sides and angles are equal and parallel.
2. Any two adjacent sides are equal. This means all the sides are equal.
3. The opposite angles are equal and none is a right angle.
4. The diagonals are unequal. They bisect each other at right angles, and they bisect the angles of the rhombus.
5. Each diagonal bisects the area of the rhombus.

What facts do we know about a trapezium (Fig. 16.5)?

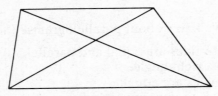

Figure 16.5

1. One pair of opposite sides is parallel.
2. There are no special relationships between the angles.
3. The diagonals have no special features.
4. The diagonals do not bisect the area of the trapezium.

The basic area is that of the square.

A square of side 1 cm covers an area of 1 cm².
A square of side 1 m covers an area of 1 m².
A square of side 1 km covers an area of 1 km².

When we wish to find the area of a rectangle we ask ourselves how many squares of a given size will cover that area. Suppose, in the first place, we have a rectangle which measures 7 cm by 3 cm (Fig. 16.6). We split the area up into squares of area 1 cm². We discover

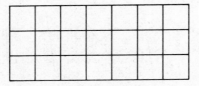

Figure 16.6

that the area can be divided into three rows each containing 7 such squares. So the area is 3×7 cm² or 7×3 cm². If the length is l units and the breadth *b* units, then the area = *l* × *b* unit squares. The formula for the area of a rectangle is, then:

$$A = lb \qquad\qquad 16.1$$

The area of a parallelogram

Consider parallelogram *ABCD* (Fig. 16.7). Imagine that we cut off area *CBN* along line *CN*. This area fits exactly on top of the space

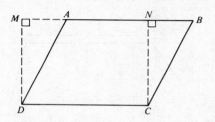

Figure 16.7

DAM. We have thus converted the area of the parallelogram *ABCD* into the area of the rectangle *MNCD*, and the area of this is *DC* × *DM*. We often call *DC* the base and *DM* the height. So the formula for the area of the parallelogram is:

$$A = \text{base } (b) \times \text{height } (h) = bh \qquad\qquad 16.2$$

The area of a triangle

Consider triangle *PQR* (Fig. 16.8). Draw *PS* parallel to *QR* and draw *RS* parallel to *QP*. Then *PSRQ* is a parallelogram. By the

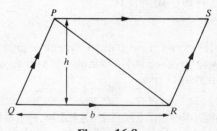

Figure 16.8

above formula its area = $b \times h$. But PR (diagonal) bisects the area of the parallelogram.

So the area of triangle $PQR = \frac{1}{2}bh$ *16.3*

The area of a trapezium

The area of a trapezium (Fig. 16.9) is:

$$\frac{1}{2}(a + b)h$$ *16.4*

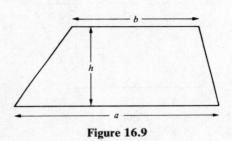

Figure 16.9

Examples

1. For a rectangle, determine: (a) A when l and b are 35.4 and 28.6 mm respectively; (b) l when A and b are 4569 mm^2 and 37.8 mm respectively.

   (a) $A = l \times b = 35.4 \times 28.6 = 1012.44 \approx 1012.4$ mm^2.
   Check: $30 \times 30 = 900$.
   (b) $l = A/b = 4569/37.8 = 120.87302 \approx 120.9$ mm.
   Check: $4400/40 = 110$.

2. For a triangle, determine: (a) A when b and h are 47.7 and 32.8 mm respectively; (b) h when A and b are 5709.2 mm^2 and 83.4 mm respectively.

   (a) $A = \frac{1}{2}bh = \frac{1}{2} \times 47.7 \times 32.8 = 782.28 \approx 782.3$ mm^2.
   (b) $h = 2A/b = (2 \times 5709.2)/83.4 = 136.91127$
        ≈ 136.9 mm.

Exercise 16.1

1. Calculate the following measurements of a rectangle (Fig. 16.10), given the other two:

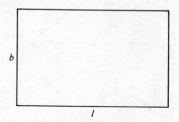

Figure 16.10

   (a) *A* when *l* and *b* are: 10 cm, 3 cm; 21 m, 7 m; 83 mm, 54 mm; 6.9 km, 3.8 km.
   (b) *l* when *A* and *b* are: 800 m², 20 m; 650 cm², 13 cm; 454 mm², 13.2 mm.
   (c) *b* when *A* and *l* are: 1500 cm², 50 cm; 90 m², 5000 cm.

2. Calculate the following measurements of a parallelogram, given the other two (Fig. 16.11):

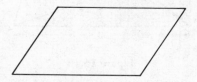

Figure 16.11

   (a) *A* when *b* and *h* are: 10 cm, 7 cm; 36 m, 9 m.
   (b) *b* when *A* and *h* are: 1200 m², 40 m; 93.4 cm², 7 cm.

3. *ABCD* (Fig. 16.12) is said to be a quadrilateral. It can be divided into two triangles, *ABC* and *ADC*, in each of which

the marked angle is a right angle. Calculate the area of *ABCD*.

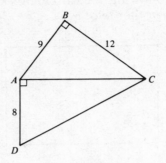

Figure 16.12

4. Calculate the area of triangles *ABC* and *BDC* in Fig. 16.13. Use these values to calculate the area of *ABDC*.

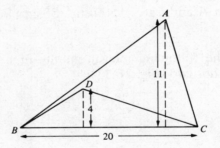

Figure 16.13

16.2 The area of the circle

Imagine that we divide a circle up into a large number of parts (sectors), all equal, by cutting along diameters as illustrated in Fig. 16.14.

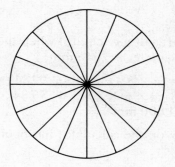

Figure 16.14

Then arrange the pieces according to the pattern indicated in Fig. 16.15. The smaller each part (sector) is, the nearer Fig. 16.15

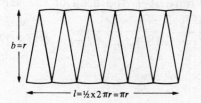

Figure 16.15

will be to a rectangle. The length will be half the circumference of the circle and the breadth will be the radius. So:

$$\text{area} = \pi r \times r = \pi r^2 \qquad 16.5$$

An alternative formula introduces the diameter, d, instead of r:

$$A = \pi r^2$$

$$= \pi \left(\frac{d}{2}\right)^2 = \tfrac{1}{4} \cdot \pi \cdot d^2 \qquad 16.6$$

Area of semi-circle is:

$$\tfrac{1}{2}\pi r^2 = \tfrac{1}{2} \times \frac{\pi d^2}{4} = \tfrac{1}{8}\pi d^2 \qquad 16.7$$

Examples

1. Calculate the area of a circle: (a) when the radius is 35.7 cm; (b) when the diameter is 2045 mm.

    (a) $A = \pi r^2 = \pi \times 35.7^2 = 4003.9284 \approx 4003.9 \text{ cm}^2$
    (b) $A = \frac{1}{4}\pi d^2 = \frac{1}{4} \times \pi \times 2045^2 = 3\,284\,554.8$
         $\approx 3\,284\,600 \text{ mm}^2$

    Here the key π on the calculator has been used, not 3.142.

2. Calculate the radius of a circle whose area is 5693.4 cm².
    $$r = \sqrt{A/\pi} = \sqrt{5693.4/\pi} = 42.570712 \approx 42.6 \text{ cm}$$

3. Calculate the diameter of a semi-circle whose area is 629.6 cm². Where A is the area of the semi-circle, by Law 16.7:
    $$d = \sqrt{8A/\pi} = \sqrt{(8 \times 629.6/\pi)} = 40.04077 \approx 40.04 \text{ cm}$$

Exercise 16.2

1. Calculate the areas of circles whose radii are 10 cm, 5 m, 1.2 km and 14.7 mm. Take $\pi = 3.142$.
2. Calculate the radii of circles whose areas are 314.2 cm², 380 m² and 0.0156 km².
3. Calculate the diameters of quarter circles whose areas are 56.1 m², 230 cm² and 5.8 km².

16.3 Volume

The basic unit of volume is that of the cube.

> A cube of side 1 cm has a volume of 1 cm³.
> A cube of side 1 m has a volume of 1 m³.
> A cube of side 1 km has a volume of 1 km³.

A solid whose faces are all rectangles (a rectangular prism) is represented by Fig. 16.16. It has length l, breadth b and height h. By dividing these into l, b and h equal units we can visualize the

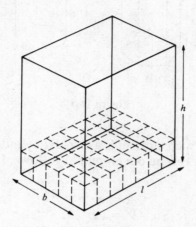

Figure 16.16

space inside the solid being divided into a number of equal cubes. Because the height is h there will be h layers of cubes. In each layer there will be $l \times b$ cubes. Total number of cubes $= l \times b \times h$. So the volume $= lbh$ units. The formula for such a solid is:

$$V = lbh \qquad\qquad 16.8$$

But that means:

$$V = (lb)h$$
$$= A \times h \quad \text{(because } lb = \text{area of base)}$$

So another method of expressing the formula is:

$$A \times h \qquad\qquad 16.9$$

where A is the area of the base.

We can have prisms with any shape of base, as, for instance, in Fig. 16.17(a) and (b). In all cases:

$$V = Ah \qquad\qquad 16.10$$

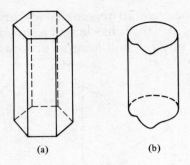

(a)   (b)

Figure 16.17

A special case of such a prism is a circular cylinder (Fig. 16.18). In this case $V = Ah$ can be developed as follows. If r is the radius of the circular base:

$$A = \pi r^2$$
$$\text{So} \quad V = (\pi r^2)h$$
$$= \pi r^2 h \qquad\qquad 16.11$$

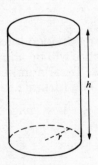

Figure 16.18

Examples

1. Calculate the volume of a prism where l, b and h take the following values: $l = 37.8$ cm, $b = 21.4$ cm, $h = 31.5$ cm.

    $$V = lbh = 37.8 \times 21.4 \times 31.5 = 25\,480.98 \approx 25\,481 \text{ cm}^3$$

2. Calculate the height of a prism whose volume and area of base are 34 756 cm³ and 580 cm² respectively.

$$h = V/A = 34\,756/580 = 59.924138 \approx 60.0 \text{ cm}$$

3. Determine the radius of the base of a circular cylinder whose volume and height are 75 036 m³ and 15 m respectively.

$$r = \sqrt{V/\pi h} = \sqrt{75\,036/(\pi \times 15)} = 39.903802 \approx 39.90 \text{ m}$$

Exercise 16.3

1. Calculate the volumes of rectangular prisms where *l*, *b* and *h* have the following values: 15, 10, 8 cm; 74 cm, 80 mm, 0.34 m; 5.2 m, 3.7 m, 2.6 m.
2. Calculate the heights of rectangular prisms where *V*, *l* and *b* are: 500 m³, 4 m, 2.5 m; 1250 cm³, 75 mm, 5 cm; 63.5 m³, 5.05 m, 4.25 m.
3. Calculate the volumes of prisms whose bases and heights take the following values: $A = 20$ cm², $h = 5$ cm; $A = 145$ cm², $h = 13$ cm.
4. Calculate the volumes of circular cylinders where *r* and *h* take the following values: 6.57 cm, 11.2 cm; 385 mm, 27.4 cm.
5. Calculate the radii of the bases of circular cylinders where *V* and *h* take the following values: 8680 cm³, 9.2 cm; 682.9 m³, 4.76 m.

Pyramids

In Fig. 16.19 *VXYZ* represents a triangular pyramid. What is the volume of such a solid? To appreciate this fully we really need a

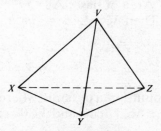

Figure 16.19

three-dimensional model, but as a second best arrangement let us look at Fig. 16.20, which is a triangular prism *ABCDEF*. The dotted lines show how we can split it up into three triangular pyramids, *ADEF*, *ABCF* and *ABEF*. *ABCF* and *ABEF* have

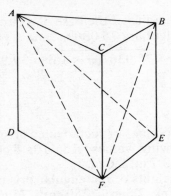

Figure 16.20

equal bases, triangles *BCF* and *BEF*, and a common vertex, *A*, so they have equal bases and equal heights. Therefore we would expect them to have equal volumes. Similarly, *ADEF* and *ABCF* have equal bases, *ADF* and *ACF*, and vertices *B* and *E* at the same level, so they have equal bases and equal heights, and therefore we would expect them to have equal volumes.

Therefore each of the three triangular pyramids is equal in volume to the others. This means each has a volume = $\frac{1}{3}$ volume of the prism = $\frac{1}{3}Ah$. So the formula for the volume of a pyramid is:

$$V = \tfrac{1}{3}Ah \qquad\qquad 16.12$$

A circular cone (Fig. 16.21) is a special type of pyramid. If *r* is the radius of the base:

$$\text{Area of base, } A = \pi r^2$$
$$\text{Then } V = \tfrac{1}{3}Ah = \tfrac{1}{3}\pi r^2 h \qquad\qquad 16.13$$

Examples

1. Determine the volume of a pyramid where the area of the base and the height are 56.37 cm^2 and 11.02 cm respectively.

    $$V = \tfrac{1}{3}Ah = \tfrac{1}{3} \times 56.37 \times 11.02 = 207.0658 \approx 207.07 \text{ cm}^3$$

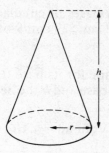

Figure 16.21

2. Calculate the height of a pyramid with a rectangular base given $V = 47\,073.6$ cm³, $l = 32.6$ cm, $b = 27.9$ cm.

   $h = 3V/lb = (3 \times 47\,073.6)/(32.6 \times 27.9) = 155.26618$
   ≈ 155.3 cm

3. Calculate the volume of a circular cone where r and h take the following values: $r = 14.3$ cm, $h = 37.4$ cm.

   $V = \frac{1}{3}\pi r^2 h = \frac{1}{3} \times \pi \times 14.3^2 \times 37.4 = 8008.8894$
   ≈ 8008.9 cm³

4. Calculate the radius of the base of a circular cone whose volume is 6608 cm³ and whose height is 12.5 cm.

   $r = \sqrt{3V/\pi h} = \sqrt{(3 \times 6608)/(\pi \times 12.5)} = 22.468067$
   ≈ 22.5 cm

Exercise 16.4

1. Calculate the volumes of pyramids where the area of the base and the height are given: 64 cm², 15 cm; 352 000 mm², 43 cm.
2. Calculate the heights of pyramids with rectangular bases, given volume and length and breadth of base: 7500 cm³, 50 cm, 25 cm; 34 m³, 6 m, 3 m.
3. Calculate the volumes of circular cones where r and h take the following values: 5 cm, 8 cm; 8.3 cm, 9.8 cm; 4.29 cm, 54.7 mm.

4. Calculate the radii of bases of circular cones where V and h take the values: 3452 cm³, 29 cm; 9407 cm³, 821.3 mm.

A cone may have any shape for its base (Fig. 16.22). In all cases, where A is the area of the base and h the height of the vertex above the base:

$$\text{Volume} = \tfrac{1}{3}Ah \qquad\qquad 16.14$$

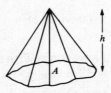

Figure 16.22

We are able to use this fact to discover the volume of a sphere. Fig. 16.23 is intended to represent a sphere, centre O. On its surface suppose we have a small area, let us call it δA (meaning a small bit of A, and of any shape). If we join all points of that area to O, the

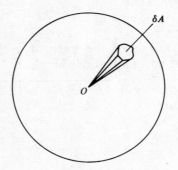

Figure 16.23

solid which is marked out is approximately a cone. The smaller δA is, the nearer that bit of surface will be to a plane surface, and the nearer the solid marked out will be to a cone. The height of the cone (distance from O to A) is r (radius of the sphere). So:

$$\text{Volume} = \tfrac{1}{3}\delta A \cdot r$$

If we divide the whole surface area of the sphere into small areas such as A and imagine them joined to O we shall obtain a series of cones which interlock and in total give the volume of the sphere. So:

$$\text{Volume of sphere} = \tfrac{1}{3}\delta A_1 r + \tfrac{1}{3}\delta A_2 r + \tfrac{1}{3}\delta A_3 r + \cdots \text{ (where}$$
$$\delta A_1, \delta A_2, \text{ etc. are small areas on sphere)}$$
$$= \tfrac{1}{3}r(\delta A_1 + \delta A_2 + \delta A_3 + \cdots \text{ (by factorizing)}$$
$$= \tfrac{1}{3}r \times \text{total area of sphere}$$

We shall assume that the area of the sphere is $4\pi r^2$. This means:

$$V = \tfrac{1}{3}r \times 4\pi r^2 = \tfrac{4}{3}\pi r^3 \qquad\qquad 16.15$$

Examples

1. Calculate the volume of a sphere whose radius is 43.6 cm.
$$V = \tfrac{4}{3} \times \pi \times r^3 = (4 \times \pi \times 43.6^3)/3 = 347\,174.71$$
$$\approx 347\,170 \text{ cm}^3$$

2. Calculate the radius of a sphere whose volume is 620 045 cm³.
$$r = \sqrt[3]{3V/4\pi} = \sqrt[3]{(3 \times 620\,045)/(4 \times \pi)} = 52.898663$$
$$\approx 52.90 \text{ cm}$$

Exercise 16.5

1. Calculate the volumes of spheres whose radii are: 10 cm; 134 mm; 0.25 m.
2. Calculate the radii of spheres whose volumes are: 1000 cm³; 892 100 mm³; 0.00249 m³.

16.4 Surface area

The surface area of a circular cylinder (Fig. 16.24(a)) is made up of three parts: the two ends (both circles) and the curved surface. The curved surface, opened out, turns into a rectangle (Fig. 16.24(b)).

The length is $2\pi r$ and the breadth is h. The total area is:

$$\pi r^2 + \pi r^2 + 2\pi rh = 2\pi r^2 + 2\pi rh$$
$$\text{Total area} = 2\pi r(r + h) \quad \text{(factorizing)} \qquad 16.16$$

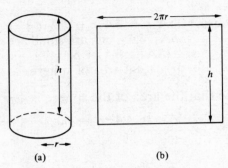

(a)   (b)

Figure 16.24

If the cylinder is hollow and one end is open:

$$\text{surface area} = \pi r^2 + 2\pi rh = \pi r(r + 2h) \qquad 16.17$$

A right prism, represented in Fig. 16.25, has two identical ends and a series of faces which are rectangles. If the areas of the ends are A, the total surface area is:

$$2A + l_1 h + l_2 h + l_3 h + \cdots = 2A + h(l_1 + l_2 + l_3 + \cdots)$$
$$= 2A + h \times p \qquad 16.18$$

where p is the perimeter of an end.

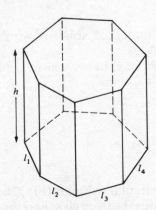

Figure 16.25

To be able to apply this formula we need to be able to calculate the areas of the polygons (the ends) and to be given the lengths of the sides. One method of calculating the area of a polygon, which may be irregular, is to divide it, as in Fig. 16.26, into triangles. This is useful only if we have sufficient information to calculate the areas of the individual triangles.

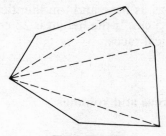

Figure 16.26

Examples

1. Calculate the curved surface area of a circular cylinder where the values of r and h are 13.6 cm and 27.9 cm respectively.
   $S = 2\pi rh = 2 \times \pi \times 13.6 \times 27.9 = 2384.0918 \approx 2384$ cm^2
   The total surface area $= 2\pi r(r + h) = 2 \times \pi \times 13.6 \times 41.5$
   $$= 3546.2298$$
   $$\approx 3546 \text{ cm}^2$$

2. Calculate the height of a circular cylinder when the total surface area and the base radius are 1635.2 cm^2 and 11.4 cm respectively.
   $S = 2\pi r^2 + 2\pi rh$
   Rearranging:
   $$2\pi rh = S - 2\pi r^2$$
   $$h = (S - 2\pi r^2)/2\pi r$$
   $$= (1635.2 - 2 \times \pi \times 11.4^2)/2 \times \pi \times 11.4$$
   $$= 11.428962 \approx 11.43 \text{ cm}$$

Exercise 16.6

1. A right circular cylinder has base radius r and height h. Calculate the curved surface area of the cylinder where r and h

take the values: 10 cm, 20 cm; 14 cm, 33 cm; 0.92 m, 687 mm.
2. Calculate the areas of top and base together in each part of question (1). Then calculate the total surface area in each case.
3. Calculate the heights of circular cylinders where the total surface area and base radius are: 872.3 cm^2, 10 cm; 0.6481 m^2, 20 cm.
4. A right prism has as base and top identical regular hexagons whose sides are 5 cm. If the height is 25 cm calculate the total area of the vertical faces.

16.5 Composite areas and volumes

In addition to the formulae which we have developed for areas and volumes, we need to use, in certain examples, one or two simple but important ideas. For instance, in Fig. 16.27, the area of

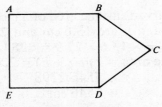

Figure 16.27

ABCDE, which in itself is not covered by any of the above formulae, is easily seen to be area *ABDE* + area *BCD*, i.e. a rectangle + a triangle. And we do have formulae for each of these.

Similarly, in Fig. 16.28, area *ABCDE* = area *ABDE* − area *BCD* = rectangle − semi-circle.

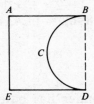

Figure 16.28

In Fig. 16.29, the volume of the solid = volume V_1 + volume V_2 + volume V_3 = volume of circular cone + volume of circular cylinder + volume of hemisphere.

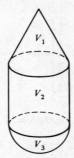

Figure 16.29

Exercise 16.7

In the following questions all dimensions are to be assumed to be in centimetres.

1. Calculate the area of the Fig. 16.30, *ABCDE*, using the dimensions given.

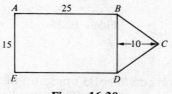

Figure 16.30

2. In Fig. 16.31 *ABDE* represents a square. *BCD* is a semicircle. Calculate the area of *ABCDE*.

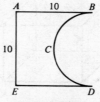

Figure 16.31

3. In Fig. 16.32 *MNP* is a semi-circle and *LMP* is an isosceles triangle. Calculate the area of *LMNP*.

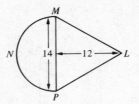

Figure 16.32

4. Fig. 16.33 represents a solid made up of a hemisphere, a circular cylinder and a circular cone. Using the measurements given, calculate the total volume of the solid.

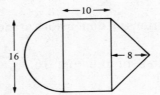

Figure 16.33

5. Fig. 16.34 represents a solid made up of a rectangular prism and a rectangular pyramid. Using the measurements given, calculate the total volume.

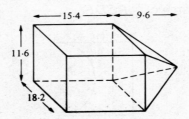

Figure 16.34

6. Fig. 16.35 represents a circular pipe. Calculate its volume.

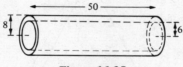

Figure 16.35

16.6 Additional formulae

As well as the formulae already considered, others of importance are referred to below:

Area of a sector of a circle

The two formulae for the area of a sector (Fig. 16.36) are:

$$A = \tfrac{1}{2}r^2\theta \quad (\theta \text{ in radians}) \qquad 16.19$$

$$A = \frac{\theta}{360} \pi r^2 \quad (\theta \text{ in degrees}) \qquad 16.20$$

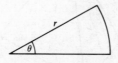

Figure 16.36

Surface area of a cone (*circular*)

Where l is the slant height and r the base radius (Fig. 16.37) the curved surface area, S, is given by:

$$S = \pi r l \qquad 16.21$$

The total surface area = S + area of base:

$$\pi r l + \pi r^2 = \pi r^2 + \pi r l = \pi r(r + l) \qquad 16.22$$

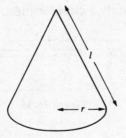

Figure 16.37

Surface area of a right square pyramid

Where the base side is a and the slant height is l (Fig. 16.38) the sloping surface area, S, is:

$$4 \times \text{area of each triangular face} = 4 \times \tfrac{1}{2}al = 2al \qquad 16.23$$

The total surface area is:

$$\text{area of square base} + 2al = a^2 + 2al = a(a + 2l) \qquad 16.24$$

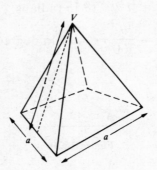

Figure 16.38

Surface area of a sphere

Where the radius of the sphere is r (Fig. 16.39):

$$\text{surface area} = 4\pi r^2 \qquad 16.25$$

Certain solids are formed by cutting off the upper parts of pyramids

Figure 16.39

and cones along planes which are parallel to the bases (see Figs 16.40 and 16.41). In each case, when the shaded part is omitted, the remaining solid is called a *frustum*.

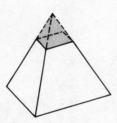

Figure 16.40

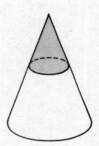

Figure 16.41

Volume of a frustum of a cone

Where r_1, r_2 and h represent the dimensions indicated in Fig. 16.42 and V is the volume of the frustum:

$$V = \tfrac{1}{3}\pi(r_1^2 + r_1r_2 + r_2^2) \cdot h \qquad 16.26$$

Sometimes it is convenient to calculate V as the difference

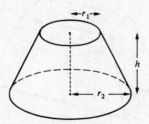

Figure 16.42

between the volumes of two cones, each of whose base radius and height are known, e.g.:

$$V = \tfrac{1}{3}\pi r_2^2 h_2 - \tfrac{1}{3}\pi r_1^2 h_1$$

Surface area of a frustum of a cone

Again, with the dimensions indicated in Fig. 16.43, the curved surface area:

$$S = \pi(r_1 + r_2)l \qquad\qquad 16.27$$

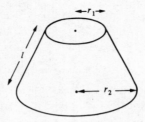

Figure 16.43

The total surface area is:

$$\pi r_1^2 + \pi r_2^2 + \pi(r_1 + r_2)l \qquad\qquad 16.28$$

Volume of a frustum of a pyramid

Where A_1 and A_2 are the areas of the parallel faces (in Fig. 16.44 each is a rectangle) and h is the height of the frustum, then the

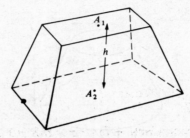

Figure 16.44

volume of the frustum is:

$$V = \tfrac{1}{3}h(A_1 + A_2 + \sqrt{A_1A_2})$$ *16.29*

Formula 16.29 is true whatever the shape of the parallel faces.

Surface area of a frustum of a pyramid

Suppose the parallel faces are rectangles whose sides are x_1, x_2 and X_1, X_2 respectively, and the slant heights of the two different kinds of sloping faces are l_1 and l_2 (Fig. 16.45). The sloping surface

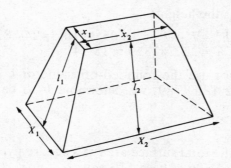

Figure 16.45

area = the sum of the areas of 4 trapezia:

$$2 \times \tfrac{1}{2}(x_1 + X_1)l_1 + 2 \times \tfrac{1}{2}(x_2 + X_2)l_2 = (x_1 + X_1)l_1 + (x_2 + X_2)l_2$$

16.30

The total surface area is:

$$x_1x_2 + X_1X_2 + (x_1 + X_1)l_1 + (x_2 + X_2)l_2$$ *16.31*

Examples

1. A cone of slant height 17 cm has a base radius of 8 cm. Calculate its total surface area.
    By formula 16.22:

    Total surface area $= \pi r(r + l) = \pi \times 8(8 + 17)$
    $= \pi \times 8 \times 25 = 628.31853 \approx 628 \text{ cm}^2$

2. Calculate the height of a cone, base radius 10 cm, and total surface area 900 cm^2.

    Then $r = 10$, and l is unknown. Substitute in 16.22:

    $$900 = \pi \times 10(10 + l)$$

    $$\frac{1}{\pi \times \cancel{10}} \times \cancel{900}^{90} = \frac{1}{\cancel{\pi} \times \cancel{10}} \times \cancel{\pi} \times \cancel{10}(10 + l)$$

    $$\frac{90}{\pi} = 10 + l$$

    $$l = 90/\pi - 10 = 18.64789 \approx 18.65$$

    Now, if h is the height:

    $$h^2 = l^2 - r^2 = 18.65^2 - 10^2 = 247.8225$$
    $$h = 15.742379 \approx 15.74$$

    If we do not use the rounded-off value of l, i.e. 18.65, but instead use 18.64789, we determine h to be 15.739879 $\approx$ 15.73.

3. Calculate the total surface area of a square pyramid of height 100 mm and side of base 110 mm.

    The formula needed is 16.24. $a = 110$ and l is unknown. By drawing a half vertical section through V and parallel to two sides of the base, we obtain the triangle in Fig. 16.46, in which the sides are l, h and $\frac{1}{2}a$. Then:

    $$l^2 = h^2 + (\tfrac{1}{2}a)^2 = h^2 + \tfrac{1}{4}a^2$$
    $$= 100^2 + 55^2 = 13\,025$$
    $$l = 114.12712 \approx 114$$

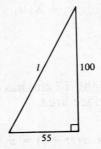

Figure 16.46

Then, by 16.24, the total surface area is:

$$110(110 + 2 \times 114.12712) = 37\,207.966 \approx 37\,208 \text{ mm}^2$$

4. Calculate the volume of the frustum of a cone with height 6 and in which the radii of top and bottom are 2 and 4 respectively.
   By formula 16.26:
   $$\begin{aligned} V &= \tfrac{1}{3}\pi(2^2 + 2 \times 4 + 4^2) \times 6 \\ &= \tfrac{1}{3}\pi(4 + 8 + 16) \times 6 = 175.92919 \approx 176 \end{aligned}$$

5. Determine the curved surface area of the frustum of a cone where $r_1 = 16.54$ cm, $r_2 = 23.83$ cm and $h = 9.27$ cm.
   Before we can use formula 16.27 we need to determine l. From Fig. 16.47, by Pythagoras:
   $$l^2 = 7.29^2 + 9.27^2$$
   $$l = 11.793091 \approx 11.79$$

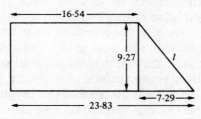

Figure 16.47

The curved surface area is:
$$\pi(16.54 + 23.83)11.793091 = 1495.6717 \approx 1496$$

6. Calculate the volume of the frustum of a square pyramid with height 16 and in which the top and base are squares of sides 12 and 20 respectively.
   By formula 16.29:
   $$\begin{aligned} V &= \tfrac{1}{3} \times 16 \times (12^2 + 20^2 + \sqrt{12^2 \times 20^2}) \\ &= \tfrac{1}{3} \times 16 \times (144 + 400 + 240) = 4181.333333 \approx 4181 \end{aligned}$$

7. Using formula 16.31 determine the total surface area of the frustum of a rectangular pyramid the dimensions of which are: $x_1 = 15.3$, $x_2 = 24.1$, $X_1 = 30.6$, $X_2 = 48.2$, $l_1 = 15.7$, $l_2 = 12.6$.

Total surface area is:

$15.3 \times 24.1 + 30.6 \times 48.2 + (15.3 + 30.6) \times 15.7$
$\quad + (24.1 + 48.2) \times 12.6$
$\quad = 368.73 + 1474.92 + 720.63 + 910.98 = 3475.26 \approx 3475$

Exercise 16.8

1. Calculate the surface area of a sphere, radius 9.2 cm.
2. Calculate the total surface area of a solid hemisphere of radius 10 cm.
3. Calculate the radius of a sphere with surface area 1000 cm².
4. Calculate the curved surface area of a cone of height 15 cm and base radius 8 cm.
5. Calculate the total surface area of a cone of base radius 10 cm and slant height 35 cm.
6. Calculate the height of a cone with total surface area 1100 cm² and base radius 10 cm.
7. A solid consists of a cone resting on a hemispherical base. The sloping edge of the cone is 185 mm and the radius of the hemisphere is 95 mm. Calculate its total surface area.
8. Calculate the sloping surface of a square pyramid in which the side of the base is 20 cm and the height is 24 cm.
9. Calculate the sloping surface of a square pyramid in which the diagonal of the base is 20 cm and the sloping edge is 26 cm.
10. Calculate the volume of a frustum of a cone of height 100 mm and in which the radii of the top and base are 50 mm and 100 mm respectively.
11. Calculate the volume of the frustum of a cone formed by cutting off at the top one-third of the height of a cone in which the height is 24 cm and the base radius is 18 cm.
12. Calculate the volume of the frustum of a cone with sloping height 14.2 cm and with radii of top and base 6.5 and 11.8 cm respectively.
13. Calculate the curved surface area of the frustum of a cone where the slant height is 10 cm and the radii of the top and base are 10 cm and 20 cm respectively.

14. Calculate the curved surface area of the frustum of a cone where the vertical height is 12 cm and the radii of the top and base are 10 cm and 15 cm respectively.

15. Calculate the volume of the frustum of a square pyramid with height 20 cm and top and bottom faces of sides 10 cm and 20 cm.

16. Calculate the volume of the frustum of a square pyramid formed by cutting off at the top one-third of the height of a pyramid of height 30 cm and in which the side of the base is 20 cm.

17. Calculate the volume of the frustum of a square pyramid with height 165 mm and where the top and bottom faces have sides 145 mm and 195 mm respectively.

18. Calculate the total area of the sloping faces of the frustum of a square pyramid of height 12 cm and in which the sides of the top and bottom faces are 10 cm and 20 cm respectively.

19. Calculate the total area of the frustum of a square pyramid of height 125 mm and in which the sides of the top and bottom are 105 mm and 195 mm.

20. A rectangular metal block 100 mm × 80 mm × 60 mm has a cylindrical hole, of radius 10 mm, cut through its centre parallel to the longest edge. Calculate the volume of metal remaining after the hole has been cut.

21. A tank for transporting chemical spray is cylindrical, with both ends hemispherical. The overall length is 7000 mm and the radius of the cylindrical section is 1050 mm. Calculate the total capacity (volume) of the tank in cubic metres.

22. Calculate the area of sheet metal required to construct the tank in question (21), assuming a wastage of 15 per cent. Give the answer in square metres.

23. A drill cuts ten conical holes each 7.5 mm deep and with maximum diameter 5 mm in a rectangular metal plate of dimensions 105 mm × 105 mm × 30 mm. Calculate the volume of metal remaining, in cubic millimetres.

16.7 Areas and volumes of similar bodies

Where bodies are similar (i.e. with the same shape but not the same size) their volumes (for solids) and areas (surface areas if they are solid) are related to one another by a simple relationship.

In Fig. 16.48 each side of the triangle ABC is divided into three equal parts. From the figure it is easy to see that the triangles ADE,

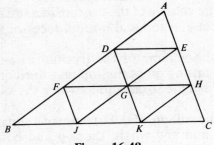

Figure 16.48

AFH and ABC are similar, that area $ABC = 9$ area ADE, and that area $AFH = 4$ area ADE. Then:

$$\frac{\text{area } ADE}{\text{area } ABC} = \frac{1}{9} = (\tfrac{1}{3})^2 = \left(\frac{AD}{AB}\right)^2, \quad \text{since } AD/AB = 1/3$$

$$AD/AF = 1/2; \; AF/AB = 2/3$$

Further: $\quad \dfrac{\text{area } ADE}{\text{area } AFH} = \dfrac{1}{4} = (\tfrac{1}{2})^2 = \left(\dfrac{AD}{AF}\right)^2$

Again: $\quad \dfrac{\text{area } AFH}{\text{area } ABC} = \dfrac{4}{9} = (\tfrac{2}{3})^2 = \left(\dfrac{AF}{AB}\right)^2$

This can be extended to similar plane figures of any shape. Where their areas are A_1 and A_2 and the corresponding lengths are l_1 and l_2, then:

$$\frac{A_1}{A_2} = \left(\frac{l_1}{l_2}\right)^2 \qquad\qquad 16.32$$

Note that in Fig. 16.49 (a) and (b), l_1 and l_2 can be any suitable pair

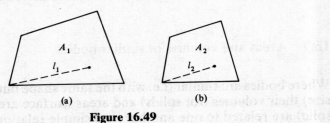

(a)   (b)

Figure 16.49

of corresponding length measurements. By extension of the principle yet again, the volumes of similar solids are related by the following rule:

$$V_1/V_2 = (l_1/l_2)^3 \qquad 16.33$$

Example

Fig. 16.50 (a) and (b) represent two similar circular cones. If their volumes and total surface areas are represented by V_1, V_2 and S_1, S_2 respectively, then:

$$S_1/S_2 = (r_1/r_2)^2 = (l_1/l_2)^2 = (h_1/h_2)^2 \qquad 16.34$$

and:
$$V_1/V_2 = (r_1/r_2)^3 = (l_1/l_2)^3 = (h_1/h_2)^3 \qquad 16.35$$

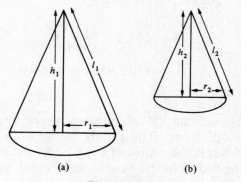

(a)   (b)

Figure 16.50

In fact the ratio of their areas is equal to the ratio of the squares on corresponding sides or lengths, and the ratio of their volumes is equal to the ratio of the cubes of the corresponding sides or lengths. These corresponding sides or lengths may be obtained in any way which is convenient. In 16.34 and 16.35 we compared radius with radius, or height with height, or slant height with slant height.

Examples

1. A cone has a volume of 637.5 cm³ and radius of base 13.4. Determine the volume of a similar cone in which the radius of base is 8.5.

Suppose the volume of the second cone is V cubic centimetres. Then:

$$V/637.5 = (8.5/13.4)^3$$

$$V = 637.5 \times \left(\frac{8.5}{13.4}\right)^3$$

$$= 162.71312 \approx 162.7$$

2. If the total surface area of the second cone in Example (1) is 461.1 cm^2 determine the total surface area of the first cone. Suppose the surface area of the first cone is S square centimetres. Then:

$$S/461.1 = (13.4/8.5)^2$$

$$S = 461.1 \times \left(\frac{13.4}{8.5}\right)^2$$

$$= 1145.9532 \approx 1146.0$$

3. Two similar circular cylinders have curved surface areas of 532.7 and 405.6 cm^2. The radius of the base of the first is 17.4 cm. What is the radius of the base of the second? Suppose the radius of the base of the second is r centimetres. Then:

$$532.7/405.6 = (17.4/r)^2$$

$$r^2/17.4^2 = 405.6/532.7$$

$$r^2 = 17.4^2 \times \frac{405.6}{532.7}$$

$$r = 17.4 \times \sqrt{\frac{405.6}{532.7}} = 15.182975 \approx 15.2$$

Exercise 16.9

1. The volume of a cone, height 23.2 cm, is 465.2 cm^3. A similar cone has a height of 18.5 cm. What is its volume?

2. The volumes of two similar cones are 649.2 cm³ and 487.6 cm³. If the height of the first is 19.5 cm, what is the height of the second?

3. The volumes of two similar cones are 649.2 cm³ and 487.6 cm³. The radius of the base of the second is 20.1 cm. What is the radius of the first?

4. Two similar cylinders have heights of 16.2 cm and 25.5 cm. The volume of the first is 1054.3 cm³. What is the volume of the second?

5. If, in question (4), the curved surface area of the second cylinder is 856.3 cm², what is the curved surface area of the first?

6. Two similar cylinders have surface areas of 707.7 cm² and 609.6 cm². If the radius of the base of the second is 31.5 cm what is the radius of the base of the first?

7. Two metal objects of similar shape and of the same material have masses of 83.6 kg and 42.5 kg. If the height of the first is 36.5 cm what is the height of the second? Note that the masses are proportional to the volumes.

8. Two similar objects have their volumes in the ratio 3:2. Determine the ratio of their surface areas.

9. Two similar bodies have their surface areas in the ratio 7:4. If the volume of the larger is 5690.3 cm³ what is the volume of the other?

10. Two similar models of the same statue have surface areas of 892.7 cm² and 1016.5 cm². If the volume of the first is 3145 cm³ what is the volume of the second?

17

The Trigonometry of Right-angled Triangles

Draw OX horizontal (Fig. 17.1). Draw $OA_1A_2A_3 \ldots$ at an angle (any angle which is acute) to OX. Mark off points A_1, A_2, A_3 etc. so that:

$$OA_1 = A_1A_2 = A_2A_3 = A_3A_4 = \cdots = 1$$

Draw A_1N_1, A_2N_2, A_3N_3 etc. perpendicular to OX. Then we have a series of right-angled triangles $OA_1N_1, OA_2N_2, OA_3N_3$ etc., all of which contain the same angle, $A_1\hat{O}N_1$.

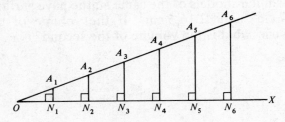

Figure 17.1

Measure, as accurately as you can, A_1N_1, A_2N_2, A_3N_3 etc. We notice that $A_2N_2 \approx 2A_1N_1$, $A_3N_3 \approx 3A_1N_1$, $A_4N_4 \approx 4A_1N_1$ etc. Again, by our construction:

$$OA_2 = 2OA_1,\ OA_3 = 3OA_1,\ OA_4 = 4OA_1 \ldots$$

In triangle OA_1N_1 write down the ratio

$$A_1N_1/OA_1$$

In triangle OA_2N_2 write down the ratio

$$A_2N_2/OA_2 \approx 2A_1N_1/2OA_1 \approx A_1N_1/OA_1$$

In triangle OA_3N_3 write down the ratio

$$A_3N_3/OA_3 \approx 3A_1N_1/3OA_1 \approx A_1N_1/OA_1$$

And so on. In other words, no matter what size the triangle is, all those ratios are equal. The sides in question were: all ANs were *opposite* angle $A_1\hat{O}N_1$ and all OAs were sides opposite the right angle, i.e. the hypotenuse. So each of those ratios represented opposite/hypotenuse.

For all right-angled triangles containing the same angle $A_1\hat{O}N_1$, the ratio opposite/hypotenuse has the same value. For right-angled triangles containing different angles from $A_1\hat{O}N_1$ the ratio opposite/hypotenuse will vary.

So opposite/hypotenuse is a ratio in a right-angled triangle depending only upon the value of the angle; let us call it α. The name we give to this ratio is the *sine of the angle*, or *sine α*, or, abbreviated still more, *sin α*. It is important to remember that the whole of this expression represents the name of the ratio in question. So we speak of sin 30°, sin 54°, sin 23°28', and so on.

Now construct right-angled triangles with angles 10°, 20°, 30°, ..., 80° in them. In each case make OA 10 cm. Then measure AN in centimetres. ($AN \approx 6.4$ cm.) From Fig. 17.2, where the

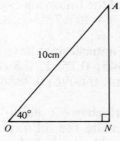

Figure 17.2

angle is 40°, we would obtain the following result:

$$\sin 40° = \frac{AN}{OA} \approx \frac{6.4}{10} = 0.64$$

For convenience, instead of having to construct a diagram each time we wish to discover the sine of a given angle, we are provided with a set of tables, called natural sines, which give us the required information. Compare the answers from the tables with those you obtained from your diagrams.

We must be able to use the tables to carry out *two* operations: *one*, given the angle, to obtain its sine, and *two*, given the sine of an unknown angle, to determine the angle. The tables are constructed in a similar way to those for squares, square roots and logarithms.

Examples

1. $\sin 16° = 0.2756$;
    $\sin 16°36' = 0.2857$;
    $\sin 16°40' = 0.2857 + (11) \text{ difference} = 0.2857 + 0.0011$
    $= 0.2868.$

2. $0.9455 = \sin 71°$;
    $0.9164 = \sin 66°24'$;
    $0.8727 = \sin 60°42' + 4' = \sin 60°46'.$

Exercise 17.1

1. Find the natural sines of the following angles: $26°$; $41°$; $17°18'$; $24°6'$; $40°12'$; $53°24'$; $64°30'$; $78°36'$; $83°42'$; $48°48'$; $7°54'$; $9°2'$; $15°7'$; $33°27'$; $44°46'$; $71°59'$.

2. Find the angles whose natural sines have the following values: 0.2756; 0.5878; 0.9945; 0.1582; 0.3616; 0.6101; 0.5120; 0.8607; 0.3942; 0.4814; 0.6096; 0.9886.

From the same figures which we used to calculate the ratios opposite/hypotenuse, calculate the following ratios: ON_1/OA_1; ON_2/OA_2; ON_3/OA_3; etc. No matter what the size of the right-angled triangle, providing the angles $A_1\hat{O}N_1$, $A_2\hat{O}N_2$, $A_3\hat{O}N_3$ etc. are all equal, the new ratios will all be approximately equal. In each triangle ON_1, ON_2, ON_3 etc. are sides which are next to, or *adjacent* to, the angle. We say these ratios are adjacent/hypotenuse. Their values depend not on the size of the right-angled triangle but on the magnitude of the angle. We call these ratios *cosine of the angle* or *cosine α* or *cos α*.

Again, from the triangles which you constructed with angles 10°, 20°, 30°, ..., 80° in them, measure the lengths of the adjacent sides and calculate the ratios cos 10°, cos 20°, cos 30° etc. Compare the results with those from the natural cosine tables.

Notice that, as the angle increases, the value of the cosine decreases. And note the consequent change in dealing with the mean differences. Just as with the sine, we must be able, with the cosine, to use the tables in two ways: to obtain the cosine given the angle, and to obtain the angle given the cosine.

Examples

1. cos 16° = 0.9613;
   cos 16°36′ = 0.9583;
   cos 16°40′ = 0.9583 − 3 = 0.9580.

2. 0.9455 = cos 19°;
   0.9164 = cos 23°36′;
   0.8727 = 0.8721 + 6 = cos (29°18′ − 4′) = cos 29°14′.

3. cos 24° = 0.9135;
   cos 24°18′ = 0.9114;
   cos 24°23′ = 0.9114 − 6 = 0.9108.

4. 0.3746 = cos 68°;
   0.3633 = cos 68°42′;
   0.3627 = 0.3616 + 11 = cos (68°48′ − 4′) = cos 68°44′;
   0.3643 = 0.3633 + 10 ≈ cos (68°42′ − 4′) = cos 68°38′.

Exercise 17.2

1. Find the natural cosines of the angles in Exercise 17.1, question (1).
2. Find the angles whose natural cosines have the values in Exercise 17.1, question (2).
3. Add the angles which are the answers to Exercise 17.1, question (2), to the corresponding answers in question (2) of this exercise. What do you notice about the results? Do you think these results are just coincidence?

Another argument which we might have used to show that the ratios opposite/hypotenuse and adjacent/hypotenuse were constant for a given angle, no matter what size the right-angled triangle happened to be, is that all the triangles are similar, and corresponding sides of similar triangles are in the same ratio. In Fig. 17.3 this means:

$$o_1/o_2 = a_1/a_2$$

i.e. $\dfrac{o_1}{o_2} \times \dfrac{o_2}{a_1} = \dfrac{a_1}{a_2} \times \dfrac{o_2}{a_1}$

i.e. $\dfrac{o_1}{a_1} = \dfrac{o_2}{a_2}$

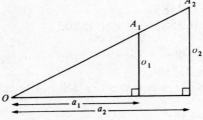

Figure 17.3

In other words, the ratio opposite/adjacent is the same in the two triangles. Check that this is the case in the following manner, using graph paper (Fig. 17.4). Mark off equal intervals ON_1, N_1N_2, N_2N_3 etc. along a horizontal line. Take ON_1 to be a simple number of divisions, say 10. Along the vertical through N_1 measure off a length A_1N_1 to be a simple number of divisions, say 1, 2, 3 etc. Join OA_1 and produce. Where this line meets the verticals through N_2,

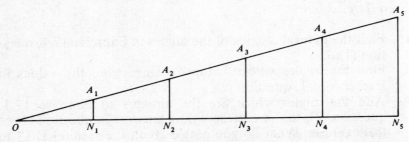

Figure 17.4

N_3 etc. mark the points A_2, A_3 etc. Measure A_2N_2, A_3N_3, and so on.

Calculate the ratios A_1N_1/ON_1, A_2N_2/ON_2, A_3N_3/ON_3, and so on. Their values are approximately equal. Measure the angle $A_1\hat{O}N_1$.

By taking different lengths for OA_1 we shall obtain different angles $A_1\hat{O}N_1$ and different values for the equal ratios. As before, the value of the ratio depends not on the size of the right-angled triangle but on the magnitude of the angle. We call this ratio *the tangent of the angle*, or *tangent α* or *tan α*.

By taking the length of A_1N_1 to be 1, 2, 3, 4, etc. and measuring the angle $A_1\hat{O}N_1$ in each case find the tangents of the different angles produced. Compare your answers with those obtained from the natural tangent tables. Notice that, as the angle increases, so does the tangent. In this respect it is like the sine. But, whereas the sine never has a value greater than 1, the tangent increases indefinitely.

Again, we must learn to operate the tables in either direction.

Examples

1. tan 41° = 0.8693;
    tan 62°18′ = 1.9047;
    tan 71°47′ = 3.0237 + 144 = 3.0381.
    Note that, from 80° onwards, the mean differences are unreliable. So if we wanted tan 84°40′, it is reasonably accurate to give the answer as 10.78, i.e. tan 84°42′, which is nearer than tan 84°36′.

2. 1.1106 = tan 48°;
    1.5166 = tan 56°36′;
    2.3369 = 2.3332 + 37 = tan (66°48′ + 2′) = tan 66°50′;
    0.8030 = 0.8012 + 18 = tan (38°42′ + 4′) to the nearest = tan 38°46′.

Exercise 17.3

1. Find the natural tangents of the angles in Exercise 17.1, question (1).

2. Find the angles whose natural tangents have the following values: 0.1763, 0.4452, 1.3270, 0.6297, 4.5864, 1.4176, 3.5150, 0.5990, 3.0600, 10.80, 25.20.

Special angles

Although we may use the tables to discover the ratios of any acute angle (in which case they are given in decimal form) there are certain angles whose ratios are best *remembered* in a somewhat different form. The angles are 30°, 45° and 60°. We shall now determine the three ratios, sine, cosine and tangent, of these angles.

The ratios of the angle 45°

Sketch a right-angled triangle with an angle 45° in it (Fig. 17.5), for example, triangle ABC in which $A\hat{C}B = 90°$ and $A\hat{B}C = 45°$.

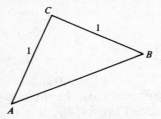

Figure 17.5

That means that $B\hat{A}C = 45°$, too, and that side BC = side AC (sides opposite equal angles are equal). Suppose $BC = 1$. Then $AC = 1$. Using Pythagoras:

$$AB^2 = AC^2 + BC^2 = 1^2 + 1^2$$
$$= 1 + 1 = 2$$
$$AB = \sqrt{2}$$

Then:

$$\text{sine } 45° = AC/AB = 1/\sqrt{2}$$
$$\text{cosine } 45° = BC/AB = 1/\sqrt{2}$$
$$\text{tangent } 45° = AC/BC = 1/1 = 1$$

The ratios of the angles 30° and 60°

Sketch an equilateral triangle, *PQR* (Fig. 17.6). Suppose each side has length 2. Each angle must be 60° ($\frac{1}{3}$ of 180°). Draw *PL* perpendicular to *QR*.

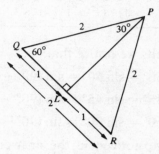

Figure 17.6

The two triangles *PLQ* and *PLR* are right-angled. They have *PQ* = *PR* (hypotenuse in each case) and they have *PL* in common. So the triangles are congruent (RHS). This means *QL* = *RL*. Since *QL* + *RL* = 2, *QL* = *RL* = 1.

Again, $Q\hat{P}L = R\hat{P}L$. Because $Q\hat{P}L + R\hat{P}L = 60°$, $Q\hat{P}L = R\hat{P}L = 30°$. By Pythagoras:

$$PL^2 + LQ^2 = PQ^2$$
$$\text{therefore} \quad PL^2 + 1^2 = 2^2$$
$$PL^2 + 1 = 4$$
$$PL^2 = 4 - 1 = 3$$
$$PL = \sqrt{3}$$

From triangle *PLQ*:

$$\sin 30° = QL/PQ = 1/2$$
$$\cos 30° = PL/PQ = \sqrt{3}/2$$
$$\tan 30° = QL/PL = 1/\sqrt{3}$$
$$\sin 60° = PL/PQ = \sqrt{3}/2$$
$$\cos 60° = QL/PQ = 1/2$$
$$\tan 60° = PL/QL = \sqrt{3}/1 = \sqrt{3}$$

Table 17.1 summarizes the above information

Table 17.1   *Ratios of special angles*

	0°	30°	45°	60°	90°
sin	0	$1/2$	$1/\sqrt{2}$	$\sqrt{3}/2$	1
cos	1	$\sqrt{3}/2$	$1/\sqrt{2}$	$1/2$	0
tan	0	$1/\sqrt{3}$	1	$\sqrt{3}$	∞

From the above results we notice that:

$$\cos 30° = \sin 60° = \sin (90° - 30°)$$

$$\cos 45° = \sin 45° = \sin (90° - 45°)$$

$$\cos 60° = \sin 30° = \sin (90° - 60°)$$

This is also what we noticed in the answers to Exercise 17.2, question (3). It appears that $\cos \alpha°$ always equals $\sin (90° - \alpha°)$. Let us see if we can prove that to be the case. In Fig. 17.7 $A\hat{B}C$ is a

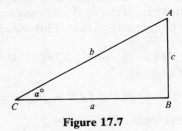

Figure 17.7

right angle. Consequently:

$$A\hat{C}B + C\hat{A}B = 90°$$

$$\alpha° + C\hat{A}B = 90°$$

$$C\hat{A}B = 90° - \alpha°$$

Now, from Fig. 17.7

$$\cos \alpha° = a/b$$

But

$$a/b = \sin C\hat{A}B = \sin (90° - \alpha°)$$

This means that

$$\cos \alpha° = \sin (90° - \alpha°)$$

Again, from the triangle

$$\sin \alpha° = c/b = \cos C\hat{A}B = \cos (90° - \alpha°)$$

Exercise 17.4

1. From Fig. 17.8, using triangle *DEF* in relation to angle θ:

$$\frac{FE}{DF} = \frac{\text{opp}}{\text{hyp}} = \sin \theta$$

If $DF = 20$ and $\theta = 20°$, then:

$$\frac{FE}{20} = \sin 20°$$

$$\frac{FE}{20} \times 20 = 20 \times \sin 20°$$

$$FE = 20 \sin 20° = 20 \times 0.3420$$

$$= 6.84$$

Calculate *FE* when *DF* and θ take the following pairs of values: 30, 10°; 25, 17°; 86.4, 45°17′.

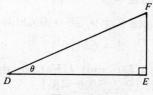

Figure 17.8

2. Again using Fig. 17.8:

$$\sin \theta = \frac{FE}{DF}$$

If $DF = 20$ and $FE = 11$:

$$\sin \theta = 11/20 = 0.5500$$

$$\theta = 33°22′$$

Calculate θ when DF and FE take the following pairs of values: 20, 13; 25, 8.6; 74.2, 63.8.

3. Using Fig. 17.8:

$$\frac{DE}{DF} = \frac{\text{adj}}{\text{hyp}} = \cos \theta$$

If $DF = 20$ and $\theta = 17°$:

$$\frac{DE}{20} = \cos 17°$$

$$\frac{DE}{20} \times 20 = 20 \times \cos 17°$$

$$DE = 20 \cos 17°$$

$$= 20 \times 0.9563 = 19.126 \approx 19.13$$

Calculate DE for the values of DF and θ given in question (1).

4. Again using Fig. 17.8:

$$\cos \theta = DE/DF$$

If $DF = 20$ and $DE = 9$:

$$\cos \theta = 9/20 = 0.4500$$

$$\theta = 63°15'$$

Calculate θ when DF and DE take the following pairs of values: 20, 7; 25, 19.2; 59.6, 48.1.

5. Using Fig. 17.8:

$$\tan \theta = FE/DE$$

If $DE = 10$ and $\theta = 15°$:

$$\frac{FE}{10} = \tan 15°$$

$$\frac{FE}{10} \times 10 = 10 \times \tan 15°$$

$$FE = 10 \tan 15° = 10 \times 0.2679 = 2.679$$

Calculate *FE* when *DE* and θ take the following pairs of values: 20, 23°; 25, 14.7°; 60.8, 71.2°.

6. Still using Fig. 17.8:

$$\tan \theta = \frac{FE}{DE}$$

If *DE* = 20 and *FE* = 13.2:

$$\tan \theta = \frac{13.2}{20} = 0.6600$$

$$\theta = 33°26'$$

Calculate θ if *DE* and *FE* take the following pairs of values: 40, 23.5; 52, 61; 103.2, 71.9.

Examples

1. Fig. 17.9 represents a tower, *AB*, of height 20 m. From two points, *C* and *D*, on the same side of the tower and at the same

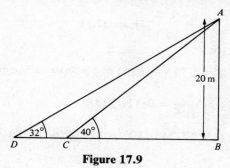

Figure 17.9

level as the base, *B*, the elevations of the top of the tower, *A*, are 40° and 32° respectively. Determine the distance *CD*.

$$C\hat{A}B = 90° - 40° = 50°; \qquad D\hat{A}B = 90° - 32° = 58°$$

From triangle *ABC*:

$$BC/20 = \tan 50°$$

$$BC = 20 \tan 50° = 23.835072 \text{ (by calculator)}$$

$$\approx 23.84$$

From triangle ABD:

$$BD/20 = \tan 58°$$
$$BD = 20 \tan 58° = 32.006691 \text{ (by calculator)}$$
$$\approx 32.01$$
$$CD = BD - BC = 32.01 - 23.84 \approx 8.17 \approx 8.2 \text{ m}$$

2. Fig. 17.10 represents a spindle. Calculate θ.

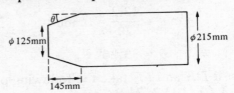

Figure 17.10

Fig. 17.11 is an extract from Fig. 17.10. It is a right-angled triangle.

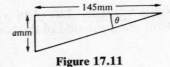

Figure 17.11

By calculator:

$$a = \tfrac{1}{2}(215 - 125) = \tfrac{1}{2} \times 90 = 45 \text{ mm}$$
$$\tan \theta = \frac{45}{145} = 0.3103448$$
$$\theta = 17.241459° \approx 17.24° \approx 17°14'$$

By logs:

$\bar{1}.4918$ lies between $\bar{1}.4916$ and $\bar{1}.4920$.
$\bar{1}.4920$ is log tan $17°15'$.
$\theta \approx 17°15'$.

Number	Log
45	1.6532
145	2.1614
	$\bar{1}.4918$

3. A taut, thin belt passes around two pulley wheels of radii 25 and 15 cm in a vertical plane. The centres of the pulleys are 2 m apart. Calculate the length of the belt. (The belt is an open belt.)

In Fig. 17.12, suppose A and B are the pulley centres and ST and UV are the straight sections of the belt. Draw BC parallel to ST. Then $A\hat{C}B$ is 90°.

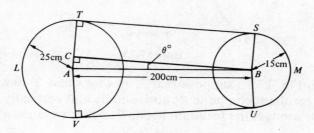

Figure 17.12

Suppose $A\hat{B}C = \theta$
$AC = AT - CT = AT - BS = 25 - 15 = 10$ cm
From triangle ABC: $\sin \theta = AC/AB = 10/200 = 1/20$
$\qquad\qquad\qquad\qquad\qquad = 0.05$
$\theta = 2.865984° \approx 2.87°$

Then $TS = AB \cos \theta = 200 \cos 2.87°$
$\qquad\qquad = 199.74984 \approx 199.75$ cm
Angle $S\hat{B}U = 360° - 90° - 90° - 2\theta° = 180° - 5.731968°$
$\qquad\qquad\qquad = 174.26803° \approx 174.27°$
Reflex angle $T\hat{A}V = 360° - 174.26803°$
$\qquad\qquad\qquad\qquad = 185.73197° \approx 185.73°$

Length of belt along TLV = angle in radians × radius
$\qquad\qquad\qquad\qquad\qquad = 81.04086 \approx 81.04$ cm.
Length of belt along SMU = angle in radians × radius
$\qquad\qquad\qquad\qquad\qquad = 45.623264 \approx 45.62$ cm
Total length of belt = $2 \times 199.75 + 81.04 + 45.62$
$\qquad\qquad\qquad\qquad = 526.16 \approx 526$ cm

4. Forces of 760 N and 1120 N act at 60° and 50° respectively to the horizontal. Determine the resultant horizontal and vertical components and the direction which the resultant force makes with the horizontal.

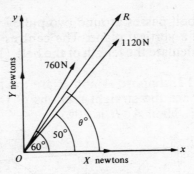

Figure 17.13

In Fig. 17.13 suppose that X newtons and Y newtons are the resultant components horizontally and vertically and that R newtons is the resultant itself. R makes an angle $\theta°$ with X.

$$X = 760 \cos 60° + 1120 \cos 50°$$
$$= 760 \times 0.5 + 1120 \times 0.6427876$$
$$= 380 + 719.92212 = 1099.9221 \approx 1100 \text{ N}$$
$$Y = 760 \sin 60° + 1120 \sin 50°$$
$$= 760 \times 0.8660254 + 1120 \times 0.7660444$$
$$= 658.17931 + 857.96978 = 1516.1491 \approx 1516 \text{ N}$$
$$\tan \theta = Y/X = 1.3784149$$
$$\theta° = 54.040205° \approx 54.04° \approx 54°2'$$
$$R = \sqrt{X^2 + Y^2} = 1873.1088 \approx 1873 \text{ N}$$

Exercise 17.5

Use both calculator and log sines etc. to calculate the answers to the following questions.

1. The angle of elevation to the top of a high tower is 35°23′ from a point 200 m away from the foot of the tower and level with its base. Determine the height of the tower.
2. A long, steadily rising road is 8 km long. The top is 1.25 km vertically above the level of the bottom. Determine the average gradient as an angle.
3. A plane is flying at 3000 m above the sea. It measures the angle of depression of a buoy in the water to be 32°24′. How far along the surface of the water is the buoy from a point directly below the plane?

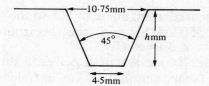

Figure 17.14

4. Fig. 17.14 represents a section of a groove for a V belt. Calculate h.
5. Fig. 17.15 represents a round machined bar. Calculate h.

Figure 17.15

6. A rectangle is 16.8 cm by 10.6 cm. Calculate the length of a diagonal and the acute angle between the two diagonals.
7. The base angles of an isosceles triangle are each 42°30′. The equal sides are each 8.6 cm long. Calculate the altitude and base of the triangle.
8. A ladder stands on horizontal ground and leans against a vertical wall. It makes an angle of 52°30′ with the ground. Calculate the length of the ladder and the distance of its foot from the wall if the top of the ladder is 7.5 m above the ground.
9. A rectangular metal plate is 12.5 cm by 19.6 cm. Find the angles between a diagonal and each of the two sides.
10. From the top of a vertical cliff 159 m high the angle of depression of a boat is 49°10′. How far is the boat from the foot of the cliff?
11. A flange has eight holes equally spread around a pitch circle of 75 mm diameter. Determine the distance between the centres of two adjacent holes.
12. Three stay wires each 15.6 m long are equally spaced around a vertical post, and firmly fixed to level ground and to the top of the post. The wires are inclined at 65° to the horizontal. Calculate the height of the post and the distance from the base of the post to the base of a wire.

13. A rocket is fired at an angle of 82° to the horizontal. If the speed is 350 km/h, find the horizontal and vertical components of the velocity.

14. The eastward component of velocity of a ship is 7.8 km/h. Its northward component is 13.4 km/h. Calculate its direction.

15. The resultant of two vectors acting at an angle of 90° to each other is 6250 N. One force is 2320 N. Find the other force and the angle which that force makes with the resultant.

16. A load of 2000 N is supported by two ropes, *CA* and *CB* (Fig. 17.16). Determine the tensions, *P* and *Q*, in the ropes.

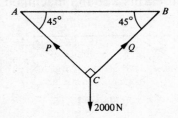

Figure 17.16

17. Ropes *QP* and *QR* support a load 3250 N (Fig. 17.17). Determine the forces, *X* and *Y*, in the ropes.

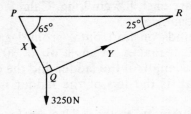

Figure 17.17

18. Calculate the longest thin straight wire which can be placed in a closed rectangular box 50 × 140 × 160 mm. Determine the angle which it makes with the 160 mm edge.

19. Fig. 17.18 represents a tapered roller. Calculate θ.

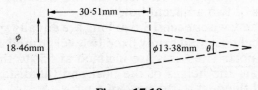

Figure 17.18

20. Fig. 17.19 represents the end view of a shed. Calculate x and y.

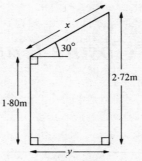

Figure 17.19

21. Fig. 17.20 represents the symmetrical end view of a building. Calculate the sloping length and the pitch of the roof. (The pitch is the inclination to the horizontal.)

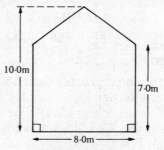

Figure 17.20

22. A straight girder rises 0.15 m for every 4 m of its length. Determine the inclination of the girder to the horizontal.

23. Fig. 17.21 represents two taut cables, AC and BC, giving temporary support to a vertical concrete column CD. The cables and post are in the same vertical plane. Determine the distance between the anchor points A and B.

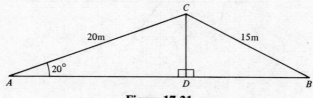

Figure 17.21

18

Sine and Cosine Curves

So far we have dealt with the three trigonometrical ratios sine, cosine and tangent of angles which are acute. Is it possible to deal with such ratios of angles of any magnitude?

If an angle is greater than a right angle we certainly cannot construct a triangle which both is right angled and contains another angle greater than a right angle, because the sum of those two angles alone would then be greater than 180°.

We must discover another idea in order to deal with angles of any magnitude. We have such an idea if we relate the subject to the x and y axes in graphs. Construct the usual axes Ox and Oy. Imagine now a point, P, which moves round the circumference of a circle, centre O (Fig. 18.1). Assume that OP has rotated into its

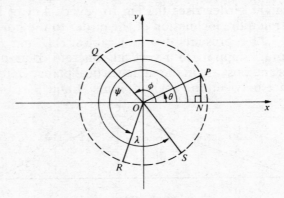

Figure 18.1

position from the direction Ox, i.e. an anti-clockwise rotation. Now θ is acute and, by drawing PN perpendicular to Ox, can be considered an angle in the triangle ONP.

Suppose the radius of the circle is r ($=OP$) and the co-ordinates of P in relation to the axes are (x, y). Then $PN = y$ and $ON = x$. From Fig. 18.1:

$$\sin \theta = \text{opp/hyp} = PN/OP = y/r$$
$$\cos \theta = \text{adj/hyp} = ON/OP = x/r$$
$$\tan \theta = \text{opp/adj} = PN/ON = y/x$$

To fit the new requirements (angles of any magnitude), we redefine our three ratios as:

$$\sin \theta = y/r$$
$$\cos \theta = x/r$$
$$\tan \theta = y/x$$

No matter what position P takes on the circle, e.g. OQ, OR, OS, we shall always be able to specify the co-ordinates of Q, R and S, and r is constant.

So we have a method of calculating each of the ratios. Using the above principles we are in a position to illustrate the graph of the sine for all angles between $0°$ and $360°$. For ease of calculation take $r = 1$. This means:

$$\sin \theta = y/1 = y$$

In Fig. 18.2 mark off points along the circumference of the circle at intervals of arc subtending $10°$ at the centre. Make the continuation of Ox the axis along which we measure angle for our sine curve and divide it into intervals of $10°$. Divide the circumference of the

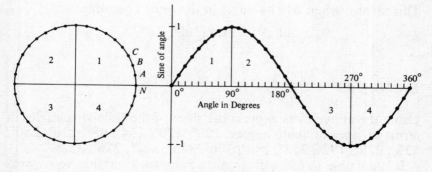

Figure 18.2

circle, starting at *N*, at *A*, *B*, *C*, etc., representing arcs subtending 10° at the centre. Project from these points parallel to *Ox* to meet the corresponding upright along the angle axis.

Notice that the curve can be divided into four sections, 1, 2, 3 and 4, corresponding to intervals of 90° for the angle. These sections are called quadrants.

In the *first* quadrant the sine is *positive*.
In the *second* quadrant the sine is *positive*.
In the *third* quadrant the sine is *negative*.
In the *fourth* quadrant the sine is *negative*.

By looking carefully at Fig. 18.2 we discover that:

$$\sin 170° = \sin 10° = \sin (180° - 170°)$$
$$\sin 160° = \sin 20° = \sin (180° - 160°)$$
$$\sin 150° = \sin 30° = \sin (180° - 150°)$$
$$\sin 140° = \sin 40° = \sin (180° - 140°)$$

This means, when θ is obtuse:

$$\sin \theta° = \sin (180° - \theta°)$$

$$\sin 190° = -\sin 10° = -\sin (190° - 180°)$$
$$\sin 200° = -\sin 20° = -\sin (200° - 180°)$$
$$\sin 210° = -\sin 30° = -\sin (210° - 180°)$$

This means, when ϕ is an angle in the third quadrant:

$$\sin \phi° = -\sin (\phi° - 180°)$$

$$\sin 350° = -\sin 10° = -\sin (360° - 350°)$$
$$\sin 340° = -\sin 20° = -\sin (360° - 340°)$$
$$\sin 310° = -\sin 50° = -\sin (360° - 310°)$$

This means, when ψ is an angle in the fourth quadrant:

$$\sin \psi° = -\sin (360° - \psi°)$$

Exercise 18.1

Using the above facts express the sines of the following angles in terms of sines of acute angles: 100°, 120°, 154°, 98°, 176°, 250°, 230°, 229°, 192°, 263°, 280°, 300°, 345°, 327°, 276°, 352°.

It is possible to use a diagram to help work out how to express the sine of any angle between 0° and 360°. We notice that the sine of such an angle is always equal to either + or − times the sine of an angle which is acute. To remember whether it is + or − we use Fig. 18.3.

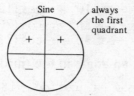

Figure 18.3

To find the required acute angle we subtract the angle from 180° if it is in the second quadrant, subtract 180° from the angle if it is in the third quadrant, and subtract the angle from 360° if it is in the fourth quadrant.

To discover the cosine curve we have to modify the method we used for sine. We rotate the quadrants in the circle anti-clockwise by 90°.

In the *first* quadrant the cosine is *positive*.
In the *second* quadrant the cosine is *negative*.
In the *third* quadrant the cosine is *negative*.
In the *fourth* quadrant the cosine is *positive*.

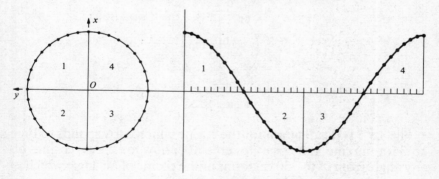

Figure 18.4

By looking carefully at Fig. 18.4 we discover that:

$$\cos 170° = -\cos 10° = -\cos (180° - 170°)$$
$$\cos 160° = -\cos 20° = -\cos (180° - 160°)$$
$$\cos 150° = -\cos 30° = -\cos (180° - 150°)$$
$$\cos 140° = -\cos 40° = -\cos (180° - 140°)$$

This means when θ is obtuse:

$$\cos\theta° = -\cos(180° - \theta°)$$

$$\cos 190° = -\cos 10° = -\cos(190° - 180°)$$
$$\cos 200° = -\cos 20° = -\cos(200° - 180°)$$
$$\cos 210° = -\cos 30° = -\cos(210° - 180°)$$

This means when ϕ is an angle in the third quadrant:

$$\cos\phi° = -\cos(\phi° - 180°)$$

$$\cos 350° = \cos 10° = \cos(360° - 350°)$$
$$\cos 340° = \cos 20° = \cos(360° - 340°)$$
$$\cos 310° = \cos 50° = \cos(360° - 310°)$$

This means when ψ is an angle in the fourth quadrant:

$$\cos\psi° = \cos(360° - \psi°)$$

Exercise 18.2

Using the above facts express the cosines of the angles in Exercise 18.1 in terms of cosines of acute angles.

Figure 18.5

Fig. 18.5 is the diagram for the cosine which corresponds to Fig. 18.3 for the sine. It helps us to remember how to express cosines of any angle from 0° to 360° in terms of the cosine of an angle which is acute.

ANSWERS TO EXERCISES

Exercise 1.1
1. 3 tens + 5 units, 4 tens + 7 units, 5 tens + 6 units, 6 tens + 3 units,
   8 tens + 2 units, 5 tens + 0 units, 3 tens + 0 units, 9 tens + 2 units,
   7 tens + 1 unit, 4 tens + 4 units.
2. 1 hundred + 7 tens + 4 units, 1 hundred + 9 tens + 6 units,
   2 hundreds + 3 tens + 8 units, 5 hundreds + 8 tens + 7 units,
   9 hundreds + 2 tens + 3 units, 1 hundred + 0 tens + 2 units,
   1 hundred + 0 tens + 5 units, 2 hundreds + 0 tens + 6 units,
   6 hundreds + 0 tens + 9 units, 7 hundreds + 5 tens + 0 units,
   8 hundreds + 0 tens + 0 units.

Exercise 1.2
1. 124   2. 1947   3. 108 774   4. 165 201   5. 1 125 376
6. 1037 V   7. 1173 m

Exercise 1.3
1. $13 \times 12 = 12 \times 13 = 156$ 2. $14 \times 17 = 17 \times 14 = 238$
3. $18 \times 21 = 21 \times 18 = 378$ 4. $34 \times 47 = 47 \times 34 = 1598$
5. $85 \times 73 = 73 \times 85 = 6205$ 6. $193 \times 102 = 102 \times 193 = 19\,686$
7. $4562 \times 3451 = 3451 \times 4562 = 15\,743\,462$
8. $1089 \times 7304 = 7304 \times 1089 = 7\,954\,056$
9. $6345 \times 7875 = 7875 \times 6345 = 49\,966\,875$

Exercise 1.9
1. 111   2. 222   3. 222   4. 87   5. 396   6. 1818
7. 4229   8. 573 800   9. 62 V   10. 32 008 kg

Exercise 1.10
1. 6   2. 12   3. 16   4. 16   5. 16   6. 51   7. 167
8. 335   9. 326   10. 8   11. 0   12. 0   13. 0   14. 0
15. 0   16. 0   17. 0   18. 0   19. 0   20. 0

Exercise 1.11
1. 13   2. 8   3. 2   4. 41   5. 3   6. 117   7. 5

Exercise 1.12
1. 2   2. 3   3. 7   4. 70   5. 13   6. −63   7. 1
8. −14   9. 33   10. −146   11. 1225   12. 93

Exercise 1.13
1. 31 2. 31 3. 151 4. 14 144 5. 3107 6. 257
7. 561 8. 736 9. 34 r. 5 10. 51 r. 1 11. 624 r. 8
12. 212 r. 20 13. 7 m/s^2 14. 56 microfarads 15. 9803 r. 714 cm^3

Exercise 1.15
1. 3/4 2. 4/5 3. 4/5 4. 3/4 5. 3/4 6. 2/3
7. −2/5 8. 1/4 9. −7/9 10. 12/13 11. 9/24
12. 96/144, 108/144, 120/144, 126/144, 117/144, 76/144, 111/144
13. 40/60, 45/60, 36/60, 48/60, 50/60, 35/60, 55/60, 25/60, 52/60, 28/60
14. 32/48, 36/48, 30/48, 42/48, 40/48, 44/48, 28/48, 26/48, 38/48, 39/48, 27/48

Exercise 1.16
1. 4/5 2. 7/8 3. 8/11 4. 21/92 5. 9/17 6. 105/371

Exercise 1.17
1. 1/48 2. 1/85 3. 1/360 4. 1/527 5. 1/156 6. 1/238

Exercise 1.18
1. 18/25 2. 28/39 3. 40/73 4. 99/124 5. 132/325
6. 9/4

Exercise 1.19
1. 12/63 2. 35/81 3. 18/55 4. 35/78 5. 15/32
6. 48/143 7. 224/255 8. 143/168 9. 437/480
10. 1421/1500

Exercise 1.20
1. 3/10 2. 7/20 3. 3/16 4. 4/5 5. 42/275 6. 35/81
7. 4/7 8. 1/2 9. 3/14

Exercise 1.21
1. 3/10 2. 7/20 3. 11/15 4. 2/3 5. 22/27 6. 4/7
7. 1/2 8. 3/14 9. 42/275 10. 35/81

Exercise 1.22
1. 3/2 2. 4/3 3. 5/4 4. 11/7 5. 23/15 6. 8/13
7. 7/15 8. 14/23 9. 2 10. 3 11. 13/7 12. 8/27
13. 8/13 14. 15/44

Exercise 1.23
1. 4/5 2. 6/7 3. 7/11 4. 11/13 5. 13/15 6. 2/5
7. 4/5 8. 5/6 9. 3/7 10. 2/3 11. 7/12 12. 8/15

Exercise 1.24
1. 7/10 2. 11/12 3. 9/16 4. 11/20 5. 8/12 = 2/3
6. 7/10 7. 7/8 8. 3/8 9. 13/20 10. 17/20

Exercise 1.25
1. 12   **2.** 24   **3.** 36   **4.** 15   **5.** 28   **6.** 48   **7.** 60
8. 72   **9.** 60   **10.** 42   **11.** 84   **12.** 96   **13.** 11/12
14. 23/24   **15.** 23/36   **16.** 11/15   **17.** 25/28   **18.** 29/48
19. 5/12   **20.** 31/84

Exercise 1.26
1. 2/15   **2.** 1/6   **3.** 27/80   **4.** 2/15   **5.** 17/72   **6.** 11/80
7. 17/80   **8.** 65/144   **9.** 31/96   **10.** 13/80

Exercise 1.27
1. $1\frac{3}{5}$ **2.** $2\frac{1}{6}$ **3.** $2\frac{1}{8}$ **4.** $1\frac{5}{9}$ **5.** $3\frac{4}{7}$ **6.** $2\frac{10}{11}$ **7.** $7\frac{5}{7}$
8. $4\frac{8}{29}$ **9.** $20\frac{7}{30}$ **10.** $41\frac{11}{25}$ **11.** 9/4   **12.** 7/2   **13.** 43/10
14. 86/5   **15.** 113/20   **16.** 81/11   **17.** 631/248   **18.** 95/4
19. 546/5   **20.** 734/17

Exercise 1.28
1. $6\frac{3}{4}$ **2.** $6\frac{4}{5}$ **3.** 6   **4.** $3\frac{1}{2}$ **5.** $3\frac{5}{8}$ **6.** $6\frac{3}{8}$ **7.** $5\frac{2}{3}$
8. $5\frac{3}{8}$ **9.** $3\frac{1}{8}$ **10.** $1\frac{3}{12}$ **11.** $7\frac{2}{5}$ **12.** 1/3   **13.** 6/53
14. 7/24   **15.** $5\frac{3}{5}$

Exercise 1.29
1. $1\frac{7}{8}$ **2.** $11\frac{1}{4}$ **3.** 6   **4.** 16/45   **5.** 1/6   **6.** $3\frac{1}{3}$ **7.** 7/8
8. $6\frac{1}{4}$

Exercise 1.30
1. 2/33   **2.** 5/8   **3.** $1\frac{1}{9}$ **4.** $1\frac{4}{15}$ **5.** $1\frac{2}{15}$ **6.** 1/5   **7.** $2\frac{13}{15}$
8. $2\frac{4}{7}$ **9.** $-1/10$ **10.** 41/89

Exercise 1.31
1. 3/5   **2.** 14/15   **3.** 3/4   **4.** 4/9   **5.** 16/9   **6.** 5/3
7. 14/9   **8.** 7/9   **9.** 7/12   **10.** 9/7

Exercise 1.32
1. $5\frac{5}{6}$ **2.** $3\frac{3}{7}$ **3.** $5\frac{3}{5}$ **4.** $6\frac{2}{3}$ **5.** $1\frac{1}{5}$ **6.** 5/16

Exercise 1.33
1. 96 kg; $56\frac{2}{3}$ kg   **2.** 981 g; $70\frac{18}{109}$ cm^3 **3.** $4\frac{8}{9}$ Ω; $32\frac{8}{11}$ m
4. 1400 m; 81 seconds   **5.** $3\frac{6}{29}$ A; $101\frac{1}{2}$ V   **6.** $2425\frac{25}{31}$ cm^3; $257\frac{11}{47}$ K
7. $428\frac{4}{7}$ N; $26\frac{22}{25}$ mm   **8.** $218\,461\frac{35}{65}$ Pa; 338 K   **9.** $169\frac{5}{7}$ cm; $54\frac{39}{44}$ cm
10. $3\frac{21}{34}$ m/s^2; $110\frac{1}{2}$ N

Exercise 1.34
1. 42 cm; 20 cm   **2.** 1 A; 630 Ω **3.** 6 kg/litre; 21 litres
4. 400 rev/min; 60 teeth   **5.** 24 cm; 180 cm^2
6. 3 atmospheres; 1920 cm^3 **7.** $v = 40$; $t = 50$; $s = 2400$
8. $a = 2\frac{17}{24}$; $m = 42\frac{1}{4}$; $F = 105\frac{5}{8}$ **9.** $I = 1\frac{1}{3}$; $V = 24$; $W = 42$
10. $M = 85$ kg; $v = 4$ m/s; $H = 136$

Exercise 1.35
1. 36 mm; 60 mm   2. 20 mm; 24 mm; 28 mm
3. 51 kg lead; 34 kg tin   4. 68 mm; 85 mm; 204 mm
5. 20 mm; $26\frac{2}{3}$ mm; $80\frac{2}{3}$ mm

Exercise 2.1
1. 3 units $+4 \times 1/10 + 5 \times 1/100 + 2 \times 1/1000$
2. 4 units $+5 \times 1/10 + 6 \times 1/100 + 4 \times 1/1000$
3. 1 unit $+5 \times 1/10 + 0 \times 1/100 + 7 \times 1/1000$
4. 6 units $+0 \times 1/10 + 4 \times 1/100 + 5 \times 1/1000$
5. 3 units $+5 \times 1/10 + 6 \times 1/100 + 0 \times 1/1000$
6. 1 unit $+0 \times 1/10 + 0 \times 1/100 + 5 \times 1/1000$
7. 0 units $+0 \times 1/10 + 4 \times 1/100 + 8 \times 1/1000$
8. 3 units $+9 \times 1/10 + 2 \times 1/100 + 7 \times 1/1000$
9. 9 units $+ 0 \times 1/10 + 0 \times 1/100 + 0 \times 1/1000 + 6 \times 1/10\,000$
10. 0 units $+ 0 \times 1/10 + 0 \times 1/100 + 0 \times 1/1000 + 3 \times 1/10\,000$
        $+ 8 \times 1/100\,000$

Exercise 2.2
1. 3/5   2. 1/4   3. 7/20   4. 3/4   5. 1/8   6. 3/8
7. 5/8   8. 7/8   9. 6/25   10. 4/25   11. 8/25   12. 24/25
13. 153/1000   14. 719/1000   15. 853/1000   16. 141/200
17. 1/50   18. 1/20   19. 1/40   20. 3/1000
21. 1003/10 000   22. 307/10 000   23. 41/20 000

Exercise 2.3
1. 0.31   2. 0.27   3. 0.306   4. 0.717   5. 0.082   6. 0.07
7. 0.00803   8. 6/10 = 0.6   9. 55/100 = 0.55
10. 95/100 = 0.95   11. 85/100 = 0.85   12. 16/100 = 0.16
13. 14/100 = 0.14   14. 58/100 = 0.58   15. 448/1000 = 0.448
16. 925/1000 = 0.925   17. 372/1000 = 0.372   18. 435/1000 = 0.435
19. 2675/10 000 = 0.2675   20. 89 750/1 000 000 = 0.08975

Exercise 2.4
1. 0.875   2. 0.5625   3. 0.8125   4. 0.84   5. 0.68
6. 0.78125   7. 0.453125   8. 0.828125   9. 0.688   10. 0.84

Exercise 2.5
1. $0.\dot{6}$ 2. 0.16   3. $0.\dot{4}$ 4. $0.6\dot{1}$ 5. $0.41\dot{6}$ 6. $0.708\dot{3}$
7. $0.638\dot{8}$

Exercise 2.6
1. $0.\dot{2}8571\dot{4}$ 2. $0.\dot{2}\dot{7}$ 3. $0.\dot{3}8461\dot{5}$ 4. $0.70588\dot{2}3\dot{5}$

Exercise 2.7
1. 3.1   2. 5.7   3. 10.3   4. 10.8   5. 4.3   6. 6.8
7. 17.7   8. 16.0   9. 23.0   10. 48.6   11. 62.1   12. 13.9

13. 41.8 **14.** 16.3 **15.** 9.14 **16.** 7.46 **17.** 19.05
18. 102.60 **19.** 63.61 **20.** 0.06

Exercise 2.8
1. 0.658; 0.66 **2.** 0.328; 0.33 **3.** 4.026; 4.0 **4.** 18.823; 19
5. 421.066; 420 **6.** 305.267; 301 **7.** 1458.005; 1500
8. 6053.256; 6100 **9.** 714.352; 710 **10.** 0.005; 0.0045
11. 0.104; 0.10 **12.** 3.004; 3.0 **13.** 10.451; 10 **14.** 16.075; 16

Exercise 2.9
1. 3/20 **2.** 9/20 **3.** 3/25 **4.** 8/25 **5.** 33/50 **6.** 21/25
7. 1/25 **8.** 3/50 **9.** 7/50 **10.** 17/50 **11.** 1/5 **12.** 1/4

Exercise 2.10
1. 60% **2.** 70% **3.** 25% **4.** $62\frac{1}{2}$% **5.** 55% **6.** $47\frac{1}{2}$%
7. $16\frac{2}{3}$% **8.** $66\frac{2}{3}$% **9.** $28\frac{4}{7}$% **10.** $31\frac{1}{4}$% **11.** $44\frac{4}{9}$%
12. $53\frac{1}{8}$%

Exercise 2.11
1. 0.625 **2.** 0.375 **3.** 0.125 **4.** 0.875 **5.** 0.085
6. 0.055 **7.** 0.112 **8.** 0.907 **9.** 1.246 **10.** 1.024
11. 0.0058 **12.** 0.0025 **13.** 0.00043 **14.** 0.000025
15. 25% **16.** 60% **17.** 12.6% **18.** 5.4% **19.** 58.2%
20. 16.7% **21.** 20.3% **22.** 0.7%

Exercise 2.12
1. 29.8 **2.** 40.1 **3.** 93.87 **4.** 93.85 **5.** 635.77 **6.** 4.2
7. 8.4 **8.** 11.8 **9.** 44.17 **10.** 71.24 **11.** 124.82 **12.** 28.94

Exercise 2.13
1. 7.36 **2.** 13.94 **3.** 136.5 **4.** 7730.16 **5.** 13.16
6. 11.3975 **7.** 235.2358 **8.** 892.544 **9.** 22.4784
10. 0.0001035 **11.** 1.17156 **12.** 204 363.18

Exercise 2.14
1. 2.5 **2.** 2.2 **3.** 2.0 **4.** 2.1 **5.** 0.5 **6.** 0.5 **7.** 7.69
8. 5.68 **9.** 0.05 **10.** 0.12 **11.** 12.00 **12.** 16.84

Exercise 2.15
1. 25 per cent tin; 71.67 per cent copper; 3.33 per cent antimony
2. 4.5 per cent increase in W **3.** 9.75 per cent decrease in A
4. 31.25 per cent **5.** 27.9 kg
6. 2.67 per cent high grade oil; 1.44 per cent bitumen; 3.6 per cent kerosene
7. 2.91 per cent decrease in density
8. 33.33 per cent for air; 24 per cent for oil; 42.67 per cent for water
9. 32.825 per cent increase in volume
10. 8 per cent decrease in velocity

Exercise 3.1
1. 4, 6, 8, 9, 10, 12   2. 8, 10, 15   3. 24, 28, 36
4. 32, 48, 30, 45, 64   5. 3, 5   6. 2, 4, 5, 10   7. 3, 7   8. 3, 9
9. 2, 3, 4, 6, 9, 12, 18   10. 2, 3, 4, 6, 8, 12, 16, 24
11. 2, 4, 5, 8, 10, 20   12. 6, 12   13. 20, 100   14. 84, 168
15. 24, 48, 96, 288

Exercise 3.2
1. $2^2 \times 3$ 2. 2×3^2 3. $2^3 \times 3$ 4. $2^2 \times 5$ 5. 5^2
6. $2 \times 3 \times 5$ 7. $2^2 \times 3^2$ 8. $2 \times 3 \times 7$ 9. $2^4 \times 3$ 10. 2×3^3
11. 2×5^2 12. 2^3 13. 2^4 14. 2^5 15. $2^3 \times 3^2$ 16. 3^4
17. 2×7^2 18. $2^2 \times 3^3$ 19. $2^3 \times 5^2$ 20. $2 \times 3 \times 5^3$
21. LCM: 360; HCF: 2   22. LCM: 300; HCF: 5
23. LCM: 756; HCF: 6   24. LCM: 588; HCF: 14
25. LCM: 648; HCF: 9

Exercise 3.4
1. 2^7 2. 3^6 3. 4^6 4. 5^5 5. 2^7 6. 6^4 7. 3^7
8. a^9 9. 6^{p+q} 10. p^7 11. a^{b+c} 12. a^{2b} 13. b^{a+c}
14. a^{3p} 15. a^{2p+q} 16. a^{p+q+r}

Exercise 3.6
1. 2^3 2. 2^2 3. 3^5 4. 4^2 5. 5^2 6. $2^1 = 2$ 7. 3^2
8. $a^1 = a$ 9. b^3 10. a^{p-2q} 11. b^{p-1} 12. a^p

Exercise 3.7
1. 2^4 2. 2^6 3. 2^6 4. 3^8 5. 3^6 6. 4^{12} 7. 3^8
8. 2^{12} 9. a^6 10. a^8 11. a^{pq} 12. a^{2p} 13. a^{3q}
14. b^{pq} 15. a^{pqr}

Exercise 3.9
1. 4^{-n} 2. 5^{-x} 3. 6^{-q} 4. 7^{-m} 5. 8^{-p} 6. 9^{-n}
7. 10^{-p} 8. a^{-n}

Exercise 3.11
1. 9   2. 4   3. 5   4. 5   5. 11   6. 13   7. 6   8. 7
9. 2   10. 2   11. 2   12. 5   13. 200   14. 42   15. 49
16. 7   17. 27   18. 27   19. 8   20. 8

Exercise 3.12
1. $6p^5 q^7$ 2. $8x^{\frac{3}{4}}$ 3. $9y^{\frac{2}{3}}$ 4. $5\dfrac{x^{\frac{1}{2}}}{y^{\frac{1}{2}}}$ 5. $3x^{\frac{3}{5}}y^{\frac{2}{5}}$ 6. $\dfrac{3}{2}\dfrac{b^{\frac{3}{2}}}{a^2}$

7. $\frac{7}{2}x^2 y$ 8. $\dfrac{1}{3}\dfrac{b^4}{a^5}$ 9. $a^3 b^3$ 10. $4x^4 y^6$ 11. $\dfrac{a^p x^{2p} y^{3p}}{z^{4p}}$

12. $3x$ 13. $4\dfrac{y^2}{x^2 z^{\frac{3}{2}}}$ 14. $\dfrac{3}{2}\dfrac{z^{\frac{4}{3}}}{x^2 y}$ 15. $\dfrac{6}{5}\dfrac{x}{y^2}$ 16. $\dfrac{7b^2}{a^{\frac{3}{2}}}$

17. $\dfrac{1}{2}\dfrac{y^3}{x^2}$ **18.** $\dfrac{4}{15}\dfrac{y^6}{xz^3}$ **19.** $24a^3b^4c^6$ **20.** $15a^3b^2c^6$ **21.** $2\dfrac{ab}{c^5}$

22. $\dfrac{4}{3}\dfrac{r^3}{p^3q^3}$ **23.** $5ab^2$ **24.** $12x^{\frac{3}{2}}y^{\frac{1}{2}}$ **25.** $15\dfrac{p^3r^2}{q}$ **26.** $4x^2y^4$

27. $27\dfrac{b^3}{a^3}$ **28.** $\dfrac{1}{36p^2q^4}$ **29.** $\dfrac{a^{\frac{1}{2}}b}{8}$ **30.** $9p^{\frac{1}{4}}q$ **31.** $\dfrac{14\,641z^{\frac{1}{2}}}{xy^{\frac{3}{2}}}$

32. $4\dfrac{a^4}{b^2}$

Exercise 4.1
1. 8.32×10^1 **2.** 6.45×10^1 **3.** 1.236×10^2 **4.** 1.015×10^2
5. 6.0497×10^3 **6.** 3.051×10^3 **7.** 8.140×10^3 **8.** 6.200×10^3
9. 1.46×10^{-1} **10.** 9.02×10^{-1} **11.** 4.3×10^{-2} **12.** 6.5×10^{-3}
13. 2.05×10^{-5} **14.** 1.3×10^6 **15.** 2.5×10^5 **16.** 2.35×10^3
17. 4.8×10^{-7} **18.** 3.75×10^3

Exercise 4.2
1. 230 **2.** 48 000 **3.** 20.1 **4.** 0.606 **5.** 0.012
6. 0.00035 **7.** 86 200 000 **8.** 0.00000108 **9.** 0.000075

Exercise 4.3
1. 6.9×10^2 **2.** 9.9×10^3 **3.** 8.5×10^4 **4.** 4.83×10^2
5. 2.76×10^3 **6.** 1.54×10^4 **7.** 1.182×10^4 **8.** 8.191×10^1
9. $8.15 \times 10^0 = 8.15$ **10.** 1.176×10^{-1} **11.** 2.384×10^{-1}
12. 2.2×10^2 **13.** 6.598×10^3 **14.** 6.32×10^4 **15.** 9.48×10^5
16. 5.44×10^1 **17.** 2.2×10^{-1} **18.** 1.3×10^{-2} **19.** 4.6×10^{-3}
20. 9×10^{-7} **21.** 351×10^{-5} **22.** 4.0×10^2
23. 3.129381556×10^5

Exercise 4.4
1. 101 **2.** 111 **3.** 1000 **4.** 1010 **5.** 1101 **6.** 10000
7. 10100 **8.** 10111 **9.** 11101 **10.** 11111 **11.** 100000
12. 100101 **13.** 101001 **14.** 110000 **15.** 110011
16. 110111 **17.** 111011 **18.** 111111 **19.** 1000000

Exercise 4.5
1. 3 **2.** 5 **3.** 4 **4.** 10 **5.** 11 **6.** 19 **7.** 25
8. 24 **9.** 56 **10.** 42 **11.** 46 **12.** 47 **13.** 60 **14.** 63

Exercise 4.6
1. 100 **2.** 101 **3.** 111 **4.** 1001 **5.** 111 **6.** 1101
7. 1100 **8.** 101010 **9.** 100111 **10.** 110001 **11.** 1000000
12. 1001011

Exercise 4.7

1. 0.01 **2.** 0.001 **3.** 0.0001 **4.** 0.00001 **5.** 0.000001
6. 0.111 **7.** 0.011 **8.** 0.101 **9.** 0.01001 **10.** 0.000101
11. 0.01101111 approx. **12.** 0.10000101 approx.
13. 0.101010111 approx. **14.** 1.1 **15.** 1110.1 **16.** 11.111
17. 1001.001 **18.** 111.0001 **19.** 1011.00001
20. 111.01101111 approx. **21.** 0.5 **22.** 0.025 **23.** 0.0125
24. 0.875 **25.** 0.625 **26.** 0.59375 **27.** 0.5775625
28. 11.75 **29.** 111.625 **30.** 100.125

Exercise 4.8

1. $43 = 53_8 = (101)(1000) + 11 = 101000 + 11 = 101011$
2. $57 = 71_8 = (111)(1000) + 1 = 111001$
3. $95 = 137_8 = 1(1000000) + 11(1000) + 111 = 1011111$
4. $536 = 830_8 = (1000)(1000000) + 11(1000) + 0 = 1000011000$
5. $1062 = 2046_8 = 10(1000)^3 + 100(1000) + 110 = 10000100110$
6. $3429 = 6545_8 = 110(1000)^3 + 101(1000)^2 + 100(1000) + 101$
$= 110101100101$
7. $5053 = 11675_8 = 1(1000)^4 + 1(1000)^3 + 110(1000)^2 + 111(1000) + 101$
$= 1001110111101$
8. $6247 = 14147_8 = 1100001100111$
9. $7178 = 16012_8 = 1110000001010$
10. $7485 = 16475_8 = 1110100111101$
11. $11011 = 11(1000) + 11 = 3 \times 8 + 3 = 33_8 = 27_{10} = 27$
12. $11111 = 11(1000) + 111 = 3 \times 8 + 7 = 37_8 = 31_{10} = 31$
13. $1001000 = 1(1000)^2 + 1(1000) = 1 \times 8^2 + 1 \times 8 + 0 = 110_8 = 72_{10} = 72$
14. $1001001000 = 1(1000)^3 + 1(1000)^2 + 1(1000) = 1 \times 8^3 + 1 \times 8^2 + 1 \times 8 + 0$
$= 1110_8 = 584_{10} = 584$
15. $1000110011 = 1(1000)^3 + 110(1000) + 011 = 1 \times 8^3 + 0 \times 8^2 + 6 \times 8 + 3$
$= 1063_8 = 563$
16. $1111111111 = 1(1000)^3 + 111(1000)^2 + 111(1000) + 111$
$= 1 \times 8^3 + 7 \times 8^2 + 7 \times 8 + 7 = 1777_8 = 1023$

Exercise 4.9

1. 456 **2.** 1167 **3.** 1113 **4.** 1511 **5.** 1645 **6.** 13 143
7. 45 340 **8.** 151 130

Exercise 4.10

1. 100 **2.** 100 **3.** 1000 **4.** 1001 **5.** 100 **6.** 10100
7. 1110 **8.** 1000010

Exercise 4.11

1. 6 **2.** 7 **3.** 6 **4.** 7 **5.** 7 **6.** 177 **7.** 232
8. 243 **9.** 116 **10.** 544 **11.** 2314

Exercise 5.1
1. 17.90 **2.** 36.62 **3.** 81.13 **4.** 126.5 **5.** 268.7
6. 665.6 **7.** 6022 **8.** 108 100 **9.** 1 118 000 **10.** 0.01523
11. 0.04252 **12.** 0.6637 **13.** 0.0009309 **14.** 0.008324
15. 0.00001310

Exercise 5.2
1. 2.236 **2.** 302.2 **3.** 4.223 **4.** 8.722 **5.** 11.13
6. 30.08 **7.** 31.70 **8.** 148.1 **9.** 2874 **10.** 0.7071
11. 0.9656 **12.** 0.3520 **13.** 0.2058 **14.** 0.2919
15. 0.04651 **16.** 0.01070 **17.** 0.1014 **18.** 0.004062

Exercise 5.3
1. 0.4619 **2.** 0.2327 **3.** 0.1550 **4.** 0.09101 **5.** 0.04395
6. 0.006546 **7.** 0.0001580 **8.** 4.619 **9.** 2.327 **10.** 25.81
11. 160.5 **12.** 2232

Exercise 5.4
1. 0.6921 **2.** 0.9282 **3.** 1.2622 **4.** 1.8044 **5.** 2.5246
6. 2.7231 **7.** 3.6836 **8.** 3.9020 **9.** 4.4830 **10.** 6.7933
11. $\bar{1}.5350$ **12.** $\bar{1}.9438$ **13.** $\bar{2}.7958$ **14.** $\bar{2}.9553$
15. $\bar{3}.4026$ **16.** $\bar{3}.8732$

Exercise 5.5
1. 2.096 **2.** 7.273 **3.** 1.331 **4.** 64.94 **5.** 461.6
6. 663.6 **7.** 2584 **8.** 2592 **9.** 1826 **10.** 10.63
11. 1.462 **12.** 0.1777 **13.** 0.2341 **14.** 0.07326
15. 0.01024 **16.** 0.005944 **17.** 1.010 **18.** 1.001
19. 0.1023 **20.** 117.6

Exercise 5.6
4. 2.0 **5.** 3.0 **6.** $\bar{2}.0$ **9.** 2.8 **10.** 1.4 **11.** $\bar{1}.7$
12. 0.1 **13.** $\bar{1}.3$ **14.** 0.3 **15.** $\bar{1}.1$ **16.** $\bar{2}.7$

Exercise 5.7
1. 30.38 **2.** 29.69 **3.** 226.6 **4.** 3211 **5.** 923.0
6. 33 820 **7.** 264 100 **8.** 37 150 **9.** 12 740 000
10. 0.8792 **11.** 7.157 **12.** 316.6 **13.** 0.1751 **14.** 0.02153
15. 0.003261 **16.** 0.000203

Exercise 5.8
3. 1.2 **5.** 0.7 **6.** 0.6

Exercise 5.9
1. 1.347 **2.** 2.26 **3.** 13.07 **4.** 27.51 **5.** 1.432
6. 1.326 **7.** 1.352 **8.** 1.62 **9.** 0.4603 **10.** 0.3273

11. 0.7984   **12.** 0.206   **13.** 0.5593   **14.** 0.4999   **15.** 0.0782
16. 0.0001161

Exercise 5.11
1. 16.01   **2.** 25.00   **3.** 64.01   **4.** 169.0   **5.** 288.9
6. 7.998   **7.** 125.0   **8.** 1331   **9.** 16.00   **10.** 80.98
11. 27.57   **12.** 64.74   **13.** 4410   **14.** 0.03999   **15.** 0.25
16. 0.06401   **17.** 0.3882   **18.** 0.000364   **19.** 0.00000001082
20. 0.00000006893

Exercise 5.13
1. 59.67   **2.** 5255   **3.** 70.87   **4.** 16 950   **5.** 99.42
6. 3646   **7.** 2.004×10^{11} **8.** 286.3   **9.** 3656   **10.** 2569
11. 7.575

Exercise 6.1
1. 92   **2.** 109   **3.** 63   **4.** 247

Exercise 6.2
1. 527   **2.** 192.64   **3.** 1456.1523   **4.** −0.15767

Exercise 6.3
1. 3600   **2.** 42 000

Exercise 6.4
1. 100   **2.** 288

Exercise 6.5
1. 6.6800896   **2.** 0.8587185   **3.** 0.8915051   **4.** 0.6896992

Exercise 6.6
1. 6.6800896×10^9 **2.** 8.5871845×10^{11} **3.** 8.915051×10^{-12}
4. $6.8964988 \times 10^{-11}$

Exercise 6.7
1. 8×10^{10} **2.** 5.34×10^{10} **3.** 6.72×10^{-10}

Exercise 6.8
1. 5.33091×10^8 **2.** 1.48813×10^9 **3.** 7.6816×10^{-8}
4. -9.3427×10^{-8}

Exercise 6.9
1. 16   **2.** 49   **3.** 121   **4.** 256   **5.** 961   **6.** 5.6644
7. 0.2704   **8.** 0.001218   **9.** 565.60928   **10.** 12 977.875
11. 0.0003954   **12.** 1.2189944   **13.** 1.8061112   **14.** 11.4674
15. 0.1865889

Exercise 6.10
1. 0.016818 **2.** 0.076558 **3.** 0.0000244 **4.** 4.7641734
5. 1332.8002 **6.** $3/5 = 0.6$ **7.** $7/4 = 1.75$ **8.** $3/5 = 0.6$
9. 0.125 **10.** 0.008 **11.** 0.0493827 **12.** 0.0000012
13. 3.6006323 **14.** 1709.0624 **15.** 0.0123457 **16.** 0.0019531
17. 0.0016 **18.** 0.0250361 **19.** 14.832582 **20.** 1.7777778

Exercise 6.11
1. 354 **2.** 1452 **3.** 8 **4.** 30 544.1 **5.** 10.665816
6. $-542\,129.8$ **7.** $-35\,089.62$

Exercise 7.1
1. $9x$ **2.** $13x$ **3.** $3y$ **4.** $5a$ **5.** $6b$ **6.** $8x$ **7.** q
8. $-x$ **9.** $-5y$ **10.** $11a$

Exercise 7.2
1. $8x$ **2.** $15x$ **3.** $2px$ **4.** $3ax$ **5.** $10ax$ **6.** $12ab$
7. $-15t$ **8.** $6t$ **9.** $12x^2$ **10.** $6x^3$ **11.** $6x^2y^2$ **12.** $12p^3q$
13. $-14x^5y^4$ **14.** $2x$ **15.** 2 **16.** -2 **17.** 4 **18.** $2a$
19. $2a/c$ **20.** $3a^2y$

Exercise 7.3
1. $2a+b$ **2.** $5a+5b$ **3.** $a+2b$ **4.** $3a+4b$
5. $a+3b+15c$ **6.** $6p-4q-4r$ **7.** $6xy$ **8.** $40xyz$
9. $60pqr$ **10.** $2x/y$ **11.** $-6x/7y$ **12.** $6ab^2$

Exercise 7.4
1. $8a+12b$ **2.** $10x-25y$ **3.** $14a+7b-21c$ **4.** $-2x+4y$
5. $5y$ **6.** $36p+4q$ **7.** $12x^2+6xy$ **8.** $14p^2+35p$
9. $6a^2+9a+4$ **10.** $10ab+35b^2$ **11.** $x^2+2xy+y^2$
12. $a^2-2ab+b^2$ **13.** p^2-q^2 **14.** $12a^2+16ab+5b^2$
15. $12l^2 - 7lm - 12m^2$

Exercise 7.5
1. $2(a+2b)$ **2.** $3(x+2y)$ **3.** $5(p-2q)$ **4.** $2(3x-4y)$
5. $2x(a+2b)$ **6.** $3a(x+2y)$ **7.** $5x(p-2q)$ **8.** $2a(3x-4y)$
9. $2x(x+2)$ **10.** $3x(y+2x)$ **11.** $5p(p-2)$ **12.** $2x(3x-4)$
13. $x^2(4x+3)$ **14.** $2yz(x+2t)$ **15.** $ax(2x+3)$

Exercise 7.6
1. $(y+1)(a+b)$ **2.** $(y+1)(y+3)$ **3.** $(x-1)(2x+5)$
4. $(a+2)(3+2a)$ **5.** $(b-3)(5-2b)$ **6.** $(x+y)(a+b)$
7. $(x+y)(a-b)$ **8.** $(x-y)(a+b)$ **9.** $(x-y)(a-b)$
10. $(2x+5)(3x+4)$

Exercise 7.7

1. $(y+1)(a+b)$ 2. $(y+1)(y+3)$ 3. $(x-y)(a-b)$
4. $(a-b)(x+y)$ 5. $(x+y)(a+b)$ 6. $(3l+4m)(2a+b)$
7. $(2x+3y)(x+y^2)$ 8. $(2x-3y)(x+y^2)$ 9. $(9a+4b)(2b+3a^2)$
10. $(p-t)(qr+3xy)$

Exercise 7.8

1. $(p+2q)^2$ 2. $(p-2q)^2$ 3. $(2a+b)(2a-b)$
4. $(3a-2b)(3a+2b)$ 5. $(3a+2b)^2$ 6. $(3x-2y)^2$
7. $(3a^2b-2c)^2$ 8. $2(a+b)^2$ 9. $2(x-y)^2$ 10. $6(x-y)^2$
11. $a(x+y)^2$ 12. $3p(a-b)^2$ 13. $(5a+7b)(5a-7b)$
14. $(8x^2-5y)^2$ 15. $2(a+b)(a-b)$ 16. $3(x+y)(x-y)$
17. $a(x-y)(x+y)$ 18. $ax(2a+3b)(2a-3b)$ 19. $(12a+5b)^2$
20. $(24ax-5y^2)^2$ 21. $(2x+3)$ 22. $8(2x+2)=16(x+1)$
23. $(3x+4)(x+2)$ 24. $(5a+b)(a+7b)$ 25. $(a+b+1)(a+b-1)$
26. $(a-b+1)(a-b-1)$ 27. $(2p+3q+r)(2p+3q-r)$
28. $(2p+2q)(2p+4q)=4(p+q)(p+2q)$
29. $(a+b+x+y)(a+b-x-y)$ 30. $(a+b+x+y)(a+b-x-y)$

Exercise 8.1

1. 9 2. 13 3. $2\frac{1}{2}$ 4. 5 5. 4 6. 21 7. 3 8. $2/3$
9. $3/16$ 10. -6 11. 2 12. 3 13. 6 14. 3 15. 3
16. 2 17. $\frac{1}{2}(b-a)$ 18. b/a 19. $b/2a$ 20. $4b/(a+b)$
21. $a(b-c)$ 22. $(b-c)$ 23. $2b-a$ 24. $(3a+b)/(a+b)$

Exercise 8.2

1. $x=4, y=1$ 2. $p=1, q=5$ 3. $p=8, q=3$
4. $p=10\frac{1}{3}, q=1\frac{2}{3}$ 5. $p=6, q=4$ 6. $a=2, b=1$
7. $x=2, y=2$ 8. $x=2, y=2\frac{2}{3}$ 9. $a=2, b=-1$
10. $x=1\frac{3}{11}, y=-2\frac{5}{11}$ 11. $x=2\frac{19}{27}, y=7\frac{4}{27}$ 12. $x=-2, y=1$
13. $x=13\frac{7}{29}, y=-9\frac{27}{29}$ 14. $x=1\frac{3}{5}, y=1\frac{2}{5}$ 15. $x=2, y=1$
16. $x=2\frac{15}{19}, y=3\frac{1}{19}$ 17. $x=15\frac{10}{61}, y=2\frac{60}{61}$ 18. $x=-\frac{31}{59}, y=-3\frac{57}{59}$

Exercise 8.3

1. (a) $x-1$ (b) $x-3$ (c) $x-9$ (d) $x-t$ (e) $x+2$ (f) $x+6$
   (g) $x+y$ (h) $2x$ (i) $2x$ (j) $2x$ 2. $(100+x)$ km; $(100+x-y)$ km

3. $(1000+3x-3.5y)\,\text{m}^3$ 4. $\dfrac{100}{q}-\dfrac{100}{p}=\dfrac{100(p-q)}{pq}$

5. $(a+b+c)$; $(a+b+c)x$ 6. $(T+20a)°\text{C}$
7. $(T-t)°\text{C}$; (a) $T-t$ (b) $2(T-t)$ (c) $3(T-t)$ (d) $4(T-t)$
8. (a) $(p-6x)-12(x+y)=(p-18x-12y)°\text{C}$
   (b) $(p-6x)-6(x+y)=(p-12x-6y)°\text{C}$
   (c) $(p-6x)-9(x+y)=(p-15x-9y)°\text{C}$
9. (a) $P+x$ (b) $P+3x$ (c) $P+9x/2$ (d) $P+xy/10$
10. $5x\times10+5y\times14+z\times48=50x+70y+48z$

Exercise 8.4
1. 9   2. 41   3. 30   4. 19, 38, 29   5. $p = 180$, $q = 60$, $r = 115$
6. 11, 33   7. 26, 16 cm   8. 4, 4, 2 A   9. 120, 60, 70 Ω
10. $67\frac{9}{13}$, $101\frac{7}{13}$, $53\frac{11}{13}$

Exercise 8.5
1. $x = 8$, $y = 7$ 2. 15, 8 years   3. $m = 5$, $c = 7$
4. $a = \frac{5}{6}$, $b = -8\frac{11}{15}$ 5. gnome 2 kg, frog $\frac{1}{2}$ kg
6. flagstone £2, brick 15p   7. 10 m, 6 m
8. 70 kg Type A, 110 kg Type B

Exercise 9.1
1. $x = y - b$; 0.9   2. $q = p + r$; 101.6
3. $x = (y - b)/a$; $0.1470588 \approx 0.15$ 4. $u = v - at$; 277
5. $I = V/R$; $1.4274673 \approx 1.43$ 6. $x = TL/k$; 523.51
7. $a = F/M$; $2.9302326 \approx 2.93$ 8. $h = E/Mg$; $6.9407238 \approx 6.94$

9. $V = \sqrt{\dfrac{2E}{M}}$; $11.664854 \approx 11.66$

10. $u = \dfrac{s - \frac{1}{2}at^2}{t} = \dfrac{s}{t} - \frac{1}{2}at$; $-90.273404 \approx -90.27$

11. $a = \dfrac{2(s - ut)}{t^2}$; $a = -1.1107844 \approx -1.11$

12. $r = \sqrt{\dfrac{A}{\pi}}$; $4.8234085 \approx 4.82$ 13. $h = \dfrac{V}{\pi r^2}$; $1.7654309 \approx 1.76$

14. $r = \sqrt{\dfrac{V}{\pi h}}$; $6.3749533 \approx 6.37$ 15. $M_1 = \dfrac{Fd^2}{GM_2}$; 2.63×10^{18}

16. $d = \sqrt{\dfrac{GM_1M_2}{F}}$; 2.27×10^2 17. $L = \dfrac{gT^2}{4\pi^2}$; $1.9184741 \approx 1.92$

18. $L_0 = \dfrac{L}{1 + at}$; $65.040619 \approx 65.04$ 19. $t = \dfrac{L - L_0}{L_0 a}$; $3.8188762 \approx 3.82$

20. $a = \dfrac{L - L_0}{L_0 t}$; 1.232×10^{-4} 21. (a) $1129.6878 \approx 1.13 \times 10^3$

    (b) $1\,110\,301.6 \approx 1.11 \times 10^6$ (c) $2.4353814 \times 10^{-8} \approx 2.44 \times 10^{-8}$
22. (a) $1.8205722 \times 10^8 \approx 1.82 \times 10^8$ (b) $2.0735175 \times 10^8 \approx 2.07 \times 10^8$
    (c) $3.1253706 \times 10^{-26} \approx 3.13 \times 10^{-26}$
23. (a) $1303.2471 \approx 1.30 \times 10^3$ (b) $1.1079086 \approx 1.11$
24. (a) $1.5471402 \times 10^{-8} \approx 1.55 \times 10^{-8}$ (b) $0.9754589 \approx 9.75 \times 10^{-1}$

Exercise 10.1

1.
Price:	10	20	30	40	50	60	70	80	90	100	110
VAT:	1.5	3.0	4.5	6.0	7.5	9.0	10.5	12.0	13.5	15.0	16.5

2.
in:	1	2	3	4	5	6	7
cm:	2.54	5.08	7.62	10.16	12.70	15.24	17.78

in:	8	9	10	11	12	13	14	15
cm:	20.32	22.86	25.4	27.94	30.48	33.02	35.56	38.1

in:	16	17	18	19	20	21
cm:	40.64	43.18	45.72	48.26	50.8	53.34

3.
lb:	11	16	21	26	31
kg:	4.994	7.264	9.534	11.804	14.074

lb:	36	41	46	51	56
kg:	16.344	18.614	20.884	23.154	25.424

4.
m.p.h.:	6.21	12.42	18.63	24.84	31.05	37.26	43.47	49.68
km/h:	10	20	30	40	50	60	70	80

m.p.h.:	55.89	62.10	68.31	74.52	80.73	86.94	93.15	99.36
km/h:	90	100	110	120	130	140	150	160

5.
Taxable income:	1000	1050	1100	1150	1200	1250	1300
Tax:	300	315	330	345	360	375	390

Taxable income:	1350	1400	1450	1500	1550	1600	1650
Tax:	405	420	435	450	465	480	495

Taxable income:	1700	1750	1800	1850	1900	1950	2000
Tax:	510	525	540	555	570	585	600

6.
Income:	2000	2100	2200	2300	2400	2500
NI:	57.5	63.25	69	74.75	80.5	86.25

Income:	2600	2700	2800	2900	3000
NI:	92	97.75	103.5	109.25	115

7. C: 4.4, 15.6, 23.9, 26.7, 32.2
F: 41, 59, 75.2, 89.6

8. V: 35, 45, 55, 62.5, 77.5
t: 1.5, 2.5, 5.6, 8.6

9. I(£): 12.75, 21.25, 28.9, 47.6, 69.7
D(£): 141, 250, 340, 560, 820

Exercise 10.2
1. $Y = X + 1$ **2.** $Y = X - 2$ **3.** $Y = 2X - 1$ **4.** $Y = 2X + 5$
5. $Y = \frac{1}{2}X + 2$ **6.** $Y = \frac{1}{2}X - 3$ **7.** $Y = -X + 1$ **8.** $Y = -X + 3$
9. $Y = 1 - 2X$ **10.** $Y = 3X + 2$

Exercise 10.5
1. T: 5000, 7500, 12 500, 3000, 1875. x: 10, 0.5, 0.2, 0.025, 300
2. V: 160, 280, 336, 32, 2. I: 1.25, 3.125, 4, 0.5625, 0.34375
3. F: 42, 59.5, 133, 297.5. a: 1.86, 22.06, 2.8, 3.2, 0.5

Exercise 10.6
1. F: 41, 59, 149, 93.2, 107.6, 208.4. C: 35, 65, 85, -5, 93.3, 65.6
2. v: 42.5, 62.5, 77.5, 46, 53.5. t: 0.5, 3.5, 6.5, 4.8, 8.6
3. I: 8.25, 35.75, 96.25, 18.15, 48.95. D: 141, 1141, 796, 1764, 1873
4. P: 23, 29, 41, 30.5, 36.5, 40.4, 41.3, 49.7. W: 30, 70, 90, 16.7, 136.7

Exercise 10.7
1. 3 2. 4 3. 3 4. 2 5. $\frac{1}{2}$ 6. $\frac{1}{2}$ 7. $\frac{1}{4}$ 8. $\frac{1}{3}$

Exercise 10.8
1. $y=3x+6$; $m=3, c=6$ 2. $y=5x+8$; $m=5, c=8$
3. $y=\frac{2}{3}x-5$; $m=\frac{2}{3}, c=-5$ 4. $y=\frac{1}{2}x+10$; $m=\frac{1}{2}, c=10$
5. $y=\frac{1}{3}x+5$; $m=\frac{1}{3}, c=5$ 6. $y=\frac{1}{2}x+2$; $m=\frac{1}{2}, c=2$
7. $y=\frac{3}{2}x+3$; $m=\frac{3}{2}, c=3$ 8. $y=\frac{3}{2}x-2\frac{1}{2}$; $m=\frac{3}{2}, c=-2\frac{1}{2}$
9. $y=\frac{1}{2}x+2$; $m=\frac{1}{2}, c=2$ 10. $y=\frac{1}{2}x+1\frac{1}{2}$; $m=\frac{1}{2}, c=1\frac{1}{2}$
11. $y=\frac{3}{2}x+4$; $m=\frac{3}{2}, c=4$ 12. $y=\frac{3}{2}x+3\frac{1}{2}$; $m=\frac{3}{2}, c=3\frac{1}{2}$
13. $y=\frac{6}{5}x-\frac{3}{5}$; $m=\frac{6}{5}, c=-\frac{3}{5}$ 14. $y=\frac{13}{10}x+1\frac{3}{5}$; $m=\frac{13}{10}, c=1\frac{3}{5}$

Exercise 10.9
1. $m=-2, c=3$ 2. $m=-\frac{1}{2}, c=4$ 3. $m=-\frac{1}{2}, c=2\frac{1}{2}$
4. $m=-\frac{1}{3}, c=2\frac{1}{3}$ 5. $m=-\frac{2}{3}, c=2$ 6. $m=-\frac{3}{4}, c=-2$
7. $m=\frac{3}{4}, c=-\frac{3}{4}$ 8. $m=\frac{3}{4}, c=\frac{1}{4}$ 9. $m=-\frac{2}{3}, c=-1\frac{2}{3}$
10. $m=-\frac{2}{3}, c=3\frac{2}{3}$ 11. $m=-3, c=5$ 12. $m=-\frac{19}{8}, c=-1\frac{5}{8}$

Exercise 10.10
1. $y=2x$; $m=2, c=0$ 2. $y=\frac{1}{4}x+4$; $m=\frac{1}{4}, c=4$
3. $y=5x-15$; $m=5, c=-15$ 4. $y=\frac{3}{2}x-\frac{5}{12}$; $m=\frac{3}{2}, c=-\frac{5}{12}$
5. $y=\frac{5}{4}x-3\frac{1}{2}$; $m=\frac{5}{4}, c=-3\frac{1}{2}$ 6. $y=\frac{17}{4}x+15\frac{2}{3}$; $m=\frac{17}{4}, c=15\frac{2}{3}$
7. $y=-2x+8$; $m=-2, c=8$ 8. $y=-\frac{1}{2}x+4\frac{2}{3}$; $m=-\frac{1}{2}, c=4\frac{2}{3}$
9. $y=-3x-5$; $m=-3, c=-5$ 10. $y=-\frac{9}{4}x-8$; $m=-\frac{9}{4}, c=-8$
11. $y=x+1$; $m=1, c=1$ 12. $y=x+3$; $m=1, c=3$
13. $y=x-1$; $m=1, c=-1$ 14. $y=-\frac{44}{39}x+9\frac{10}{39}$; $m=-\frac{44}{39}, c=9\frac{10}{39}$
15. $y=-\frac{3}{5}x+3$; $m=-\frac{3}{5}, c=3$ 16. $y=-\frac{5}{2}x+2$; $m=-\frac{5}{2}, c=2$
17. $y=\frac{11}{7}x+\frac{1}{7}$; $m=\frac{11}{7}, c=\frac{1}{7}$ 18. $y=\frac{11}{8}x+\frac{1}{2}$; $m=\frac{11}{8}, c=\frac{1}{2}$
19. $y=-x-9$; $m=-1, c=-9$ 20. $y=\frac{10}{11}x-3\frac{5}{11}$; $m=\frac{10}{11}, c=-3\frac{5}{11}$
25. $m=1$ 26. $4\frac{1}{3}$

Exercise 10.11
1. 1.02, 1.05, 1.09, 1.13 2. 1.80, 1.96, 2.14, 2.36, 2.60
3. 0.98, 0.87, 0.64, 0.34 4. 1.39, 1.87, 2.08, 2.35

Exercise 11.4

2. Relative frequencies: 0.015, 0.046, 0.085, 0.100, 0.146, 0.169, 0.146, 0.123, 0.092, 0.054, 0.023

3. Relative frequencies: 0.020, 0.010, 0.140, 0.300, 0.240, 0.120, 0.100, 0.040, 0.030

4. Relative frequencies: 0.040, 0.120, 0.280, 0.240, 0.160, 0.100, 0.060

Exercise 12.1

1. 12.0   **2.** 16.7   **3.** $17.82 \approx 17.8$ **4.** $1000.5 \approx 1000$

Exercise 12.3

1. 89   **2.** 13.9   **3.** 234.2

4. Word value 384.5 attached to interval 380–389. Mean $409.9 \approx 410$.

Exercise 12.4

1. 46.3   **2.** 9.07   **3.** 49.94   **4.** 26.6 for men, 23.3 for women

Exercise 12.5

1. (1) modes 11.95, 12.00, 12.05   (2) mode 16.7   (3) modes 17.10, 17.11, 18.4   (4) mode 995

2. (1) 89 seeds   (2) 14 defectives   (3) modal class 230–239 kg/cm^2, value 235 kg/cm^2 (4) modal class 410–419, value 414.5 words

3. (1) modal class 40–49, mode 44.5   (2) modal class 9.06–9.08 kg, mode 9.07 kg   (3) modal class 49–51 per cent, mode 50 per cent   (4) modal class (husbands) 23–27, mode 25.5; modal class (wives) 18–22, mode 20.5

Exercise 12.6

1. 7   **2.** 56   **3.** 6.5

4. 5.5, i.e. average of 5.4 and 5.6 *or* not less than 5.4 and not greater than 5.6

5. 48

6. average of 133 and 142 = 137.5 *or* not less than 133 and not greater than 142

7. (1) 12.00   (2) 16.7   (3) average of 17.11 and 18.1 = 18.0 *or* not less than 17.11 and not greater than 18.1   (4) average of 995 and 1000 = 997.5 *or* not less than 995 and not greater than 1000

Exercise 12.7

1. Range = 16 − 3 = 13   **2.** Range = 7.2 − 3.2 = 4.0

3. Range = 9.4 − 2.3 = 7.1   **4.** Range = 8.6 − 3.9 = 4.7

5. Range = 92 − 11 = 81   **6.** Range = 178 − 103 = 75

Exercise 13.3

1. (e, g); (f, h); (a, c); (b, d); (l, n); (k, m)

2. (p, r); (q, s); (x, z); (y, t); $(1, 3)$; $(2, 4)$; $(5, 7)$; $(6, 8)$

Exercise 13.4

1.

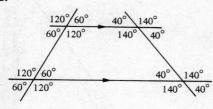

2.

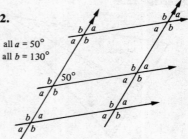

all a = 50°
all b = 130°

Exercise 14.1

1.

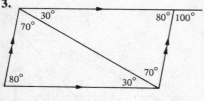

2.

3.

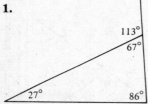

4.

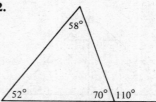

5.

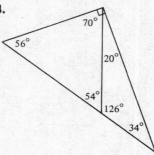

6.

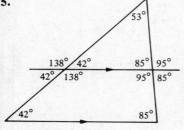

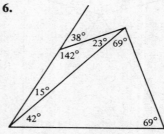

Exercise 14.2

1.
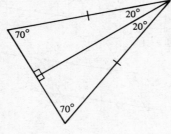

2.
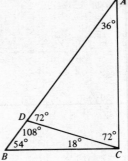

3. Triangles *ABC* and *BCD* are equilateral. Therefore $A\hat{B}C = 60° = B\hat{C}D$. These are alternate angles. *AB* is parallel to *CD*.

4.
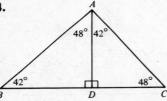

5.
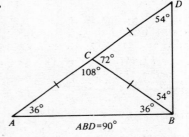

$ABD = 90°$

6.
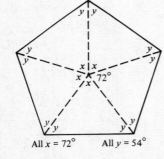

All $x = 72°$ All $y = 54°$

7.
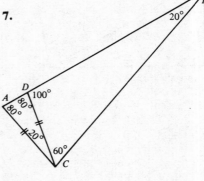

8.
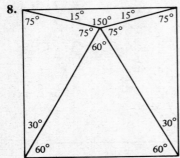

Exercise 14.4
1. $z = 10$ 2. $z = 15$ 3. $z = 25$ 4. $z = 35$ 5. $z = 26$
6. $z = 39$ 7. $y = 48$ 8. $y = 6$

Exercise 14.5
1. $ED = 2\frac{2}{5}$; $EB = 3\frac{3}{5}$ 2. $OD = 6\frac{1}{2}$; $OC = 2\frac{1}{2}$ 3. $p = 1\frac{1}{2}$
4. $BD = 12$; $DC = 9$; $AD = 16$ 5. $QR = 15$; $ST = 5\frac{5}{8}$; $PT = 6\frac{3}{8}$
6. $MN = 7$; $PQ = 3\frac{1}{2}$

Exercise 14.6
1. $RQ = 3\frac{1}{2}$; $RP = 3$; $PQ = 4$ 2. $XY = \frac{2}{3}$; $MN = 4\frac{2}{3}$; $L\hat{Y}X = \theta$
3. $A_1C_1 = 6$; $B_1C_1 = 10$; $A_1B_1 = 12$ 4. $DC = 8$; $AD = 5$
5. $LM = 5\frac{1}{4}$ 6. $V\hat{W}Y = 110°$

Exercise 14.7
1. $A\hat{C}B \approx 47°$ 2. $X\hat{Y}Z \approx 84°$ 3. $r \approx 5.8$; $P\hat{Q}R \approx 58°$
4. $a \approx 63$; $A\hat{B}C \approx 11°$ 5. $b \approx 41$; $c \approx 76$ 6. $z \approx 62$; $x \approx 59°$
7. $P\hat{R}Q \approx 43°$; $R\hat{P}Q \approx 47°$ 8. $B \approx 30°$; $C \approx 60°$

Exercise 15.1
1. (a) 31.42 (b) 188.52 (c) 21.30 (d) 83.77
2. (a) 2 (b) 3 (c) 5 (d) 7.56
3. (a) 5 (b) 10 (c) 5.58 (d) 16.96
4. (a) 6.284 (b) 25.136 (c) 37.70 (d) 17.46 (e) 9.86
5. (a) 45° (b) 90° (c) 135° (d) 237.9° (e) 353.5°

Exercise 15.2
1. (a) 45°, 27.5°, 67.5°, 90° (b) 60°, 120°, 180°, 150°
2. (a) 40°, 30°, 60°, 70° (b) 70°, 50°, 150°, 94°
   (c) 70°, 50°, 150°, 94° (d) 27.5°, 26°, 31.5°, 43.5°
3. (a) 50° (b) 32° (c) 45° (d) 60° (e) 70° (f) 80°
4. (a) $A\hat{Q}O = 40°$, $B\hat{Q}O = 60°$, $A\hat{Q}B = 100°$
   (b) $A\hat{Q}O = 45°$, $B\hat{Q}O = 55°$, $A\hat{Q}B = 100°$
   (c) $A\hat{Q}O = 65°$, $B\hat{Q}O = 65°$, $A\hat{Q}B = 130°$
   (d) $A\hat{Q}O = 70°$, $B\hat{Q}O = 80°$, $A\hat{Q}B = 150°$
   In each case $A\hat{Q}B = \frac{1}{2}$ reflex angle $A\hat{O}B$.
5. (a) $A\hat{O}B = 180°$ (b) $A\hat{Q}O = 20°$, $B\hat{Q}O = 70°$, $A\hat{Q}B = 90°$; $A\hat{Q}O = 30°$,
   $B\hat{Q}O = 60°$, $A\hat{Q}B = 90°$; $A\hat{Q}O = 40°$, $B\hat{Q}O = 50°$, $A\hat{Q}B = 90°$; $A\hat{Q}O = 10°$,
   $B\hat{Q}O = 80°$, $A\hat{Q}B = 90°$
   (c) In each case $A\hat{Q}B = 90°$.
6. 31.42, 15.71, 47.13, 19.90, 9.95

Exercise 15.3

1.

$P\hat{T}X$	$O\hat{P}T$	$T\hat{O}P$	$P\hat{O}S$	$O\hat{P}S$	$O\hat{S}P$	$T\hat{P}S$
60°	30°	120°	60°	60°	60°	90°
50°	40°	100°	80°	50°	50°	90°
40°	50°	80°	100°	40°	40°	90°
30°	60°	60°	120°	30°	30°	90°
28°	52°	76°	104°	38°	38°	90°
88°	2°	176°	4°	88°	88°	90°

2.

$P\hat{T}X$	$O\hat{T}P$	$O\hat{P}T$	$P\hat{O}T$	$P\hat{Q}T$
24°	66°	66°	48°	24°
38°	52°	52°	76°	38°
49°	41°	41°	98°	49°
83°	7°	7°	166°	83°
57°	33°	33°	114°	57°

3.

$A\hat{O}B$	$A\hat{C}B$	reflex $A\hat{O}B$	$A\hat{D}B$	$A\hat{C}B + A\hat{D}B$
120°	60°	240°	120°	180°
110°	55°	250°	125°	180°
100°	50°	260°	130°	180°
140°	70°	220°	110°	180°
160°	80°	200°	100°	180°
170°	85°	190°	95°	180°

4.

$T\hat{A}B$	$D\hat{A}B$	reflex $D\hat{O}B$	$D\hat{O}B$	$D\hat{C}B$
50°	130°	260°	100°	50°
60°	120°	240°	120°	60°
70°	110°	220°	140°	70°
80°	100°	200°	160°	80°
55°	125°	250°	110°	55°
61°	119°	238°	122°	61°
37°	143°	286°	74°	37°

Exercise 15.4

1. 114°35′, 28°39′, 85°56′, 180°, 360°, 154°41′, 60°9′, 7°20′

2. 0.567 rad, 0.834 rad, 2.761 rad, 4.715 rad, 0.620 rad, 1.287 rad, 3.401 rad

Exercise 15.5
1. 12.568 rad, 37.704 rad, 628.4 rad, 9426 rad, 540.424 rad
2. 11.61 revs, 23.55 revs, 8.85 revs, 3.13 revs

Exercise 15.6
1. 10 m; 13 m; 57 cm; 0.64 km; 19.775 m; 63.7 cm
2. 5 m; 2 cm; 3565 km; 2185 mm; 0.636 m
3. 3.839 rad; 3.269 rad; 1.610 rad; 0.795 rad

Exercise 16.1
1. (a) 30 cm^2; 147 m^2; 45 152 mm^2; 26.22 km^2 (b) 40 m; 50 cm; 34.4 mm
   (c) 30 cm; 1.8 m
2. (a) 70 cm^2; 324 m^2 (b) 30 m; 1.21 cm
3. 114 **4.** ABC: 110; BCD: 40; $ABCD = 110 - 40 = 70$

Exercise 16.2
1. 314.2 cm^2; 78.55 m^2; 4.524 km^2; 679 mm^2
2. 10 cm; 11 m; 70.5 m **3.** 16.9 m; 34.2 cm; 5.43 km

Exercise 16.3
1. 1200 cm^3; 20 128 cm^3; 50.02 m^3
2. 50 m; 33.3 cm; 2.96 m **3.** 100 cm^3; 1885 cm^3
4. 1519 cm^3; 127 600 cm^3 **5.** 17.3 cm; 6.76 m

Exercise 16.4
1. 320 cm^3; 50 400 cm^3 **2.** 18 cm; 5.67 m
3. 209 cm^3; 707 cm^3; 105 cm^3 **4.** 10.7 cm; 10.4 cm

Exercise 16.5
1. 4190 cm^3; 10 080 cm^3; 0.0654 m^3 **2.** 6.20 cm; 5.97 cm; 0.084 m

Exercise 16.6
1. 1257 cm^2; 2903 cm^2; 39 700 cm^2
2. 628.4 cm^2, 1885 cm^2; 1230 cm^2, 4133 cm^2; 53 200 cm^2, 92 900 cm^2
3. 3.9 cm; 31.6 cm **4.** 750 cm^2

Exercise 16.7
1. 450 cm^2 **2.** 60.7 cm^2 **3.** 119 cm^2 **4.** 3620 cm^3
5. 3930 cm^3 **6.** 4400 cm^3

Exercise 16.8
1. 1060 cm^2 **2.** 943 cm^2 **3.** 8.92 cm **4.** 427 cm^2
5. 1410 cm^2 **6.** 22.9 cm **7.** 82 100 cm^2 **8.** 1040 cm^2
9. 708 cm^2 **10.** 18 300 cm^3 **11.** 7840 cm^3 **12.** 3560 cm^3
13. 943 cm^2 **14.** 1020 cm^2 **15.** 4670 cm^3 **16.** 3850 cm^3
17. 4800 cm^3 **18.** 780 cm^2 **19.** 1290 cm^2 **20.** 449 cm^3
21. 21.8 m^3 **22.** 53.1 m^2 **23.** 330 000 mm^3

Exercise 16.9
1. 235.9 cm^3 2. 17.7 cm 3. 20.1 cm 4. 4112 cm^3
5. 345.6 cm^2 6. 33.9 cm 7. 29.1 cm 8. $1.31:1$
9. 2458 cm^3 10. 3821 cm^3

Exercise 17.1
1. 0.4384, 0.6561, 0.2974, 0.4083, 0.6455, 0.8028, 0.9026, 0.9803, 0.9940, 0.7524, 0.1374, 0.1570, 0.2608, 0.5512, 0.7042, 0.9510
2. $16°$, $36°$, $84°$, $9°6'$, $21°12'$, $37°36'$, $30°48'$, $59°24'$, $23°13'$, $28°47'$, $37°34'$, $81°21'$

Exercise 17.2
1. 0.8988, 0.7547, 0.9548, 0.9128, 0.7638, 0.5962, 0.4305, 0.1977, 0.1097, 0.6587, 0.9905, 0.9876, 0.9654, 0.8343, 0.7100, 0.3093
2. $74°$, $54°$, $6°$, $80°54'$, $68°48'$, $52°24'$, $59°12'$, $30°36'$, $66°47'$, $61°13'$, $52°26'$, $8°39'$
3. $74° + 16° = 90°$; $54° + 36° = 90°$; $6° + 84° = 90°$; etc.
   $30°36' + 59°24' = 90°$, etc.

Exercise 17.3
1. 0.4877, 0.8693, 0.3115, 0.4473, 0.8451, 1.3465, 2.0965, 4.9594, 9.058, 1.1423, 0.1388, 0.1590, 0.2701, 0.6607, 0.9919, 3.0739
2. $10°$, $24°$, $53°$, $32°12'$, $77°42'$, $54°48'$, $74°7'$, $30°55'$, $71°54'$, $84°42'$, $87°42'$

Exercise 17.4
1. 0.821; 7.31; 61.4 2. $40°32'$; $20°7'$; $59°18'$ 3. 29.5; 23.9; 60.8
4. $69°31'$; $39°50'$; $36°11'$ 5. 8.49; 6.56; 179 6. $30°26'$; $49°33'$; $34°52'$

Exercise 17.5
1. $142.04506 \text{ m} \approx 142 \text{ m}$ 2. $8.9892993° \approx 8.99° \approx 8°59'$
3. $4727.2436 \text{ m} \approx 4727 \text{ m}$ 4. $7.5444174 \text{ mm} \approx 7.5 \text{ mm}$
5. $15.696856 \text{ mm} \approx 15.70 \text{ mm}$
6. diagonal $= 19.864541 \text{ cm} \approx 19.9 \text{ cm}$; angle $= 64.499948° \approx 64.50° = 64°30'$
7. altitude $= 5.8100758 \text{ cm} \approx 5.8 \text{ cm}$; base $= 12.68117 \text{ cm} \approx 12.7 \text{ cm}$
8. base $= 5.7549524 \text{ m} \approx 5.8 \text{ m}$; length of ladder $= 9.4535431 \text{ m} \approx 9.5 \text{ m}$
9. angle $1 = 57.472098° \approx 57.47° \approx 57°28'$;
   angle $2 = 32.527902° \approx 32.53° \approx 32°32'$
10. $137.40662 \text{ m} \approx 137 \text{ m}$ 11. $28.701257 \text{ mm} \approx 28.7 \text{ mm}$
12. height $= 14.138401 \text{ m} \approx 14.1 \text{ m}$; base $= 6.5928449 \text{ m} \approx 6.6 \text{ m}$
13. $V = 346.59382 \approx 347 \text{ km/h}$; $H = 48.710585 \approx 49 \text{ km/h}$
14. bearing $030.203238° \approx 030.20°$
15. other force $= 5803.4559 \text{ N} \approx 5800 \text{ N}$;
    angle $= 21.789643° \approx 21.79° \approx 21°47'$
16. $P = Q = 1414.2136 \text{ N} \approx 1410 \text{ N}$
17. $X = 2945.5003 \text{ N} \approx 2950 \text{ N}$; $Y = 1373.5094 \text{ N} \approx 1370 \text{ N}$
18. length $= 218.4033 \text{ mm} \approx 218 \text{ mm}$; angle $= 42.896063° \approx 42.90° = 42°54'$

19. $9.5179584° \approx 9.52° \approx 9°31'$
20. $y = 1.5934867 \text{ m} \approx 1.59 \text{ m}; \ x = 1.84 \text{ m}$
21. Sloping length = 5.0 m; pitch = $36.869898° \approx 36.87° \approx 36°52'$
22. $2.1490956° \approx 2.15° \approx 2°9'$
23. $32.143343 \text{ m} \approx 32 \text{ m}$

Exercise 18.1
$\sin 100° = \sin 80°$; $\sin 120° = \sin 60°$; $\sin 154° = \sin 26°$;
$\sin 98° = \sin 82°$; $\sin 176° = \sin 14°$; $\sin 250° = -\sin 70°$;
$\sin 230° = -\sin 50°$; $\sin 229° = -\sin 49°$; $\sin 192° = -\sin 12°$;
$\sin 263° = -\sin 83°$; $\sin 280° = -\sin 80°$; $\sin 300° = -\sin 60°$;
$\sin 345° = -\sin 15°$; $\sin 327° = -\sin 33°$; $\sin 276° = -\sin 84°$;
$\sin 352° = -\sin 8°$

Exercise 18.2
$\cos 100° = -\cos 80°$; $\cos 120° = -\cos 60°$; $\cos 154° = -\cos 26°$;
$\cos 98° = -\cos 82°$; $\cos 176° = -\cos 4°$; $\cos 250° = -\cos 70°$;
$\cos 230° = -\cos 50°$; $\cos 229° = -\cos 49°$; $\cos 192° = -\cos 12°$;
$\cos 263° = -\cos 83°$; $\cos 280° = \cos 80°$; $\cos 300° = \cos 60°$;
$\cos 345° = \cos 15°$; $\cos 327° = \cos 33°$; $\cos 276° = \cos 84°$;
$\cos 352° = \cos 8°$